G000123151

First published June 1991
Second edition published June 1993
Third edition published April 1995
Fourth edition published November 1997
Fifth edition published June 2000
Sixth edition published October 2002

ISBN 0-907337-25-2

Design by Doughnut Design
(With thanks to Ket)

Printed by KSC Printers,
High Brooms Industrial Estate,
Tunbridge Wells, Kent TN2 3DR

Technical Support by Spirit Quest - www.spiritquest.co.uk

Published by The Vegan Society, Donald Watson House, 7 Battle Road, St Leonard's-on-Sea, East Sussex TN37 7AA, United Kingdom
(Tel 01424 427393)

CONTENTS

● Although, as far as is practical, the publisher has taken care to ensure the accuracy and reliability of information supplied to it, the reader should bear in mind that manufacturers may make alterations to the constituents, derivation and testing of their products at any time. The diligent animal free shopper always checks a product's ingredients listing (where one is provided!) before making a purchase.

Remember to check *www.vegansociety.com* for updates.

● The absence of an (apparently) animal free product does not necessarily mean it does not meet the Society's **ANIMAL FREE CRITERIA** (page270). Product categories that are obviously or typically animal-free (tinned fruit, tea, coffee, nuts, dried pulses, beans, jams etc) have been excluded. Additionally, despite repeated approaches, some manufacturers/distributors (including a number whose products have appeared in previous editions) failed, or simply refused to supply the information requested.

● In order to make effective use of this guide, it is suggested that the new reader familiarises him/herself with the location of the **KEY** (page iii) and **CONTENTS** (page i) — and, at least initially, regularly consults the **INDEX** (page 312).

● The inclusion of a product should not be construed as constituting Vegan Society approval for the product, its intended use, or its manufacturer/distributor (see **OTHER ETHICAL CONSIDERATIONS**, page 277).

● The listing of products under 'Healthcare' is not intended to take the place of advice provided by health care professionals.

The entire range of the company's products is animal-free
(see **ANIMAL FREE CRITERIA**, page 270) ☺

The company is an authorised user of the Vegan Society Trade Mark
(but not all its animal-free products may be registered)
(see **VEGAN SOCIETY TRADE MARK**, page 6) **TM**

The company has at least one vegan proprietor ❶

The company's entire product range is organic ✿

The company has a policy of ensuring that
(as far as is possible and practical) the production
of its products has not involved the use of genetically modified material
(see **GENETICALLY-MODIFIED ORGANISMS**, page 34) ⊘

The company has a policy of not
conducting nor commissioning animal testing 🐾

The company has signed up to the Humane Cosmetics Standard
(see **ANIMAL TESTING CRITERIA**, page 276) 👁

The company has a policy of using only ingredients which have not
been tested on animals by, or at the initiative of, the company or its
suppliers since a specified date (Note: In the product listings, the year
follows this symbol — eg a 1976 cut-off date appears as ✂76)
(see **ANIMAL TESTING CRITERIA**, page 276) ✂

Food and Drink products in **bold** have been organically produced

w = with (product listings only)

Many thanks to the following companies who have chosen to 'sponsor' their listing in the guide.
Their entries throughout the book are highlighted by their logos.

Beanie's Healthfoods (Wholesale) Limited is an import/distribution business. Their ethos is to procure natural, quality, chemical and GMO free vegetarian and vegan foods and to make them widely available! They currently import Fry's Special Vegetarian Foods and Bionade isotonic drinks. More product import rights are presently under discussion!

Beanie's Health Foods (Wholesale) Ltd.,
Unit 6,
Cherry Tree Industrial Park,
312, Botley Road,
Burridge,
Southampton,
SO31 1BQ.
Tel. (01489) 574593
Fax. (01489) 582003
Email. info@beanieshealthfoods.co.uk

Ethical Wares is an ethically based company run by vegans who seek to trade in a manner which does not exploit animals, humans or the wider environment. We will not trade with countries that have oppressive regimes or who allow exploitative working practices. By the sale of these vegan products we hope to play our part in the promotion of a cruelty-free lifestyle.

Ethical Wares
Caegwyn
Temple Bar
Felinfach
Cerdigion
SA48 7SA
01570 471155
ethicalwares@veganvillage.co.uk

Plamil – Pioneers in 1965 of Vegan Milk (fortified) Watch our adverts in Vegan magazine on new lines. Publishers of most comprehensive cover of Vegan Infants Case Histories booklet. See page 47

Bowles Well Gardens
Folkestone
Kent
CT19 6PQ
01303 850588
www.plamil-foods.co.uk
contact-us@plamilfoods.co.uk

veganline.com

Veganline
All-vegan shoes made in the UK or Europe without sweated labour.
Most are specially-made for Veganline.com with breathable Lorica tops.
One - the Equity sandal - is made by a 100 year-old co-op. Veganline.com was the first internet vegan shoe shop.

www.veganline.com - John Robertson - veg@animal.nu
Freepost LON 10506
London SW14 1YY
Tel. 0800 458 4442
Fax. 020 8286 9947

ACKNOWLEDGEMENTS

Compiled by Catriona Toms and Debbie Holman with the kind assistance of Gemma Barclay, Wendy Crathern, Liz Costa and Jennifer Toms. Thanks also to The Vegan Society Information Group as well as all staff and council members who have offered their assistance.

Special thanks go to Sandra Hood, Ket at Spirit Quest, and Barney at Doughnut Design for all their hard work and endless patience. Last, but not least, a big big thankyou to everyone who wrote, emailed, faxed and phoned with information on vegan products – keep up the good work!

WWW.VEGANSOCIETY.COM

Log on to the website of the world's premiere vegan organisation.

- Shop securely online for Vegan Society goods
- View listings of all Vegan registered products
- Become a member
- View Factsheets
- Information
- News and developments
- 'Why Go Vegan' section
- Links to other great vegan/veggie web pages

Return for updates and latest information

THE NO. 1 SITE FOR VEGAN SURFING

Hello! Welcome to the sixth edition of *The Animal Free Shopper*.

This little gem of a book has been produced by The Vegan Society for over ten years now, and whilst we'd like to say that no vegan's bookshelf should be without one, this would be far from the whole story. Because this book doesn't belong on the shelf: it's made for going out and about. So, when you're lost in a list of E numbers or confronted with unspecified 'flavourings,' you can just reach into your pocket, pull out your Shopper and indulge in some hassle-free animal-free shopping.

You see, we've done all of the hard work for you. We've contacted thousands of manufacturers of food, drink, toiletries, cosmetics, footwear, clothing - the list goes on - and asked them which of their products satisfy our **animal-free criteria** (see page 270), then we've put them all together into one easy-to-use guide. And for this edition we've made things even simpler: all the supermarket products are listed together in one section, allowing you to flick straight to the store you require, or if you prefer to buy your groceries from independent wholefood shops you can simply ignore the supermarket section altogether.

We've also included a brief introduction to nutrition, as well as some good reasons for staying animal-free. In fact, there's so much packed into this pocket-sized book that we could have called it 'The Vegan Handbook.' But that wouldn't do it justice, because *The Animal Free Shopper* is not just for vegans. Over the years, it has proved invaluable to vegetarians, allergy-sufferers, and many others, as well as being a great starting point for those taking their first tentative steps towards decreasing their dependence on animal products.

Now in its eleventh year, *The Animal Free Shopper* continues to play an essential role in helping people to go vegan and stay vegan. Never leave home without it!

www.vegansociety.com/afs

For those of you with internet access, we've added a searchable Animal Free Shopper database to The Vegan Society website. This allows you to search under manufacturer, type of product or product name – so at the touch of a button you'll be able to find out which products you can use.

It also means that updates can be made as and when we receive new product information. Updates will be flagged so that you can see what's changed since the last time you visited the site. It may not be as portable as this little book, but with internet shopping on the increase (and many mail-order companies included in *The Animal Free Shopper*) you'd be wise to add the page to your favourites before getting out that credit card.

MISSING, PRESUMED VEGAN

Although we've tried to make The Animal-Free Shopper as comprehensive as possible, you may still come across products that are vegan but are not listed. There are a number of reasons for this, the main ones being:

- companies repeatedly failing to respond to questionnaires, emails, telephone calls and faxes;
- lack of confidence on the part of the compilers that the manufacturers/ suppliers really understand the **animal-free criteria** (see page 270);
- companies supplying incomplete or inadequate product information;
- claims that the information requested is 'commercially sensitive'.

PLAYING DETECTIVE

Though experienced in investigating the animal-free credentials of a product, there are limits to The Vegan Society's capabilities. Food processing technology is a vast, complex and rapidly changing subject. At the end of the day, unless it obtains evidence to the contrary — or the details provided are clearly suspect - The Vegan Society has to accept the information provided to it (normally in the form of a written declaration) in good faith.

However, playing detective isn't the sole province of the Society. An increasing number of companies understand a vegan's requirements and enquiries from members of the public are often at least as effective as those from an organisation. Use the **animal-free criteria** (see page 270) as the basis for your approach and check **additives** (see page 271) to identify E numbers that could be animal derived. You will quickly be able to determine whether the person responding to your enquiry is sufficiently knowledgeable to provide you with plausible product information. Confirming the animal-free status of a product can be thrilling, but be

FRY'S

S P E C I A L

V E G E T A R I A N   F O O D S

Approved by **The Vegetarian Society** and suitable for vegans.

All products are Kosher Parev Mehadrian, Halal and Shudda

 BEANIE'S HEALTH FOODS (WHOLESALE) LIMITED

Unit 6, Cherry Tree Industrial Park, Botley Road, Burridge, Southampton SO3 1BQ
Tel: 01489 574593 Fax: 01489 582003
email: info@beanieshealthfoods.co.uk
www.beanieshealthfoods.co.uk

7 WIVES
THE LEADING NATURAL BODYCARE RANGE

Vegans are famous for their care of the environment and understanding of the relationship between themselves and what they eat and use on their bodies. 7 Wives has spent 4 years researching natural body-care and have discovered that soaps, skincare and deodorants can meet Vegan standards, producing real benefits. People with skin problems usually find their symptoms greatly reduced when using 7 Wives products.

For details on our range of wonderful products please contact **7 Wives Natural Bodycare**
Tel: 01736 74 12 74   Fax: 01736 74 12 80
Email: mail@7wives.co.uk

prepared also for frustration and disappointment! That said, discovering that an apparently animal-free product is not suitable certainly isn't wasted effort. Manufacturers take note of consumer interest and will, sooner or later, act. Recent examples of companies deciding to alter their products in response to demand for animal-free products include: Cadbury's changing the ingredients of the Fry's Chocolate Cream range; Kellogg's removing vitamin D3 from Frosties and Coco Pops; Ecover producing a new 'whey-free' washing-up liquid.

In addition to drawing the attention of manufacturers to the unmet needs of animal-free shoppers, it is equally important to tell them that you buy their products precisely because they are animal-free!

It is all too easy to complain and accuse companies of 'discriminating against vegans' or 'condoning animal suffering', but letters and phone calls of an encouraging nature are more likely to elicit a receptive response and, ultimately, produce the desired outcome.

LOOKING AHEAD . . .

Research for *The Animal Free Shopper* never ceases and the Vegan Society needs you to be part of this process! If you stumble across a new animal-free product, or discover that a manufacturer has introduced an animal ingredient into a product that was previously animal free, please share your findings by contacting us at: The Vegan Society, Donald Watson House, 7 Battle Rd, St Leonards-on-Sea, East Sussex TN37 7AA t 01424 427393 f 01424 717064 e info@vegansociety.com

To keep up to date with new animal-free products, just check the website for updates.

A LITTLE BIT ABOUT US

The Vegan Society was formed in England in November 1944 by a group of vegetarians who had recognised the ethical compromises implicit in lacto-vegetarianism. "It was a Sunday, with sunshine and a blue sky, an auspicious day for the birth of an idealistic movement." (Elsie B Shrigley, *The Vegan,* Spring 1962)

Among the founding members was Donald Watson, who coined the word 'vegan' by taking the first three and last two letters of 'vegetarian'.

He described the Society's early days:

"We were few in number and widely dispersed…We had no funds, no private transport – apart from bicycles – no precedents to work on, no office, little experience in public speaking, and none in publishing."
(*The Vegan*, Summer 1988)

But from little acorns great oaks do grow. Today, the Society continues to highlight the problems caused by an unhealthy dependence on animal products. We are now a registered educational charity, focused on the provision of information on all aspects of veganism. Our message is simple: **go vegan - for people, animals and the environment.**

LOCAL CONTACTS

In addition to our central offices in St Leonards-on-Sea (where volunteers are always welcome), The Vegan Society has a large network of local contacts throughout the UK. These are members who have offered to act as a point of contact for those interested in the Society's work. So if you are interested in becoming more involved on a local level, or if you need any advice on being vegan in your area, they are the people to speak to. Details are published in *The Vegan* every quarter or contact the Local Contacts Co-ordinator care of The Vegan Society.

OUR TRADEMARK

The Vegan Society trademark was conceived as a way of helping people to shop for animal-free products. Only Vegan Society authenticated products carry the trademark, and each one has been independently checked by us.

The trademark allows consumers to make easy, informed choices about the suitability of purchases and enables us to work with companies who are willing to recognise their vegan customers. With thousands of items now bearing our familiar logo, and through recent international recognition of the trademark, the influence has never been greater. We have registered vegan alternatives to just about everything: vegan ice cream, margarine, vegan cheese, vegan bacon, wines, chocolate and even champagne. The Trademark covers household items such as cosmetics and bath products, cleaners and soaps, and has attracted a lot of interest from producers of remedies and supplements.

Once a quarter we keep you up-to-date on vegan issues around the globe. In every edition you can find articles on important issues concerning veganism, nutrition and animal-rights, and keep up with the Society's latest developments.

Discover new recipe ideas, 'Shoparound' product reviews and check out the classifieds for that vegan-friendly holiday you deserve!

Regulars in each issue include:

- News ■ Book and Product Reviews ■ Dietary Advice
- Readers Letters ■ Articles ■ Diary of Vegan Events
- Advertising for Vegan / Ethical companies ■ Recipes
- Vegan Groups ■ Classified ads ....and much more

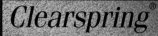

This book is full of animal-free products, many of which you will be able to identify by looking out for our symbol: remember to ask the manufacturer of your favourite products whether they have registered with us yet.

VEGAN SOCIETY TRADEMARK STANDARD

no animal ingredients
The manufacture and/or development of the product, and where applicable its ingredients, must not involve, or have involved, the use of any animal product, by-product or derivative.

no animal testing
The development and/or manufacture of the product, and where applicable its ingredients, must not involve, or have involved, testing of any sort on animals conducted at the initiative of the manufacturer or on its behalf, or by parties over whom the manufacturer has effective control.

genetically modified organisms
The development and/or production of genetically modified organisms (GMOs) must not have involved animal genes or animal-derived substances. Products put forward for registration which contain or may contain GMOs must be labelled as such.

AND A LITTLE BIT ABOUT VEGANISM

Veganism is very much on the rise. The Food Standards Agency's 2001 'Consumer Attitudes to Food Standards Report' showed that around 5% of the population would describe themselves as vegetarian and 0.4% were vegan. This means that around a quarter of a million people in the UK alone are choosing to avoid all animal products, more than double the figure found by the Realeat/Gallup Poll in 1993.

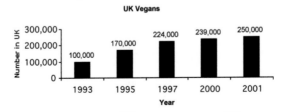

UK Vegans

(Source: The Vegan Research Panel www.imaner.net/panel)

9

Similar polls conducted in the USA suggest that as many as 1% of Americans are vegan.

But that is only part of the story. Even among the meat-eating masses, overall consumption of meat and dairy products has been declining for the better part of fifty years. Statistics show that the average person is now drinking around two-thirds less wholemilk than they were in the 1940s. There has, however, been a corresponding increase in milk consumed in other forms, so the overall decline in milk and cream intake in this period is around 17%. Meat consumption peaked in 1979, when the average person consumed 1.142kg of meat per week; by 2000 the figure was down to 0.966kg. The most dramatic changes, however, have been in egg consumption. Average consumption of eggs in 2000 was 1.75 per person per week, compared with 4.78 in 1965.

UK Consumption of Liquid Wholemilk

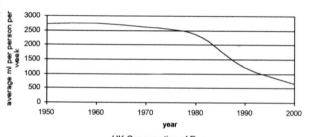

UK Consumption of Eggs

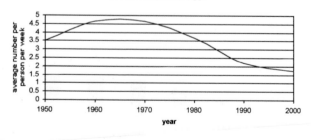

(Source: DEFRA National Food Survey, March 2001)

DOLMA
Vegan Perfumes, Toiletries & Skin Care

Perfumes

P1. CUSHIE B (Spicy citrus)
P2. ANAHITA (Floral)   NEW
P3. PRELUDE (Deep rich oriental)
P4. RAGA (Delicate apple tinged fragrance)
P5. CALISTA (Floral Bouquet)   NEW
P6. SARABANDE (Green and oriental)
P7. SONATA (Light Floral with Peach overtones)
P8. AMETHYST MIST (Deep rich floral)
P9. QUINTET (Green/Tropical/Spicy)
P10. VEGAMUSK (Animal free Musk)

Special Offer: Boxed set of 10 trial size perfumes, as above - £15.95 the lot (including UK postage). Makes a lovely gift.

Dolma offer an exclusive range of high quality original vegan perfumes, skin care and toiletries based on pure essential oils, herbal extracts, floral waters & vegetable oils. All products are carefully blended from safe, long established vegan ingredients and a fixed cut-off date of 1976 applies.

The perfumes include a large proportion of natural essential oils with perfumery synthetics and ethyl alcohol.

For free brochure send SAE (1st class stamp) or for a set of perfumes send cheque/postal order (made payable to DOLMA) to address below.

DOLMA, 19 Royce Avenue, Hucknall, Nottingham. NG15 6FU
Email: dolma@tinyworld.co.uk Website: www.veganvillage.co.uk/dolma Tel/Fax: 0115 963 4237

Goodness direct

Healthy shopping made easy

mailorder & e-shopping for health, diet & alternative health products

Where can I get ***vegan products**
***organic foods**
***special diet foods**
***cruelty free toiletries**
***natural skincare**
***herbal remedies**
***eco-friendly household items**
***on-line nutrition advice**

www.GoodnessDirect.co.uk
tel: 0871 8716611

The clear overall trend is a decreasing dependence on animal-products. This is happening for a number of reasons, many of which are explored below.

WHY ANIMAL-FREE?

ANIMAL WELFARE

Animals slaughtered for meat in the UK in 2001:

Cattle	2,164,000
Pigs	10,630,000
Sheep	12,891,000
Broilers	805,710,000
Boiling Fowl (spent laying hens)	39,240,000
Turkeys	24,470,000

(Source: DEFRA)

The popular vision of cattle grazing undisturbed in lush green fields or pigs snuffling happily in the earth, blissfully unaware of their intended fate, has long been defunct. The myth of the 'short but happy' lives of the animals that end up on the plates of 95% of British consumers may help to ease the collective conscience, but it also provides a façade to hide some of the most inhumane and appalling treatment of our fellow creatures.

POULTRY

The majority of the broilers reared each year in the UK are factory farmed. They are kept in huge windowless sheds so overcrowded that the floor can barely be seen.

A major welfare problem is that the birds have been selectively bred to reach their slaughter weight in 42 days, which is half the time taken 35 years ago. While the muscle grows quickly enough, the supporting structure of legs, joints, heart and lungs fails to keep pace. As a result, every year millions of chickens suffer from painful, sometimes crippling leg disorders, while millions more die of heart disease. By the time they reach slaughter weight, many of them can barely walk to their feeding areas.

PIGS

Pigs raised for meat are often kept indoors in overcrowded, ill-lit, barren, conditions. More than half of the fattening pigs raised in the UK are not provided with straw, but are forced to sleep on bare floors, leading to extreme discomfort and stress.

Sows kept for breeding normally give birth to their piglets and nurse them in farrowing crates. These small cramped containers, designed to stop the mother from rolling onto her piglets, allow the sow very little room to turn around or lie down comfortably. Until recently, most breeding pigs were kept in these conditions all year round.

The piglets would naturally be weaned at about 4 to 5 months, but they are often removed before 4 weeks, causing great stress to both mother and child. The piglets' traumatic existence has only just begun: in their short life they will endure painful procedures such as tail docking to prevent the distressed animals from biting each others tails, often carried out by unqualified persons and without anaesthetic.

BEEF CATTLE

Beef cattle have been gradually becoming dissociated from life on the range for some time now. Whilst twenty years ago the average cow raised for beef could expect to spend roughly two years roaming the fields, the average time spent outside is now around six months, before they are rounded up to be transported to the feedlot for 'finishing'. They are often transported over long distances in cramped, badly ventilated conditions. When they reach the feedlot, they are fed a rich mixture of grain and whatever else comes cheaply and will fatten them up. This unnatural diet can lead to a number of illnesses, not least of which is BSE.

They are often also subjected to a range of painful procedures. Male calves are castrated either surgically, or using tight rubber rings that restrict blood flow, or by crushing the spermatic cord of each testis. When they are 4 to 6 weeks old, they are 'disbudded' with a hot iron to prevent their horns from growing. This is done to stop the distressed, closely confined animals from injuring each other. If this is not done straight away, the cattle will often be de-horned later in life. This can involve the use of saws, horn shears or cutting wire. At the end of their short lives (UK law does not allow

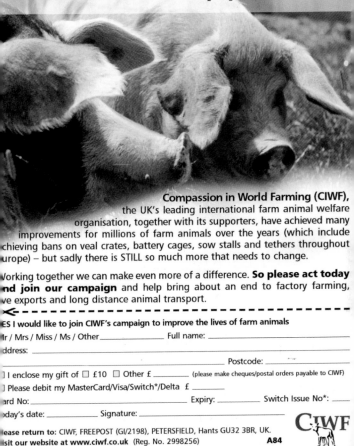

YOU may be a meat-free zone
but most of the world's population isn't.

Compassion in World Farming (CIWF), the UK's leading international farm animal welfare organisation, together with its supporters, have achieved many improvements for millions of farm animals over the years (which include achieving bans on veal crates, battery cages, sow stalls and tethers throughout Europe) – but sadly there is STILL so much more that needs to change.

Working together we can make even more of a difference. **So please act today and join our campaign** and help bring about an end to factory farming, live exports and long distance animal transport.

✂ -

YES I would like to join CIWF's campaign to improve the lives of farm animals

Mr / Mrs / Miss / Ms / Other _____ Full name: _____

Address: _____

_____ Postcode: _____

☐ I enclose my gift of ☐ £10 ☐ Other £ _____ (please make cheques/postal orders payable to CIWF)

☐ Please debit my MasterCard/Visa/Switch*/Delta £ _____

Card No: _____ Expiry: _____ Switch Issue No*: _____

Today's date: _____ Signature: _____

Please return to: CIWF, FREEPOST (GI/2198), PETERSFIELD, Hants GU32 3BR, UK.
Visit our website at www.ciwf.co.uk (Reg. No. 2998256)   **A84**

Call our credit card hotline today on 01730 237 365

CIWF
campaigning
for farm animals

the sale of beef from cattle over 36 months old, though a cow's natural lifespan is about 25 years) they are loaded into lorries for their final journey. When they reach the slaughterhouse, they are herded along cramped corridors and into pens where their heads are restrained and a bolt is shot through their skull destroying part of the brain. The cow is then stuck and allowed to bleed to death. All too often the initial stunning is inadequate and the animals may be conscious as they bleed to death.

DAIRY

If the lot of the cow raised for beef alone is to be pitied, the dairy cow deserves even more of our concern. To bring milk to the breakfast tables of the West, cows are kept in a constant cycle of pregnancy and lactation. This unnatural breeding regime results in painful udder infections such as mastitis, affecting 35 to 40% of the UK dairy herd. This condition is aggravated by unsanitary living conditions: for at least six months of the year cows often have no choice but to stand and sleep in their own filth, while some herds never leave the milking shed at all.

Frequent milking stimulates feed intake, increasing milk yields, so cows are often milked three times a day, usually by machines. The average dairy cow produces 5,915 litres per year, more than twice the amount produced by her ancestors in the 1950s. With milk yields increasing all the time, each cow's body is forced to work harder and harder.

"The amount of work done by the cow in peak lactation is immense…To achieve a comparably high work rate a human would have to jog for about 6 hours a day, every day." (Professor AJF Webster, Dept of Animal Husbandry, Bristol University)

The strain is such that after only a very few years her fertility decreases, her milk levels drop, and she is quickly replaced with a more profitable animal. As with all other intensively farmed animals, she is destined for the dinner plate: the white stuff is inseparable from the red stuff.

And it is not only the cow that suffers. Male calves are of the wrong breed to be raised for beef, so their only economic worth is as veal. Quotas and subsidy systems mean that each pint of milk is worth much more to the farmer than its market value, so little can be spared for the calf and they are often ripped from their mothers after just a few hours, causing enormous distress to both mother and child. The notorious veal crates are now being phased out throughout Europe, but legal recommendations for the housing and feeding of veal calves still fall well below recognised welfare requirements.

EGGS

In the European Union around 90% of laying hens are kept in battery cages so small that they cannot stretch their wings, peck, scratch the ground or perform most of their other natural behaviours. Up to 90,000 caged hens may be crammed into one windowless shed, with cages often stacked up to 9 storeys high.

This close confinement not only causes major psychological stress, but can also cause physical damage to the birds. The lack of exercise and the unnatural diet lead to brittle bones that are easily broken. This problem has become so bad that it is now thought to be responsible for around 35% of premature deaths in battery systems: the injured birds are unable to reach food or water and simply starve to death.

Battery systems are to be outlawed in Europe from 2012, but the so-called 'enriched cages' that will replace them are little better. Each hen will have roughly a postcard-sized piece of extra space. This may be an improvement of sorts, but evidence (and common sense) suggests that birds will continue to suffer both physical and psychological stress.

"But," says the ethical egg-lover, "I only buy free-range eggs." The myth of the free-range egg continues to salve the consciences of many British consumers. Images of fat, feathery farmyard chickens pecking and scratching in the dust couldn't be further from the reality of the majority of "free-range" systems. The birds are often kept in flocks of up to 16,000 to a shed, and although there must be access to the outside, this is often through a hole so small and so difficult to reach that up to half the birds in large scale so-called free-range units never see the light of day.

After a year of egg production, fertility decreases and most laying hens are sent for slaughter: worth as little as two pence per bird, they end up in soups, pasties, pies, etc where the pathetic condition of their bodies will not put consumers off their meal.

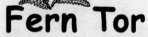

As with dairy calves, laying hen chicks are of the wrong strain to be raised for meat. Male chicks are therefore completely worthless and are killed when they are just one day old; common slaughter methods include gassing, neck dislocation and the 'homogeniser,' a device that minces chicks alive.

FISH

Fish farming is now the world's fastest growing sector of animal production. Up to 50,000 salmon can be crowded together in a single sea cage, resulting in each 75cm long salmon having the equivalent of a bathtub of water to swim in. Trout are usually stocked at even higher densities (as many as 27 trout to one bathtub). The stress caused by these unnatural conditions (a wild salmon will swim thousands of miles to return to its spawning ground) leads to physical injuries and increased susceptibility to disease. Official figures show that disease-related death rates among farmed fish are as high as 10 to 30%.

Parasites are another devastating problem for intensively farmed fish. The large concentrations of fish attract sea lice that feed on the host salmon, often causing such severe damage to the fish that the skull becomes visible, a condition that has become known as the 'death crown.' The highly toxic products used to treat these infestations cause considerable environmental damage.

And it is not only the fish themselves that suffer. Every year hundreds of fish-eating species (notably seals, birds, mink, and otters) are attracted to these vast stocks of fish and are shot by fish farmers attempting to protect their livelihoods.

HONEY

Non-vegans are often surprised to learn that honey and other bee-products are unsuitable for vegans. One of the commonest queries we get at The Vegan Society is "I'm a vegan, but I don't really understand why I can't eat honey." Again it's the old storybook image that confuses us: we see honey bees flying around, gathering nectar and taking it back to their hives – what cruelty could possibly be involved?

In fact, bees are manipulated in similar ways to other farmed animals to provide a whole range of products, including honey, beeswax, propolis, bee pollen, bee brood, royal jelly and venom.

The major welfare problems associated with bee keeping are centred around the egg-laying process. The queen is routinely artificially inseminated by sperm from decapitated bees (they would normally mate in flight). She is usually killed after 2 years, when her egg-laying abilities begin to decline, and replaced by a new queen, often purchased by mail order from specialist breeding companies. The queens' wings are clipped to force the hives to remain in a single location.

Honey, stored by the bees for the lean winter months, is removed for human use and replaced with nutrient-deficient glucose or corn syrup. Synthetic pesticides and antibiotics are also used. A bee will, on average, fly about 800km to provide half a teaspoon of honey.

SHELLAC

Lac are insects (Lacifer lacca) living on lac trees, where the female secretes a protective resin over herself. It is this resin, along with encrusted live insects, that is scraped from the trees and manufactured into shellac. 100,000 lac insects are killed for 333g of shellac. India is the world's main producer of shellac at around 20,000 tonnes per year.

Shellac is used as a glaze for fruit (such as those surprisingly shiny supermarket apples), nuts, coffee beans; in paint, varnish, tablets, cosmetics, confectionery, floor polish; and in hats as a stiffener. Whilst synthetic resin could easily replace shellac entirely, public demand for 'natural' products may actually be encouraging greater production.

COCHINEAL

Cochineal, a red dye used in clothing and foodstuffs, consists of dried bodies of Dactylopius coccus, an insect indigenous to Central and South America. The female insects are picked by hand after mating and dried in shade for 20 to 30 days. About 100,000 to 150,000 insects yield 1 kg of raw cochineal. Total world production, though fluctuating, is estimated at 150 to 180 tonnes per year with Peru accounting for 90% and the rest coming from the Canary Islands.

OR THOSE WHO KNOW...

a good thing when they see it!

Now you can enjoy the good things in life with Swedish Glace from Winner, a luxurious dessert and the perfect alternative to dairy ice cream for vegetarians and vegans.

What's more, it's completely free from lactose, cholesterol, animal fats, gluten and genetically modified ingredients! So, if you're looking for a fabulous dessert in the style of luxurious ice cream, Winner Swedish Glace is perfect!

Experience it for yourself ...
If you know what's
good for you!

Authentic
SWEDISH GLACE

Recipe supplied by
The Vegetarian Society

ayrefield Foods Ltd, Crewe, Cheshire CW1 5UF. Tel: 01270 589311 Website: www.fayrefield.com

SILK

The most common species of silkworm (moth larvae) used in commercial silk production, Bombyx mori, has been 'cultivated' over many centuries and no longer exists in the wild. The female annually lays 300-400 eggs on mulberry trees, secreting a sticky substance to fasten them to the surface.

The silkworm secretes a fine thread to make a cocoon around itself consisting of about 300,000 figure of eight movements. The pupa stage would then be followed by the production of an alkaline substance that would eat through the threads, allowing the moth to emerge, but as the industry requires the threads intact, the pupa is killed by immersing the cocoon in boiling water, steaming, oven drying or exposure to the hot sun.

Only a tiny amount of usable silk is obtained from each cocoon: it takes around 80kg of cocoons and 200kg of mulberry leaves to produce just 1kg of silk. The dead pupae are typically composted to feed the mulberry trees.

WOOL

The majority of sheep are shorn for the first time at 14 to 15 months and thereafter annually. Early season shearing in wet, windy and cold conditions can result in severe chilling, a high incidence of mastitis and even death.

Australia is the world's largest wool-producing country with 118.5 million sheep. 20 to 40% of Australian lambs die either at birth or before the age of 8 weeks, from exposure after shearing, starvation, heat exhaustion, or following castration, tail docking, mulesing (removing strips of flesh, without anaesthetic, from around anal and vaginal areas to deter egg-laying flies) and other stock operations. Lambs are susceptible to shock, blood poisoning, tetanus, dislocated joints and arthritis.

Raw wool contains 10 to 25% grease or lanolin, which is recovered during the scouring process. Lanolin consists of a highly complex mixture of esters, alcohols, and fatty acids and is used in adhesive tape, printing inks, motor oils, and machine lubrication. It can also be refined for use in cosmetics and pharmaceuticals.

FUR

The trade in wild furs is responsible for the decline of many species and the extinction of some. As the larger cats became commercially extinct or protected, the fur trade turned to the smaller ones. Thousands of lynx and bobcat are still being trapped each year in North America using steel leg-hold traps (now banned in Europe) which do not kill the animal outright and cause immeasurable suffering.

World wide, more than 30 million minks and foxes are imprisoned in row upon row of wire cages to produce fur. In the UK there are currently 11 fur farms rearing mink. Animals kept in fur factory farms (with small, barren cages averaging at about 90cm by 30cm by 40cm) show stereotypical behaviour, self-mutilation and cannibalism. They are killed by gassing, neck-breaking, lethal injection, or anal electrocution. Thanks to determined campaigning by animal welfare charities, fur farms are to be outlawed in England and Wales by 2003.

LEATHER

Vegans don't eat the inside and, increasingly, they also don't wear the outside. Leather is simply fur with the hairs scraped off one side and the flesh scraped and chemically removed from the other side. The sale of leather makes a sizeable contribution to the viability of the meat industry – it is not a by-product of animal suffering, it is a contributing factor.

Synthetic alternatives such as lorica, from which vegetarian shoes and jackets are made, are superior to leather: with micropores which allow perspiration out but don't allow water droplets in, they do not become waterlogged or need drying out.

See the clothing section of The Animal Free Shopper for a range of vegan footwear suppliers.

VIVISECTION

Home Office statistics show that the total number of procedures on animals in the UK in 2001 was 2,622,442 and 59% of these were conducted without anaesthetic.

THEY CALL IT TESTING.
TO HER IT'S TORTURE

You could help end animal testing forever

In the UK nearly three million animals suffer in laboratories every year. The BUAV opposes all animal experiments and campaigns peacefully and effectively to end them. Visit www.buav.org to find out more.

Call the BUAV on 020 7619 6963 or email fundraising@buav.org

- To ask for a free copy of our *Little Book of Cruelty Free* products
- To support the BUAV with a donation
- To get active in support of our campaigns, as a BUAV *Campaigner*

British Union for the Abolition of Vivisection, 16a Crane Grove, London, N7 8NN

BUAV
campaigning to end animal experiments

There are three main areas of research in which these experiments are claimed to be useful: to increase scientific knowledge, to aid the development of new products, and to test the safety of new products and their ingredients.

Some of the more common experiments are the LD-50 (now banned in the UK, but common throughout the rest of the world), the Draize test, and skin irritancy tests. LD-50 (Lethal Dose 50%) involves giving animals increasing amounts of a chemical or drug to find the dosage required to kill 50% of the test group. The Draize test is performed on rabbits – substances such as laundry products, bleaches and washing-up liquids are dripped into their eyes, which are then examined for signs of damage such as ulcers, bleeding, swelling, or discharge. In skin irritancy tests, the skin of the rabbit or other rodent is shaved and the substance is applied to the wound, which is then examined for adverse reactions.

There is currently a proposal to retest more than 30,000 commonly used chemicals as part of the EU's new chemicals policy. This would constitute the largest animal-testing programme in Europe's history.

Cosmetics testing was banned in the UK in 1998, but many companies continue to test products and ingredients in mainland Europe and elsewhere. There is no legislation to prevent these products being sold in the UK.

HEALTH

HEART DISEASE AND CANCER

Replacing animal foods with plant foods and thus reducing intakes of saturated fat and cholesterol and increasing intakes of fibre, vitamin C, folate and carotenoids promotes good health.

Meat has around 40% of calories from fat and cheese has around 70% of which more than 60% is the dangerous saturated fat. Eggs are the richest source of cholesterol: more than one egg a day would exceed recommended cholesterol intakes even if no other animal products were consumed.

Dietary guidelines across the world, including the meat-guzzling USA, now acknowledge the vegan alternative. Fortified plant milks are accepted as an alternative to dairy products as a source of calcium, and beans and nuts are accepted as an alternative to meat and fish as a source of protein. Recommended vegetable and fruit intakes continue to rise, with many experts replacing the familiar five-a-day advice with nine-a-day or more. Research has shown that a diet rich in fruit and vegetables can decrease the risk of having a heart attack or stroke, protect against a variety of cancers, lower blood pressure, reduce risk of intestinal ailments and guard against loss of vision in the elderly.

Compared with lacto-ovo-vegetarians and meat eaters, vegans usually have significantly higher intakes of nutrients associated with reduced risk of cardiovascular disease - including fibre, vitamin C, potassium, magnesium, and folate - as well as lower intakes of sodium. They also consume less total fat and less saturated fat, and have lower levels of total cholesterol as well as a better ratio of total cholesterol: to HDL cholesterol.

Research has confirmed reduced risk of heart disease in vegans and other vegetarians. This is believed to be due to lower intakes of saturated fat and cholesterol and higher intakes of fruit and vegetables. However, research has also indicated that some vegans are not getting the full potential benefit of their diet, due to less than optimal intakes of vitamin B12 and omega-3 fatty acids. This is easily remedied by getting at least 3 micrograms of B12 per day from fortified foods or supplements and including some omega-3 rich foods such as rapeseed oil or flaxseed oil (see Nutrition section p.46). We look forward to even better results from studies of vegan health once this advice becomes widely adopted.

Evidence is also growing that diets high in milk and dairy products increase the risk of prostate cancer and that diets high in processed meats and low in fibre increase the risk of colon cancer. In this context, it is good news that plant protein sources are now almost universally accepted as providing all the protein we need: when it comes to health, there is nothing second rate about plant foods.

DAIRY ALLERGY AND INTOLERANCE

Dairy products are a common trigger for eczema in infants and can also cause chronic constipation. Most people of African or Asian descent and a significant minority of Caucasians are lactose intolerant: milk sugar causes

digestive problems such as bloating and diarrhoea because they lack the enzymes to break it down.

It should therefore come as no surprise that in the UK that 31% of all consumers (17 million people) are attempting to reduce their consumption of dairy products, 13% (more than 7 million people) never or hardly ever eat dairy foods, and 22% claim to purchase 'regularly' non-dairy products such as soya milk.

FOOD POISONING

Studies have demonstrated that 53% of bovine carcasses and 83% of pig carcasses were contaminated with E-coli, while 18% of raw chicken from Britain and 64% of imported poultry contained salmonella. In a 1996 study, more than half of UK-bred chickens purchased from retail outlets contained campylobacter. Eggs and egg-containing foods were involved in 10% of outbreaks of food poisoning in England and Wales between 1992 and 1999. Almost 17,000 cases of salmonella infection in humans were confirmed in 1999. In fact, food poisoning from eggs has become such a problem that in 2001 the Government's Food Standards Agency stated that eating raw eggs may pose a health risk. They went on to advise that vulnerable groups, "should only consume eggs that have been cooked until the white and yolks are solid." Diarrhetic, paralytic and amnesic shellfish poisoning has also been found in several areas of the UK.

CJD

There is now convincing evidence that the agent that causes BSE is the same as that which causes new variant Creutzfeld Jacob disease (nvCJD) in humans. More than 100 people have now died in the UK. There is still a real possibility that the final death toll will be over 10,000, but earlier estimates of millions of deaths now seem unlikely. This is a matter of luck, as the difficulty of controlling the recent foot and mouth disease epidemic illustrates how easily and quickly infections can spread in modern factory farms: anyone continuing to consume animals is therefore taking a major gamble on their health and that of their family.

Prions, the 'rogue' proteins believed to be responsible for BSE and CJD, have not been found in milk or milk products, but the prion agent is contained in white blood cells which are legally permitted in milk at levels up to 2 million per teaspoon!

ANTIBIOTICS

British farmers are some of the heaviest users of antibiotics in Europe, accounting for more than 20% of the 1225 tonnes of antibiotics used annually on farm animals. Antibiotic-resistant bugs — long feared, but now found for the first time in a Glasgow hospital — have resulted from the use of antibiotic growth promoters in farm animals, not the overuse of antibiotics in hospitals. For example Vancomycin is chemically identical to Avoparcin which from 1976 until 1997 was the most widely used antibiotic growth promoter in the UK being fed to most chickens, turkeys, pigs and about 30% of all cattle. DNA sequencing showed that Vancomycin resistance in bugs infecting humans has come entirely from the use of Avoparcin and not from the use of Vancomycin. Approximately 1 tonne of Avoparcin was used for every 1kg of Vancomycin.

GMOs

Of concern to the consumer wishing to avoid genetically modified organisms (GMOs), because of possible long-term effects on health or the implications of their release into the environment, is the presence in the UK food supply of GM soya, containing genes derived from a bacterium, a virus and a petunia. Soya is found in around 50% of all processed foods.

So far, there has been very little research to assess the health and safety implications of GMOs. The insertion of foreign genes can have many harmful unexpected effects: for instance the insertion of a Brazil nut gene into soya resulted in a reaction in people allergic to nuts. There is also a risk of increasing antibiotic resistance in bacteria. Critics warn of unexpected and irreversible effects on agriculture and biodiversity. They condemn the immorality of the 'patenting of life' — transgenic animals, plants and seeds. From a vegan perspective, even if no animal gene was used during the modification process, it is likely that animal-derived enzymes were employed.

GM material can cross species barriers to other crops and weeds, and once released it is impossible to 'clean up' any unforeseen consequences. Plants designed to kill 'pests' can kill beneficial insects as well and stimulate the development of resistance in the pests. Plants engineered for herbicide resistance will encourage increased use of chemicals. Most American farmers who have turned to GM crops seem to be getting yields no better

VERSATILE Fry Light

THE ONLY 1 Cal SPRAY

Fry Light Extra Virgin Olive Oil and Sunflower Oil can be found at Asda, Budgens, Tesco, Safeway and Sainsburys, while the Sunflower Oil variety is also available from Co-Op and Morrisons and many independent shops.

Most recipes call for a precise amount of ingredients, so it's hardly surprising that Fry Light cooking sprays are so popular. It is the only patented oil spray which delivers a measured one calorie of oil per spray so it can help you follow a healthier eating plan. Award winning Fry Light lets you roast, sauté, fry and bake using up to 30 times less fat and calories than regular oils. It's so versatile that you can prepare delicious soups, sauces, pastas, meat and fish dishes as well as delectable puddings – with professional results every time!

If you would like to receive a free set of Fry Light recipes send a large sae to Fry Light, HPR Ltd, PO Box 36, Brackley, Northants NN13 5FN

than farmers growing traditional varieties. They also appear to be using similar quantities of pesticides.

The Soil Association believes that genetic modification has no place in the production of safe and healthy food. Organic farming systems aim to produce food with care for human health, the environment and animal welfare.

In keeping with its vegan ethic, The Vegan Society is totally against the use of animal genes or animal substances in the development and production of GMOs. The Vegan Society believes that all foods that contain, may contain, or have involved GMOs should be clearly labelled, and has signed up to the Five Year Freeze campaign for a moratorium on genetic engineering and patenting in food and farming.

ECOLOGY

More and more people are becoming aware of the direct correlation between what they eat every day and the health of the planet. Environmentally conscious consumers are concerned not only with food miles, over-packaging, pesticide use and GM foods, but increasingly question the environmental sustainability of modern animal husbandry. Farmers used to be seen as 'custodians of the countryside,' but the overriding image of modern industrial farming is one of destruction and waste.

The meat-intensive diets of the West contribute, among other things, to global warming, deforestation, desertification, water pollution, and loss of fossil fuels.

GLOBAL WARMING

Global temperatures continue to rise at an alarming rate. Whilst no one can say for certain what the consequences may be, sea level rise, climate change, and species loss are just a few of the possibilities that we face.

Intensive animal husbandry contributes to this environmental crisis in a number of complex ways. The most straightforward statistic is that 16% of anthropogenic emissions of methane come from cattle. Methane is one of the three gases thought to be responsible for global warming; it is produced by bacteria in the stomachs of ruminants such as sheep, cattle, and goats and is farted and belched out by the animals. Dairy cows have been calculated to produce roughly 30kg more methane per year than free-range beef cattle (84kg and 54kg respectively), largely because of differences in diet and levels of exercise. When manure is kept in anaerobic conditions (as in the liquid systems commonly used on intensive farms), even more methane is produced. Manure is also responsible for 7% of emissions of nitrous oxide (a more aggressive greenhouse gas).

In addition to these direct impacts on global warming, animal husbandry also has some more well hidden costs. The felling of forests to provide land to grow food for cattle (see below) means that there are fewer and fewer trees to absorb carbon dioxide, the major greenhouse gas. The feed crops are then grown using artificial fertilisers that release nitrous oxides. Their processing, transport and storage use up fossil fuels, releasing carbon dioxide.

Changing to a vegan diet will not stop global warming, but if you worry about using your car, having baths, turning on the heating, and using energy saving lightbulbs, you should also be worrying about the amount of damage the food you eat is causing.

DEFORESTATION

We need forests. They store large amounts of carbon dioxide, release oxygen, protect soils, and harbour millions of varieties of plant and animal species. Yet they are being destroyed at an alarming rate. The United Nation's Food and Agriculture Organisation estimates that the net loss of forests for the 1990s as a whole was 94 million hectares. This represents an area larger than Venezuela. Forests are being destroyed not only to provide wood, paper and fuel, but also to provide land for grazing cattle and for growing crops to feed to animals (see 'Resource Use' below).

DESERTIFICATION

The felling of forests and over-grazing also contributes to soil loss and desertification. Thin layers of topsoil previously protected by a fine network of roots are extremely vulnerable when the forest cover is removed and are

Pharma Nord

For quality products that work choose Pharma Nord.

The Pharma Nord range includes:

Bio-Biloba
Bio-Carnitine
Bio-Chromium
Bio-C-Vitamin
Bio-Garlic
Bio-Lipoic Acid
Bio-Magnesium
Bio-MSM+Silica
Bio-Pycnogenol
Bio-Trim
Bio-Fiber 80

FOR INFORMATION AND TO PLACE AN ORDER CALL FREEPHONE 0800 591 756

Pharma Nord (UK) Ltd, Telford Court, Morpeth, NE61 2DB

often simply washed away or compacted and broken down by heavy cattle.

The UN estimates that more than 250 million people are directly affected by desertification and around one billion people in more than a hundred countries are at risk from famine and malnutrition as a result of the rapid decrease in the fertile land available for growing crops for humans.

WATER POLLUTION

Every year farmers spread about 200 million tonnes of animal manures and other organic farm wastes on to the land as fertiliser. Slurry and silage effluent can pollute a nearby river or stream by encouraging algal blooms that block sunlight and encourage bacteria that deplete the water of oxygen, in the worst cases killing all the fish and endangering the health of other animals in the area. This process is known as eutrophication, and farming is the major cause of the problem.

Slurry, which is made up of manure and urine, contains high levels of ammonia. This encourages bacteria that produce acid that directly contributes to acid rain. Slurry can be up to 100 times more polluting than raw untreated domestic sewage. Silage effluent, the liquid produced when preserving crops for fodder, is up to 200 times more polluting.

TANNERIES

In its natural state as hide or skin, leather would be totally unsuitable for its current uses and would rot rapidly. To make it pliable and longer lasting, hide is treated with a wide range of environmentally damaging chemicals such as lime, sodium sulphate solution, emulsifiers, non-solvent degreasing agents, salt, formic acid, sulphuric acid, chromium sulphate salts, lead, zinc, formaldehyde, fats, alcohol, sodium bicarbonate, dyes, resin binders, waxes, coal tar derivatives and cyanide-based finishes. Tannery effluent contains large amounts of other pollutants such as proteins and hair. Overall, the production of leather is far more polluting than modern synthetic versions such as lorica.

ENVIRONMENT EMERGENCY HOTLINE

The Environment Agency's emergency hotline number 0800 807060 operates 24 hours a day, 365 days a year, for people to report pollution, fish in distress, illegal disposal of waste, poaching and danger to the natural environment.

RESOURCE USE

LAND

Meat and dairy production is a notoriously inefficient use of energy. All animals use the energy they get from food to move around, keep warm and perform their day to day bodily functions. This means that only a small percentage (around 10%) of the energy that farmed animals obtain from plant foods is converted into meat or dairy products.

Yet livestock use roughly 3.4 billion hectares of grazing land, and the production of around one quarter of all croplands. In all, the raising of livestock takes up more than two-thirds of agricultural land, and one third of the total land area (Food and Agricultural Organisation)

Quite simply, we do not have enough land to feed everyone on an animal-based diet. So while we continue to waste two-thirds of agricultural land by obtaining only 10% of its potential calorific value, almost 1 billion people are undernourished. A third of the children in the world suffered from malnutrition during the 1990s. More than 24,000 people still die every day from hunger-related causes. Shocking statistics indeed when enough plant foods are grown to feed everyone. It has been estimated that 10 acres of land could feed just 2 people on a diet of cattle meat, but 61 people on soya beans.

Obviously access to food is an extremely complex issue, and all too often war, corruption and lack of infrastructure mean that even when food is available people starve. However, with a rapidly increasing world population the fact remains that a plant-based diet is the most environmentally sustainable option available.

WATER

Only 0.06% of the earth's water is fresh, and even less than this is available as drinking water. Yet we continue to squander vast amounts of this most precious of natural resources on farmed animals. Growing 1kg of potatoes

GREEN PEOPLE

100% free from

Sodium Lauryl Sulphate, Synthetic fragrances, PABA sunscreen, GM organisms,
Petro-chemicals, DEA, TEA, Ethyl Alcohol or any unnecessary ingredients.

Not tested on animals and approved by The Vegan Society

ORGANIC LIFESTYLE

FREE Catalogue and Trial Sachet: 01444 401 444   www.greenpeople.co.uk

requires 500 litres of water, while producing the same amount of beef takes 100,000 litres of water. In fact, it has been estimated that a day's food for a meat eater requires more than 15,000 litres of water, compared with 5,000 for a vegetarian and a mere 1,500 for a vegan.

Water required for food production

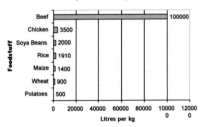

Foodstuff	Litres per kg
Beef	100000
Chicken	3500
Soya Beans	2000
Rice	1910
Maize	1400
Wheat	900
Potatoes	500

(Source: New Scientist Global Environment Report)

UNICEF investigations suggest that approximately 1.1 billion people have no access to safe water.

SPIRITUAL

Central to the beliefs of many of those following an animal-free lifestyle is the conviction of harmlessness or reverence for life, embodied in the spirit of ahimsa, the Sanskrit word for non-killing and non-injury championed by Mahatma Ghandi.

Some animal-free shoppers are allied to a particular church such as the pacifist Society of Friends (Quakers) or Seventh Day Adventists, to a particular faith such as Buddhism, Jainism or Christianity or empathise with paganism (eg Wicca, druidry) or humanism.

Many consider that their animal-free lifestyle, its practical application and sense of inner peace, provide for most of their spiritual needs and there is a tendency towards vegetarianism and veganism within the modern spiritual/personal growth movements.

Liberation of animals from human tyranny, health benefits for humans, resource use, and ecological and spiritual considerations, are five very good reasons for adopting an animal-free lifestyle. With The Animal Free Shopper in your pocket, it's never been easier or more fun to GO VEGAN!

HEALTHY EATING FOR VEGANS

Sandra Hood BSc(Hons) SRD

One of the most important ways to influence our health is through our diet and as vegans, we often feel that we have to prove that we can be healthy and that we are getting enough of this or that particular nutrient. However, it is all too easy to become obsessed with meeting the nutritional requirements of the general population and forget to look at the other side of the coin and how protective a vegan diet can be.

The mainstay of a healthy diet is plenty of unrefined carbohydrates, such as cereals, pulses and whole grains, plus the important vitamins, minerals and phytochemicals found in fruits and vegetables, and the essential fatty acids found in nuts, seeds and oils. This healthy eating diet has been shown not only to prevent illness but also to treat it. Compared with omnivores, vegetarians have been shown to be at lower risk for conditions such as constipation, diverticular disease, gallstones and appendicitis. Vegan diets have also been used to treat diseases such as angina, diabetes, high blood pressure, rheumatoid arthritis and kidney disease.

In recent years there has been a lot of emphasis on vegans adopting a more raw food oriented or fruitarian diet, and no doubt we should all be including more raw foods in our diet. However, it can also be very bulky and unsuitable for infants and children. Cooking may damage some plant nutrients, but in many cases it alters the structure of nutrients in a way that may actually increase the availability of phytochemicals, resulting in significant health effects. For instance, lycopene (a carotenoid and precursor of vitamin A) is far better absorbed from cooked tomatoes than from raw ones. To maximise benefit from the plant nutrients in the diet, therefore, it is best to include a variety of both raw and cooked foods.

The following paragraphs give a brief outline of nutrients that may be of particular interest to vegans. There are very few rules about what you should or should not eat, but it is important to ensure a reliable source of vitamin B12, and if sun exposure is limited vitamin D supplements or fortified foods should be used.

WORLD VEGAN DAY

The first World Vegan Day was held in 1944 to celebrate the 50th Anniversary of the invention of the word 'vegan' and the founding of the first Vegan Society by Donald Watson in November 1944.

Veganism is now celebrated worldwide on **1st November** every year.

Why not visit
www.worldveganday.org
for interactive forums, news, events etc.

You can contact The Vegan Society for a World Vegan Day Pack which contains all you need to start planning an event or party to celebrate the Vegan Birthday.

Aim to eat a variety of whole foods, including the following food groups on a daily basis:

- Fruits
- Vegetables
- Nuts and seeds
- Cereals
- Pulses

ENERGY

Carbohydrates
These are the main energy foods, and half your energy should come from carbohydrates. There are two types of carbohydrates: starchy foods and sugary foods. Try to choose mainly starchy foods such as whole grain bread, pasta, rice, potatoes and cereals. Vegans generally have a high fibre diet with less reliance on refined carbohydrates; in the refining process, essential nutrients are lost.

Fibre
This is the part of a plant that cannot be digested. All plant foods contain fibre. There are two categories of fibre, soluble and insoluble, and most plants contain a mixture of the two. Insoluble fibre adds bulk to stools and ensures that food passes quickly and easily through the intestinal tract. Soluble fibre, found in peas, beans, oats and lentils, has been shown to reduce blood cholesterol levels. Vegans have been shown to consume 40 to 50g of fibre per day compared with 30 to 40g per day for vegetarians and 10 to 20g per day for omnivores. Recommended minimum intakes are 18g per day and the World Health Organisation (WHO) recommends an upper limit of 54g per day. It has been suggested that intakes comparable with those of vegans would be beneficial for health.

It has been reported that excess fibre may reduce the absorption of certain minerals, but high fibre whole foods provide enough extra minerals to more than compensate for any losses incurred. When fibre does bind with minerals, they can be partly released during the fermentation of fibre by bacteria in the large bowel.

Fats
Fats provide vitamins and energy, are essential for the manufacture of hormones and are important for insulation and protection. Fat should

provide approximately 30% of adult energy requirements while infants need a higher intake. Most people are confused about the type and quantity of fats. Whether a fat is solid or liquid at room temperature, it will contain the same amount of calories. The main constituents of all fats are fatty acids, which may be saturated, monounsaturated or polyunsaturated, depending on the number of double bonds between the carbon atoms in the molecule. As the number of double bonds increases, the fats become more unsaturated or oily. There are more than 40 fatty acids found in nature.

There is no physiological requirement for dietary fat, only for essential fatty acids. These are the polyunsaturated fats:

- Linoleic – sunflower, corn, safflower and soya oils
- Alpha-linolenic – linseed, walnut and rapeseed oils

Humans and other mammals lack the enzyme to synthesise them, so they are essential in the diet.

Saturated fats
Saturated fat has been linked with heart disease; it raises cholesterol levels in the blood, and the higher your cholesterol level the greater the risk of suffering a stroke or heart attack. Meat and saturated fat go hand in hand, and animal products are the greatest sources of saturated fat in the Western diet. Milk fat is more than 60% saturated fat, compared with 6 to 25% for plant fats, most being in the 10-15% range. The exceptions are tropical oils such as coconut and palm oil.

Monounsaturated fat
Studies have shown that monounsaturated fats (MUFAs) can reduce the risk of heart disease. Vegan dietary sources include olives and olive oil, rapeseed oil, nuts [such as almonds, cashews, hazelnuts, macadamias] and avocados. MUFAs should provide the main source of fat intake.

Polyunsaturated fat
The main dietary sources are vegetable oils, seeds, nuts, grains, legumes and other plant foods. Studies regarding their health effects are inconsistent, but when they replace saturated fats and trans fatty acids in the diet there is no doubt that they are beneficial. The two essential fatty acids are linoleic and alpha-linolenic acid. Linoleic acid is found in vegetable seeds and oils such as soya, corn, sunflower, safflower, walnuts and grains.

Alpha-linolenic acid is found in linseed, rapeseed and walnuts. A high ratio of linoleic to alpha-linolenic acid inhibits the production of eicosapentaeonic acid (EPA) and docosahexaenoic acid (DHA), so it is important that vegans achieve a good balance of polyunsaturated fatty acids to ensure adequate levels of EPA and DHA.

Trans fatty acids (hydrogenated oils)
People believe that they are making healthier choices by changing from butter to margarine, but trans fatty acids produced in the manufacture of margarine have been shown to be as harmful as saturated fat. Therefore, choose margarines which do not contain hydrogenated oils and avoid processed foods such as crackers, chips, biscuits, pastries and crisps.

PROTEIN

Protein provides the building blocks for new tissue and is vital for the growth and repair of all cells. It can also be used for energy production, if needed, or stored as fat. Protein is made up of 22 amino acids, the building blocks of protein; 8 of these are essential amino acids because the human body cannot make them, but they are easily supplied by plants. Plant sources can provide adequate amounts of essential and non-essential amino acids. Good sources of protein include nuts, seeds, grains (wheat, oat, rice, barley, buckwheat, millet, pasta, bread) and pulses (peas, beans, lentils).

Many people erroneously believe that animal protein is necessary for human health and that plant protein is inferior. Omnivores tend to have protein intakes above recommendations while vegan intakes meet the recommendations. Combining amino acids is unnecessary as they are stored in protein pools which can be drawn upon as needed.

Summary
- Use whole grains in preference to refined grains.
- Ensure a good balance of polyunsaturated fatty acids.
- Monounsaturated fatty acids should provide the main source of fat intake.
- Avoid hydrogenated oils.

VITAMINS

Vitamins are found in small quantities and are essential for normal body functioning. Fat soluble vitamins are A, D, E and K. Water soluble vitamins

are B and C. With few exceptions, vitamins cannot be synthesised by the body and must be obtained from the diet. A vegan diet can provide all the vitamins necessary for good health. The following are of particular interest to vegans:

Vitamin C

Vitamin C is a powerful water soluble antioxidant, neutralising harmful reactions in the blood and the fluid inside the surrounding cells. Vegans and vegetarians are at a distinct advantage here and need to lead the way in the health revolution.

Vitamin D

Vitamin D3 is normally obtained from lanolin, which is derived from sheep's wool and not acceptable to vegans. However, most people get sufficient vitamin D through the action of sunlight on the skin. Spending time outside reduces your need for foods fortified with vitamin D. When sun exposure is limited, a vitamin D supplement may be necessary. Vitamin D promotes the absorption of calcium and is essential for bones and teeth. Foods fortified with a vegan source of vitamin D (vitamin D2, ergocalciferol) include margarine, fortified cereals and some fortified non-dairy milks.

Sentenced!
...because she's a mother

This sow will try to feed and mother her young for 28 days in a cage only inches bigger than her body.

Her piglets will be torn away, kept in filthy, concrete pens and given drugs daily until being killed at six months old

This is normal, this is factory farming, this is animal abuse

Viva! works to protect animals, people and the planet from greed and exploitation.

We do it through energetic campaigning, by exposing the sickening conditions in which farmed animals are kept and by encouraging people to become vegetarian or vegan.

Add your voice to ours and help *Viva!* throw open the cages.

For a FREE *Go Vegan* pack, including our new merchandise and book catalogues, contact:

Viva!, 12 Queen Square, Brighton BN1 3FD, UK
T: 0845 4568220   E: info@viva.org.uk   W: www.viva.org.uk

Vitamin B12

This vitamin is essential for the formation of red blood cells and a healthy nervous system. Some plant foods may contain vitamin B12 on their surface from soil residues, but this is not a reliable source. Much of the vitamin B12 present in spirulina, sea vegetables, tempeh and miso has been shown to be an inactive form rather than the active vitamin. So if you are not taking foods fortified with vitamin B12, ensure that you take a supplement. The UK government recommends 1.5 micrograms per day as sufficient to reliably prevent clinical deficiency, but higher intakes are required to avoid elevated homocysteine and associated increased mortality. The Vegan Society therefore recommends that all vegans get at least 3 micrograms of B12 every day to maximise the health benefits of their diet. (For further details, see www.vegansociety.com or contact the Vegan Society for a B12 information sheet.)

Summary
- Ensure regular exposure to sunlight for adequate vitamin D.
- Ensure a daily source of vitamin B12.

MINERALS

There are a number of minerals essential for health, but most are only needed in small amounts which come from a varied diet of whole grains, fruits, vegetables, nuts and seeds. The two main minerals needed in larger amounts which are of some interest to vegans are iron and calcium.

Calcium

Studies have found that vegan diets may be below current recommendations for calcium. Claims are commonly made that vegans require less calcium than omnivores, based on the lower acid production resulting from metabolism of plant proteins. This has not been resolved. Although oxalates, phytates and fibre in plant foods decrease calcium availability, research shows that absorption of calcium from many plant foods is excellent. Calcium absorption from low oxalate vegetables such as broccoli and kale is better than for cow's milk while absorption from beans, nuts and seeds is lower. Good vegan sources of calcium include dark green leafy vegetables such as spring greens and kale, calcium-set tofu, baked beans and fortified foods.

Iron

Vegan diets are higher in total iron content than omnivorous diets, but iron stores are lower in vegans because the iron from plant foods, known as non-haem iron, is less well absorbed than the haem iron found in meat. However, iron deficiency anaemia is no more common in vegans than in omnivores. Vitamin C and other organic acids commonly found in vegetables strongly enhance the absorption of non-haem iron. Vitamin C intakes of vegans are frequently high and this, in conjunction with generous levels of dietary iron, may compensate for the lower bioavailability of non-haem iron. Good iron sources include whole or enriched grains and grain products, iron-fortified cereals, legumes, green leafy vegetables and dried fruits.

Zinc
Diets of vegan and non-vegans often contain similar amounts of zinc. However, zinc from plant foods is less well absorbed as some plant foods contain phytate which interferes with zinc absorption. However, no reports of zinc deficiency in vegans have been found. Zinc is an essential component of a number of enzyme systems within the body and is widely distributed in plant foods. Good sources include nuts, seeds, beans and cereals.

Iodine
Iodine is needed by the thyroid gland to produce the thyroid hormone which regulates physical and mental development, including growth, reproduction and other essential functions. Iodine deficiency is rare in the UK. The main source of iodine in the UK is cow's milk, due to iodine supplemented cattle feed and the contamination of milk from teat dips containing iodophors as sterilising agents. Sea foods are rich sources of iodine, with dried seaweed being a popular choice for vegans. Two kelp tablets per week will ensure sufficient iodine; more than this is not desirable.

Summary
- Calcium absorption from low oxalate vegetables such as broccoli and kale is good.
- Vitamin C aids iron absorption.
- Good sources of zinc are nuts, seeds, beans and cereals.
- Seaweed is rich in iodine.

PHYTOCHEMICALS

It has been known for a long time that fruits and vegetables, grains, seeds, nuts and pulses are good for you, being rich in vitamins, minerals and fibre, but in the past few years there has also been interest in the phytochemicals, which have been shown to have many health benefits.

Some phytochemicals are strong antioxidants which mop up free radicals (active harmful molecules circulating in the body).

A special group of phytochemicals are the plant oestrogens, which block the deleterious action of the potent form of oestrogen either by competing with it for receptor sites or by reducing production of the potent form while increasing production of the less potent form, possibly reducing the risk of osteoporosis and certain types of hormone-dependent cancers. Concerns have been raised regarding the potential adverse effects of phytoestrogens in soya infant formulas, and the best food for babies is certainly breast milk. Nevertheless, where breast feeding is not possible there is a role for soya infant formulas, which have been used for many years without any reports of adverse effects other than occasional allergy. For children and adults, soya should be regarded as another healthy food to be added to the diet in moderation.

Another important group are the plant sterols - a type of fat which has been shown to protect against heart disease. There are no dietary recommendations for sterols, but plant sterols have been shown to be beneficial in lowering cholesterol; high levels of cholesterol in the blood can cause heart disease. The average Western diet contains 180 to 400mg plant sterols per day while the vegan diet contains 600 to 800mg per day.

Useful references

Davis B, Melina V (2000) *Becoming Vegan: the complete guide to adopting a healthy plant-based diet*, Book Publishing Co. Summertown.

Key TJ, Davey GK, Appleby PN (2001) *Health benefits of a vegetarian diet*, Proc Nutr Soc 58 271-275.

Langley G (1988) *Vegan Nutrition*, Vegan Society.

FOOD

BISCUITS

ANDUTRA LTD ⊘

Oskri Organic

ASHBOURNE BISCUITS LTD ⊘

Gingerbread Men, **Organic Biscuits: Ginger, Lemon, Oat & Raisin**

BAKEBEST ⊘

Prewetts Organic: Brazil, Choc Chip, Oatbran

CRAWFORD'S ⊘

Bourbon Creams: 500g, Portion Pack; Cream Crackers Portion Pack, Finger Nice, Jam Rings, Morning Coffee, Oat & Wholemeal Portion Pack, Pink Wafer, Shortcake

DOVES FARM FOODS ⊘

Apple & Sultana Flapjack, **Biscuits: Digestive, Fruity Oat, Plain Choc Digestives**; Cookies: **Choc Chip (Gluten Free), Lemon (Gluten Free), Seven Secrets, Vanilla Swirls**

ELKES BISCUITS ⊘

Digestive Biscuits, Ginger Nuts

FIRST QUALITY FOODS ☺⊘

Ma Baker Giant Bar: Almond, Apple, Apricot, Banana, Cherry, Peanut, Sesame, Walnut; **Ma Baker Organic Bar: Apple, Apricot, Orange**

FOX'S BISCUITS ⊘

Biscuits & Herbs, **Ginger Snaps,** Original Thick Tea, **Stem Ginger Crinkle**

GRANOVITA UK LTD ⊘

Castus Bar: Date & Apricot, Date & Nut, Raisin; **Organic Flapjack: Ginger, Pumpkin, Raisin & Linseed, Traditional Oat**

HEMP SHOP LTD ❶⊘⊘

Hemp Flapjack

HERON QUALITY FOODS LTD ☺❶✿⊘

Gluten-free Organic Biscuits: Chocolate Chip, Coconut & Cherry, Coconut & Raisin, Crunchy Nut, Shortbread

JACOBS ⊘

Bourbon Creams, Fig Rolls, Lemon Puff, Shortcake

JORDAN (CEREALS) LTD ⊘

Organic Crunchy Bar

KALLO FOODS ⊘

Flapjacks: Natural, Raisin

McVITIE'S ⊘

Abbey Crunch, Butter Puffs, Fruit Shortcake, Ginger Nuts, Go Ahead Ginger Crisp, Hob Nobs, Lincoln, Teletubbies Favourite Things

PANTRI NOLWENN ⊘™

Cookies: Almond, Chocolate Drop, Oat Lace

R J FOODS LIMITED ☺⊘™

98% Fat-Free Flapjacks: Cherry & Sultana, Fruit, Original; Crispy Rice Bar w Real Chocolate, *Flapjacks:* **Organic Chocolate**, Apple & Apricot, Cherry & Coconut, Cherry & Sultana, Date & Walnut, Fig, Fruit Bar, Mincemeat Bar, Muesli, Plain, Raspberry, Rum & Raisin

TRUFREE ™⊘

Bourbon, *Cookies:* Chocolate Chip, Gingernut; Custard Creams, Shortcake

VEGANSTORE.CO.UK ☺™❶✔⊘

ABC Cookies, Nature's Choice Multigrain Cereal Bars, Traditional Choc Chip Cookie Mix

VILLAGE BAKERY ✿⊘

 Apricot Slice, Date Slice, Oatcakes, Organic Trophy Bars: 4 Fruit, 4 Nut, 4 Seed; Savoury Seed Biscuits

VITALINEA ⊘

Fig Rolls

WHOLEBAKE LTD ⊘

Crisp Bar: Cherry & Almond, Cranberry, Original, Pecan; *Fruit Slice:* Apple & Cinnamon, Apricot & Apple, Date, Fig, Plum; Hemp Flapjack, *Luxury Flapjack:* Apricot, Cherry & Coconut, Cranberry, Date & Walnut, Fruit & Nut, Original;

Organic Crisp: Citrus, Hazel & Choc Chip, Raisin & Almond; *Organic Flapjack:* Coconut, Hazelnut, Original, Sunflower Seed; Pineapple & Almond Carob Topped Bar

ZEDZ FOODS ⊘

Date & Ginger Flapjack

BREADS, ROLLS, PIZZA BASES ETC

BAKEOVEN

Bread: Blackforest, Danish Three-Seed Malted, Eight-Grain Tinned, Pumpkin & Sunflower, Walnut Bavarian Long Sliced; *Farmhouse:* Bloomer, Ring; *Goldgrain:* Standard, w Sesame, Walnut; Mischbrot, *Muesli:* Bread, Rolls; *Pretzels:* Crescent, Rolls, Selection, Standard, Sticks; *Rye:* **Organic**, Backhaus, Backhaus Long Tin Sliced, Bavarian Bloomer, Bloomer, Caraway, Danish Light, Four-Grain, Light Caraway, Malted, Onion, Polish Light, Russian, Square, Sunflower Tinned, Vollkorn, Walnut Tinned; *Sandwich Bread:* Three-Malts, Wholemeal; *Special:* Blackforest, Ciabatta, Paderborner, Pain d'Alsace; *Special Rye:* Backhaus, Bavarian, Eight-Grain, Four-Grain, Onion, Six-Grain, Steinofen, Sunflower Tin, Walnut Tinned, Yeast-Free; *Stoneground Rye:* Bloomer, Onion, Round; Vintschgauer,

Wholemeal: Baps, Large, Long Loaf, Small

COOPLANDS LTD ⊘

Breads: All

DOVES FARM FOODS ⊘

Malt Loaf

ECO-ZONE ☺ ◢ ⊘

Organic Part-Cooked Bread w Seaweed

ENJOY ORGANIC CO LTD ✿ ⊘

Loaves: Seeded Batch, Soft White Flour Dusted Thick Sliced, Soft Wholemeal, White Farmhouse, Wholemeal Farmhouse; Soft Brown Seeded Rolls

H J HEINZ ™⊘

Danish Bread: Brown, Malted, White; *Rolls:* Soft Malted Grain, White Soft

HEMP SHOP LTD ❶ ◢ ⊘

Hemp Sprouted Wheat Bread

HERON QUALITY FOODS LTD ☺❶✿⊘

Gluten-free Organic Mixes: Bread, Bread & Cake, Hi-Bran Bread, Wheat-Free Bread

NATURE'S PLATE ™✿⊘

Breakfast Baguette

NEW YORK BAGEL CO. LTD ⊘

Bagels (NOT Longlife): **Organic**

Original, Cinnamon & Raisin, Onion, Original, Poppy, Sesame

ORGRAN ⊘

Bread Mix, Gourmet Pesto Bread Mix, Pizza & Pastry Mix

PANTRI NOLWENN ™⊘

Banettes: aux Noix, Seigle, Seigle Special, Walnut; Boule Integrale, *Bread:* Banana, Brith, Irish Soda, Olive, Pepper, Raisin, Sundried Tomato; Date-Walnut Ffrengig, Demi-Baguette aux Raisins, Klondike Gold, Onion Rye, Rustic Rye, Rye, Spelta

PAUL'S TOFU ™

Bread: Brown Rice Bread, Cornutopia, Foccacia, Four Seed, Fruit Rye, La Tabatiere, Light Rye, Melton Loaf, Olive, Pain de Campagne, Pane Basilicum, Sechskorn, Tempeh, Tomato, Unbleached White; *Gluten Free Sourdough Bread:* Number One, Number Two, Number Three; **Organic Bread: Herb, Individual Baguette, Melton loaf, Unbleached White; Organic Tea Cakes; *Organic Yeasted Bread:* Malthouse, Mixed, Plain, Spelt, Stoneground Wholemeal, Wheatfree Rye**; *Rolls:* **Organic, Organic Sesame**, White; *Sourdough Bread:* 4 Seed, Rice, Rye & Sweetcorn, Spelt, Sprouted Kamut Wheat, Tsampa, Yeast Free

PRIMO D'ORO ⊘

Torinesi: Black Pepper, Original

SHARWOOD & COMPANY LTD, J.A. ⊘

Naan Bread Mix

THE STAMP COLLECTION ⊘

*Organic & Wheat-free Bread w
Seed Topping:* **Poppy**, **Rolled Oat**,
Sunflower

TRUFREE ™⊘

Bread Mix, *Part Baked White:* Bread,
Rolls

VILLAGE BAKERY ✿⊘

**Baltic Rye, Borodinsky, Campagne,
Gluten-Free, Hadrian, Pane
Toscano, Raisin Borodinsky,
Rossisky, Ten-Seed**

WARBURTONS SOREEN ⊘

Soreen Loaf: Banana Fruit, Lincolnshire
Plum, Rich Fruit Loaf

BREAKFAST FOODS

BAKEBEST ⊘

Sunwheel Special Deluxe Museli

DOVES FARM FOODS ⊘

Biobiz, Corn Flakes, Multi Flakes

GRANOVITA UK LTD ⊘

Classic Flakes

GREENCITY WHOLEFOODS ❶⊘

Highland Bramble Crunch, *Muesli:*
**Organic Base, Organic Deluxe,
Organically Produced Special (no
coconut)**, Base, Crunchy, Deluxe, Five
Star, Gluten-Free, High Fibre, Paradise,
Super, Super (no coconut), Traditional;
Paradise Nuts & Fruit

H J HEINZ ™⊘

Perfect Balance Breakfast Cereal

HERON QUALITY FOODS LTD
☺❶✿⊘

Gluten-free Muesli

JORDAN (CEREALS) LTD ⊘

Country Crisp: Four Nut, Raisin,
Raspberry, Strawberry, Wild About
Berries; *Luxury Crunchy:* Maple &
Pecan, Red Berry & Almond; *Muesli:*
Organic, Natural, Special; Nature's
Wholegrain Maple & Pecan, **Organic
Four Berry Crisp, Organic Raisin &
Coconut Crunchy**

KALLO FOODS ⊘

Puffed Rice Cereal - Natural

KELLOGGS

Apricot Bites, *Coco Pops:* Caramel,
Original; Corn Flakes, *Frosties:* Original,
Toffee; Fruit 'n Fibre, Just Right, Oat Bran
Flakes & Fruit, Raisin Wheats, Rice Krispies

LITTLE SALKELD MILL ☺✿⊘

Watermill Muesli

MARIGOLD HEALTH FOODS ❶⊘

Organic Sultana Crunch, Super Muesli

NESTLE UK LTD

Force, Shredded Wheat, Shredded Wheat Bitesize

PERTWOOD ORGANIC CEREAL COMPANY LTD ☺✿⊘

Organic Barley Crisp: **Cocoa**, **Maple Syrup**, **Original**; **Organic Crunchy w Raisins & Almonds**, *Organic Muesli:* **w Delicious Fruit**, **w Fruit & Seeds**

QUAKER OATS LTD ⊘

Harvest Crunch: Nut, Raisin, Redberries; Oat Bran Crispies, Oat Krunchies, *Oatso Simple:* Baked Apple, Berry Burst, Golden Syrup, Original; Puffed Wheat, Scotts So Easy Original Cereal

RYVITA ⊘

Sunblest: Bran Flakes, Cornflakes, Frosted Flakes

SHEPHERDBOY ™⊘

Organic Muesli w Hempseed

SUMA WHOLEFOODS ™⊘✔

Branflakes, Bransticks, *Crunch:* Cranberry, Sultana; *Muesli:* Base, Gluten Free, Luxury Tropical, Roast Hazelnut, Super; **Organic Meusli: Base, De Luxe, Standard**

WEETABIX LTD ⊘

Alpen: Crunchy Bran, Wheat Flakes; *Nature's Own Organic:* **Malt Wheat Squares**, **Wheat Biscuits**; *Ready Brek:* Original, Rip Mix & Micro Bursting Banana, Rip Mix & Micro Saucy Strawberry; *Weetabix:* Mini Crunch Fruit & Nut, Original

WHOLE EARTH FOODS LTD ✿⊘

Cornflakes, Maple Frosted Flakes, Swiss Style Muesli

'BURGERS', 'SAUSAGES', 'MEAT' SLICES ETC

AMBROSIAN VEGETARIAN FOODS ☺™⊘

Organic Burgers: **Chilli Bean**, **Savoury**, **Sesame & Sunflower Seed Vegetable**; **Organic Savoury Burger Mix**, *Organic Sosages:* **Hot as Mustard**, **Plain**, **Savoury Herb**, **Tomato & Garlic**

CAULDRON FOODS LTD ⊘

Burgers: Chilli, Savoury, Spicy Bean, Vegetable Burger

DIRECT FOODS ⊘

Dry Mixes: Beef Style Mince, Burgamix, Chicken-Style Savoury Bake, Sosmix, Sosmix Country Herb

DRAGONFLY FOODS ☼ ⊘

Organic Beany Savoury (Soya-Based Burger): **Baked, Curry, Mushroom, Natural, Nut, Olive, Smoky, Spicy, Tomato, Vegetable**; *Organic Beany Sweet (Soya-Based Burger):* **Apple, Apricot, Chocolate, Date, Fig, Fruity**; **Original Organic Soysage**

FRY'S ☺ ❶ ⊘   *Beanie's Health Foods*

Special Vegetarian Frozen Foods: (BBQ) Sausages, Cutlets, Hot Dogs, Nuggets, Polony Slicing Sausage, Schnitzels, Spiced Burgers, Traditional Burgers, Traditional Sausages

GOODLIFE FOODS ⊘

Nut Burger, **Organic Spicy Bean Quarter Pounder, Organic Vegetable Burger**

GRANOSE ⊘

Vegetarian Sausages

GRANOVITA UK LTD ⊘

Vitamix: Burger, Sausage

IT'S SOYA GOOD ⊘

Soya Chunks, Soya Mince

JUST WHOLEFOODS ☺⊘

Mixes: **Banger, Burger**

ORGANIC ⊘ ☼

Dry mixes: **Burgamix, Sosmix, Soya Mince**

PAUL'S TOFU™

Five Grain Tofu Burgers: **Organic Bengal, Organic Mexican Chilli**, w Herbs, w Nuts

REALEAT ⊘

Fishless Fish Cake, Herb & Vegetable VegeBurger (dry mix), *VegeBangers:* Herb (dry mix), Meaty style (frozen), Spicy (dry mix); VegeMince

REDWOOD WHOLEFOOD COMPANY ☺™❶⊘

Cheatin' Bites: Chicken Style, Chicken Style Barbeque, Chicken Style Tikka, Chicken w 5-spice; *Cheatin' Roasts:* Beef, Celebration, Turkey; *Cheatin' Slices:* Beef, Chicken, Garlic Sausage, Ham, Pepperoni, Turkey; **Organic Sausages: Frankfurter Style, Lincolnshire Style**; **Organic Vegetarian Rashers,** *Rashers:* Streaky-Style, Tempeh; Vegetarian Breaded Fish-Style Fingers, *Vegi-Deli Sausages:* Oregano & Basil, Sage & Marjoram, Sage & Marjoram (ready to eat); *Vegi-Deli Slices:* Boston Baked Bean Style, Provencal Style, Spicy Chilli Style, Spicy Thai Style; *Wafer Thin Cheatin' Slices:* Chicken, Ham, Turkey

SOTO TOFU ⊘

Veg Sausages: **Bavarian, Curry, Spicy**

SUMA WHOLEFOODS ™⊘ ⚓

Burger Mix, Sausage Mix

TAIFUN ☺✿⊘

Tofu Green-Spelt Hazelnut Cutlet, *Tofu Sausages:* **Grill, Herb, Party, Sombreros, Thuringer, Wiener; Tofu-Spelt Cutlet**

VEGANSTORE.CO.UK ☺™❶✓⊘

Burgamix, Mock Meat Strips, *NOT!:* Chicken Breast Fillets 'n' Sauce, Chicken Nuggets, Chicken Salad Mix, Tuna Salad Mix; Pepperoni Slices, Sosmix, Stonewall's Jerky

VEGETARIANS CHOICE ™☺❶⊘

Vegetable Protein: Burgers, Sausage Mix, Sausages

VEGGIES CATERING CAMPAIGN ☺™❶⊘

Burgers: Chilli, Hemp, Veggies; *Mixes:* Hemp-seed Burger, Veggies Burger, Veggies Sosage; *Sosages:* Savory, Tomato, Veggies

WICKEN FEN ⊘

Lime, Coriander & Garlic Fillets, Meaty Style Burger, Mini Nuggets, *Sausages:* Country Herb, Crumbed Cumberland Style, Cumberland Style Meaty, Mediterranean Roasted Vegetable, Mushroom & Tarragon, Seasonal (Thai Spinach), Tasty Mexicana, Tomato & Garlic

ZEDZ FOODS ⊘

Burgers: Herb & Aubergine, Sage & Onion, Tofu & Ginger

CAKES & CAKE MIXES

LYONS ⊘

Apple Pies, Assorted Tarts, Real Fruit Jam Tarts, Treacle Lattice Tart

MR KIPLING ⊘

Bramley Apple Fruit Pie Bars, *Fruit Pies:* Apple & Blackcurrant, Summer Fruit; *Fruit Selection:* Apple & Blackcurrant, Apricot

ORGRAN ⊘

Gluten-Free Pancake Mixes: Apple & Cinnamon, Buckwheat; *Gluten-Free Sponge Pudding Mix:* Chocolate, Lemon

PANTRI NOLWENN ™⊘

Bisgeden, *Cake:* Carrot, Fruit; Cnau Cyll a Syltanas, Joch o Lemon

PAUL'S TOFU ™

Gluten Free Banana & Date Cake

STILETTO FOODS ⊘

Mrs Crimble's: Chocolate & Orange Cake, Dutch Fruit Loaf

TRUFREE ™⊘

Cake Mix

VEGANSTORE.CO.UK ☺™❶✓⊘

Carob Coated Doughnuts, Cinnamon Pecan Danish, Crostatina Mini Fruit

Tarts, Double Dark Devil's Food Cake Mix, **Dove's Organic Easy Bar, No Bake Organic Tofu Cheesecake Mix,** Rich & Thick Brownie Mix

VILLAGE BAKERY ☼ ⊘

Celebration Fruit Cake

ZEDZ FOODS ⊘

Rich Fruit Cake Slices, Spiced Apple Mirabel Sweet Pasty, *Sweet Muffins:* Apricot & Ginger, Banana, Banana, Carrot & Orange, Carrot & Orange - sugar-free, Carrot & Raisin, Carrot & Raisin - sugar-free, Cherry & Coconut, Chocolate, Chocolate, Chocolate & Orange, Coconut & Date, Coconut & Date, Coffee & Walnut, Date & Ginger, Poppy Seed & Lemon

'CHEESE' & 'CHEESE' SPREADS

BIDDY MERKINS ™⊘

Vegerella

BUTE ISLAND FOODS ☺❶⊘

Scheese: Blue Flavour, Cheddar Style, Cheddar w Chives, Cheshire Style, Edam Style, Emmental Flavour, Gouda Style, Hickory Smoked Style, Mozzarella Style

FAYREFIELD FOODS LTD

Swedish Soft: Garlic & Herb, Original

FLORENTINO ™⊘

Parmazano Parmesan Replacer

REDWOOD WHOLEFOOD COMPANY ☺™❶⊘

Cheezly: Feta Style, Garlic & Herb Flavoured, Mature Cheddar Style, Mature Cheddar Style w Cranberries, Nacho Style, Smokey Style w Added Bacon Style Pieces; *Cream Style Cheezly:* Garlic & Herb Flavour, Original, Sour Cream & Chive Flavour

TOFUTTI UK LTD ⊘

Soft Cheese: French Onion, Garlic & Herb, Herb & Chives, Original

VEGANSTORE.CO.UK ☺™❶☀⊘

Parmazano

CHOCOLATE

ANIMAL AID ☺❶☀⊘⚓76

Chocolate Bars: All; *Chocolate Boxes:* Coffee Cremes, Orange Cremes, Pecan Parfait, Peppermint Fondant Cremes, Rose & Violet Cremes; Fair Trade Plain Chocolate Brazils, *Truffles:* All; Vegan Chocolate Box Selection

CELTIC CHOCOLATES LTD ⊘

Celtic Fine Dark Chocolate: Bars, Mint Crisps

D & D CHOCOLATES ☺⊘

Dark Chocolate: Bar, Dinosaur Shapes, Flower Shapes, Peppermint Fondant Creams, Plain Chocolate Chips for Cooking / Eating, Praline Hearts

DR HADWEN TRUST ☺⋪⊘

Champagne Truffles, Chocolate Brazils, Chocolate Fudge Cubes & Coconut Ice Cubes, Chocolate-coated Orange Bites, Classic Gold Vegan Chocolate Assortment, Coffee Creme Dream, Fine Mint Chocolates, **Hazelnut Crunch Rocher,** Luxury 1lb Vegan Chocolate Assortment, **Organic Gourmet Chocolate Truffles Selection**

ELIZABETH SHAW LTD ⊘

Afterdinner Mints, Coffee Crisp, Mint Crisp, Orange Crisp, Twist Wrapped Mint Creams (Pick 'n' Mix)

EQUAL EXCHANGE TRADING ⊘

Fairtrade Chocolate Covered Brazil Nuts

GREEN & BLACKS ✿⊘

Organic Dark Chocolate: 70%, Fairtrade Maya Gold, Hazelnut & Currant

KALLO FOODS ⊘

Plain Chocolate

LIFESTYLE HEALTHCARE LTD ™⊘

Whizzers: Chocolate Beans, Chocolate Footballs, Chocolate Mint Balls, Speckled Eggs

LINDT & SPRUNGLI ⊘

Excellence: 70%, 85%; Swiss Thins Dark

LYME REGIS FINE FOODS LTD ⊘

Marzipan Bar - Plain Chocolate Coated

NATURAL COLLECTION, THE ⋪⊘

Chocolates: All

OSCAR BARS ™⊘

Oscar Chocolate Coated Bars: Coconut Ice, Date & Hazelnut, Peanut & Raisin

Plamil ☺™❶⊘

Organic Chocolate: Cayenne, Drops, Expressions, Mint, Orange, Plain; *Soya Based Chocolate*: Hazelnut, Martello, Mint, Plain

RITTER S ⊘

Ritter Sport: Marzipan, Peppermint, Plain Chocolate

ROCOCO CHOCOLATES ⊘

Rococo Artisan Bars: Black Pepper, Boozy (Raisin & Armagnac), Caramelised Almond, Cardamom (Dark), Chilli, Cocoa Nibs, Crystallised Ginger, Earl Grey, Lavender, Lime & Basil, Orange & Geranium, Orange Confite, Peppermint, Pink Pepper, Rosemary, Toasted Coconut; *Rococo English Selection:* Alm Marzip, Banana, Coffee, Geranium, Ginger, Lavender,

Pist Marzip, Raspberry, Rose, Strawberry, Violet; *Rococo Swiss Recipe:* Almond Lubecker Marzipan, Dipped Apricot, Dipped Glace Orange, Orange Stick, Walnut Lubecker Marzipan

SUMA WHOLEFOODS ™⊗✔

Organic Dark Chocolate Coated: **Brazils**, **Peanuts**, **Raisins**

THE BOOJA BOOJA COMPANY LTD ☺™✿⊗

Hazelnut Crunch Rocher, *Truffles:* **Around Midnight Espresso, Champagne, Cognac Flambed Banana, Ginger Wine**

THE STAMP COLLECTION ⊗

Organic & Dairy-free Dark Chocolates w Sun-Dried Fruit Centres: **Sun-Dried Apricot**, **Sun-Dried Sultana, Sunflower Seed**

VEGANSTORE.CO.UK ☺™❶✔⊗

Booja Booja Truffles, *Montezuma Speciality Bars:* All; **Organic Chocolate Brazils,** Tiny Tasty Turtles, *Whizzers Chocolate Treats:* All

VIVA! ☺❶✔⊗

Belgian Pralines, Gourmet Truffle Selection, Handmade Vegan Chocolate Selection, Hazelnut Crunch Rocher, Mint Pounds, Orange Cremes, Pecan Parfait, Plain Chocolate Bar, Whizzers Chocolate Beans

CONFECTIONERY & SWEET SNACKS

ANIMAL AID ☺❶✔⊗☃76

Stem Ginger

AUSTRALIAN NOUGAT COMPANY ™⊗

Macadamia Bliss Nougat w Pistachio

CLEARSPRING ☺™❶⊗

Organic Snack Bar: **Almond, Sesame, Sesame & Raisin**; *Sweets:* Butterscotch, Ginger, Lemon, Peppermint, Sour Plum, Vanilla

COMMEX FOODS LTD ⊗

Coolabar: Apricot & Nuts, Cashew & Sesame, Macadamia & Fruit, Macadamia & Nut

D & D CHOCOLATES ☺⊗

Siesta Carob Confectionary: Animal Shapes (original, orange, peppermint), Bar (original, orange, peppermint), Carob Drops, Carob Flakes for Cooking, Dinosaur Shapes, Flower Shapes, Heart Shapes (Original, Orange, Peppermint), Teddy Bear

DEXTRO ENERGY

Glucose Tablets: Blackcurrant, Lemon, Orange, Original, Tropical

DOVES FARM FOODS ⊗

Cereal Bars: **Easy, Tasty**

FOOD

DR HADWEN TRUST ☺ ✔ ⊘

Fruit Bonbons, Rose & Lemon Turkish Delight, Vanilla Fudge

FIRST FOODS ☺⊘

Peak Bars: Apple, Banana; *Tropical Fruit Bar*

FRUTINA ⊘

100% Fruit Snacks

JUST WHOLEFOODS ☺⊘

VegeBear's: **Frooty Fruits**, **Fruit Jellies**, **Go Liquorice!**

KELLOGGS

Real Fruit Winders: Blackcurrant, Orange, Strawberry

LIFESTYLE HEALTHCARE LTD ™⊘

Silhouette Dark Carob Bar, Whizzers Mint Humbugs

LYME REGIS FINE FOODS LTD ⊘

Fruitus: **Apple**, **Apricot**, **Marzipan Bar**, **Sultana & Hazelnut**; *La Fruit:* Apricot, Banana, Date & Fig, Ginger & Pear, Raspberry; *Max Power:* Apricot & Peach, Hazelnut & Raisin; *Zaps:* Apricot, Orange

MOTHER HEMP LTD. ™✔ ⊘

Bag o' Seed "small & fruity", **Organic Motherhemp Bar w Apple & Cranberry**

NESTLE UK LTD

Fox Glacier: Fruits, Mints; *Polo:* Citrus Sharp, Extra Strong, Fruits, Original, Spearmint, Sugar-Free, Super OJ's, Supermint

ORGRAN ⊘

Gluten-Free Fruit Bars: Apricot, Banana, Blueberry-Filled, Figs

Plamil ☺™❶⊘

Carob Confections: Drops, Hazelnut, No Added Sugar, Orange, Plain

POWER HEALTH PRODUCTS ✔ ⊘

Herb Candy Sticks: Aniseed, Barley Sugar, Blackcurrant, Cinnamon, Lemon, Liquorice Juice Sticks, Orange, Pineapple, Strawberry; *Sugar-free:* Fruits, Mints; White Aniseed Balls

RADFORDS OF DEVON ⊘

Dairy-free Fudge: Cherry, Coconut Ice, Ginger, Rum & Raisin, Vanilla, Walnut

SHEPHERDBOY ™⊘

Fruit Bars: **Organic Sunflower**, Apple, Carob Fruit & Nut, Coconut / Pineapple Fruit & Nut, Cranberry Bar, Ginger Fruit & Nut, Multi Fruit, Sunflower Fruit & Nut; Hempower Bar, *Just / So Carob Bars:* Crispy, Ginger, Mint, Orange

SWIZZELS MATLOW LTD ⊘

Climpies, Mr Fruits, Rainbow, *Deposited:* Barley Sugar, Menthol Eucalyptus; *Deposited Crystal:* Fruits,

Licorice, Mints; *Lolly:* Fruity Pops, Ice-Cream Pops, Swizz Kid Fruity

THORNTONS PLC ⊘

Fruit Jellies, *Jelly:* Blackcurrant Bat, Fish, Raspberry Spider, Teddies; Mint Crumbles, *Mr Men:* Assorted Jelly Bag, Hard Boiled Lolly Bag, Sugar Paste Decorated Lollies

VEGANSTORE.CO.UK ☺™❶✔⊘

Holy Cow Fudge: Bars, Gift Box; Just Wholefood Vegebears

VIVA! ☺❶✔⊘

Dairy-Free Fudge, Fizzy Cola Bottles, Sour Frenchies, Vegebear's Frooty Fruits, Vegebear's Fruit Jellies

WILLIAM SANTUS & CO LTD ⊘

Uncle Joe's Mint Balls

WRIGLEY CO LTD ⊘

Airwaves: Blackcurrant, Menthol & Eucalyptus; Doublemint, *Extra:* Cool Breeze, Peppermint, Spearmint, Winterfresh; *Hubba Bubba:* Atomic Apple, Awesome Orange, Seriously Strawberry, Juicy Fruit, *Orbit:* Ice White, Peppermint, Spearmint, Sweetmint, White; Spearmint, *X-cite:* Delight, Rush

COOKING AIDS — SAVOURY

CLEARSPRING ☺™❶⊘

Agar Agar Flakes, Arame, Brown Rice Mochi, *Danival Sea Salt:* Coarse, Fine; Dulse - Atlantic Coast USA, Green Nori Flakes, Hijiki, Japanese Brown Rice Syrup, Kombu, Kombu - Breton, Kuzu, Lotus Root Slices - Dried, Maitake Mushrooms, *Malt Syrup:* **Organic Barley**, **Organic Japanese Millet**, **Organic Rice**, Corn & Barley, English Barley; Mikawa Mirin, Mirin, Mugwort Mochi, Nori, Nori-Flavoured Strips, *Organic Amazake:* **Brown Rice**, **Millet**; **Organic Mikawa Mirin, Organic Pumpkin Puree, Organic Umeboshi Plums,** Sake, Sea Salad, *Seagreens:* **Organic Culinary Ingredient, Organic Table Condiment,** Fluted Glass Shaker - Half Filled w Culinary Ingredient, Grinder - Half Filled w Table Condiment; Shiitake Mushrooms, Shiso Condiment, Shredded Daikon - Dried, *Sushi:* Cucumber, Daikon, Garlic (w Umeboshi), Ginger; Sushi-Nori Toasted, Takuan (pickled daikon radish), *Tamari:* **Organic Mansan**, Mansan, San J; Tekka (Miso Condiment), Tsuyu, Ume Concentrate, Ume Plum Seasoning, Umeboshi Plums, Umeboshi Puree, Wakame, Wasabi

CROSSE & BLACKWELL

Bonne Cuisine: Sauce a L'Orange, Sauce de Paris; *Classic Creations Recipe Mixes:* Chicken Chasseur, Lamb Ragout, Sheperds Pie; *Indian Creations Recipe Mixes:* Chicken Balti, Chicken Curry, Chicken Korma; *Mexican Creations Recipe Mixes:* Chicken Fajitas, Chilli Con Carne; *Stir Fry Creations Recipe Mixes:* Black Bean Stir Fry, Lemon Chicken, Oriental Chicken, Orietal Beef, Sizzling Black Bean, Sweet & Sour Pork

ECO-ZONE ☺✔⊘

Lemon Wakame, Noirmoutier Island Sea-Salt w Seaweed Flakes, Seaweed Stock

JUST WHOLEFOODS ☺⊘

Stuffing Mixes: **Apple & Sage**, **Mushroom & Sweet Pepper**, **Sage & Onion**; VegeRen, *Wholemeal Croutons:* **Garlic & Herb**, **Lightly Salted**

LIFESTYLE HEALTHCARE LTD™⊘

Allergycare: Gluten-free Baking Powder, Herb & Onion Stuffing Mix

MARIGOLD HEALTH FOODS ❶⊘

Engevita Nutritional Yeast Flakes

ORGRAN ⊘

All Purpose Gluten-Free Crumbs

PATAKS FOODS LTD ⊘

Pastes for Rice: Coconut, Garlic &

Coriander, Pilao

PAUL'S TOFU™

Fresh Yeast

PLANTATION TRADING LIMITED™

Pepperdillos

SAXA & CEREBOS ⊘

All Table & Cooking Salt, Iodised Salt, Low Sodium Salt

SCOTTISH HERBAL SUPPLIES ™✔⊘

Dried Organic Herbs

SEAGREENS CO LTD ☺™✿⊘

Culinary Ingredient Shaker, Culinary Seaweed Ingredient, Pulse Granules, Seaweed Table Condiment, Table Condiment Grinder

SHARWOOD & COMPANY LTD, J.A. ⊘

Creamed Coconut, Vegetable Ghee

TRUFREE ™⊘

Pastry Mix

VEGANSTORE.CO.UK ☺™❶✔⊘

Agar Agar Flakes, Engervita Yeast Flakes

WHITWORTHS LTD ⊘

Sage & Onion Stuffing

COOKING AIDS – SWEET

CLEARSPRING ☺™❶◌

Organic Puree: **Apple**, **Apple / Apricot**, **Apple / Blueberry**, **Apple / Plum**

GREEN & BLACKS ✿◌

Organic 72% Cooking Chocolate

JUST WHOLEFOODS ☺◌

All Natural Custard Powder

NESTLE UK LTD

Creamola: Custard Powder, Rice; Pan Yan Bramley Apple Sauce

PLANTATION TRADING LIMITED

Wild Marula Jelly

SUMA WHOLEFOODS ™◌✔

Cherries: All

VEGANSTORE.CO.UK ☺™❶✔◌

JW Custard Powder

WHITWORTHS LTD ◌

Glace Cherries, Glace Ginger, Luxury Rum Soaked Mixed Dried Fruit

YORK FOODS ™◌

Menier Cooking Chocolate

CRACKERS, CRISPBREADS ETC

ANDUTRA LTD ◌

Newbury: **Organic Corn Slims**, **Organic Crackerello**, Original Corn Slims

CLEARSPRING ☺™❶◌

Brown Rice Sesame Wafers, *Organic Courtney's Crackers:* **Classic**, **Cracked Pepper**, **Savoury Herb**, **Sun-Dried Tomato**; *Organic Rice Cakes:* **Multi-Grain**, **Plain**, **Salted**; *Organic Rice Crackers:* **Extra Virgin Olive Oil & Sea Salt**, **Tamari**; *Rice Cakes:* Double Sesame, Sesame Garlic, Teriyaki; Tamari Brown Rice Crackers

DOVES FARM FOODS ◌

Rye Crackers (Wheat Free)

JACOBS ◌

Crackers: Bran, Cream, Water High Bake; Cornish Wafers, Herbs & Spice Selection

KALLO FOODS ◌

Rice Cakes: **Savoury**, Low Fat; *Snack Size Rice Cakes:* **No Added Salt**, **Savoury**, **Slightly Salted**, **Slightly Salted w Cracked Pepper**; *Thick Slice Rice Cakes:* **No Added Salt**, **No Added Salt w Sesame**, **Slightly Salted**, **Slightly Salted w Sesame**;

Thin Slice Rice Cakes: No Added Salt, **Slightly Salted, Slightly Salted w Sesame, Black Pepper Water Crackers, Corn Cakes,** Low Fat Corn Cakes, **Lower Sugar Rusks, Mini Original Breadsticks, Natural Crackers,** Oat & Rice Cakes, **Original Breadsticks, Original Crisp Rolls, Rosemary Crackers, Rusks, Wholemeal Rye Crispbread**

LITTLE SALKELD MILL ☺ ✿ ⊘

Rice Cakes w Sesame

MILLERS DAMSEL ⊘

Organic Wafers: **Rye (Wheat Free), Wheat**; *Wafers:* Celery, Charcoal, Poppy, Sesame, Wheat

NAIRNS ⊘

Oatcakes: **Organic Rough,** Fine, Traditional Rough

NETWORK OF WHOLEFOOD WHOLESALE CO-OPERATIVES ™⊘

Organic Oatcakes: **Low Salt,** No Salt

ORGRAN ⊘

Gluten-Free Corn Cakes, *Gluten-Free Crackers:* Mediterranean, Natural; *Gluten-free Crispbreads:* Corn, Rice, Rice & Cracked Pepper, Rice & Garden Herb, Rice & Millet, Salsa Corn

PRIMO D'ORO ⊘

Traditional Breadsticks

QUAKER OATS LTD ⊘

Snack-a-Jacks Rice Cakes: Crispy Minis, Jumbo Apple Danish, Jumbo Chocolate

RYVITA ⊘

Allinson Crackerbread: High Fibre, Original Wheat, Wholemeal; **Allinson Organic Wholemeal Crispbread,** *Crispbreads:* Dark Rye, Multigrain, Original Rye, Sesame; *Organic Rice Cakes:* **Original, Sesame**

SANCHI ⊘

Arare: Five Flavour, Quinoa & Tamari; *Crackers:* Black Sesame, Brown Rice, Brown Rice Mini, Tamari, White Sesame

SHARWOOD & COMPANY LTD, J.A. ⊘

Pappads: Bombay Spiced, Green Chilli & Garlic; *Puppodums:* Plain, Spiced; *Ready To Eat Puppodums:* Plain, Spiced

SUMA WHOLEFOODS ™⊘ ✦

Japanese Rice Crackers

TRUFREE ™⊘

Herb & Onion Cracker

VITALINEA ⊘

Cream Crackers

CREAM REPLACERS

ALPRO (UK) LTD ⊘

Soya Dream

GRANOSE ⊘

Soya Creem

RICH PRODUCTS

Coffee Rich: 12 x 1 kg, Single Serve

VEGANSTORE.CO.UK ☺™❶✔⊘

Soya Dream

DESSERTS

ALO SABOR ⊘

Organic Nut Desserts: **Almond, Apple & Apricot, Hazelnut, Hazelnut & Chocolate**

ALPRO (UK) LTD ⊘

Pot Desserts: Chocolate, Hazelnut, Vanilla

H J HEINZ ™⊘

Frozen Apple Crumble w Sultanas

JUST WHOLEFOODS ☺⊘

Jelly: Lemon, Raspberry, Strawberry, Tropical

LEEORA VEGETARIAN FOOD ™⊘

Apple Crumble

MAXIM MARKETING COMPANY ™

Weikfield Jelly Crystals: Cherry, Mango, Orange, Pineapple, Raspberry, Strawberry

NATURAL FEAST CORPORATION ™⊘

Pies: Natural Apple Gourmet Struesel, Peach Gourmet Struesel

NESTLE UK LTD

Rowntree's Ready To Eat Jelly: All

ORGANIC PUDDING ™✿⊘

Puddings: **Chocolate Fudge, Sticky Toffee, Summer Fruit, Tangy Lemon**

PAUL'S TOFU ™

Apple Strudel, Fruit Pie w Kuzu

RICH PRODUCTS

Whip Topping

VEGANSTORE.CO.UK ☺™❶✔⊘

Jelly Mixes, *Organ:* Apple & Cinnamon Pancake Mix, Pudding Mixes

DIPS & DRESSINGS

AINSLEY HARRIOT ™⊘

Marinades: All; *Salad Dressings:* Balsamic Bliss, Mango

ANGLIA OILS LTD ⊘

Organic Midsummer: **French Dressing, Italian Dressing, Low Fat Vinaigrette, Sun Dried Tomato Dressing**

BIDDY MERKINS ™⊘

Alavon Egg-Free Mayonnaise, Coleslaw (made with Alavon mayonnaise)

EQUAL EXCHANGE TRADING ⊘

Organic Tahini: **Dark**, **Light**

GRANOVITA UK LTD ⊘

Mayola!: Garlic, Lemon, Original

HELLMANN'S

Pourable Salad Dressings: Luxury French, Luxury Orange & Balsamic Vinegar, Reduced Calorie Italian Dressing

KALLO FOODS ⊘

Liquid Seasoning

KNORR

'Marinades In Minutes' Flavours: Cajun, Tikka

KP FOODS ⊘

Phileas Fogg Dips: Barbecue, Chunky Salsa, Sweet Chilli

LEEORA VEGETARIAN FOOD ™⊘

Chives Tofu Dip, Greek Tahini, Labanese Humous Mesabha

LIFE ™⊘

Mayonnaise-style Dressing

NESTLE UK LTD

Sarsons For Salads, *Waistline:* Creamy 1000 Island Dressing, Vinigrette

Plamil ☺™❶⊘

Egg-Free Mayonaise: **Organic Plain**, Chilli, Garlic, Plain, Tarragon

PLANTATION TRADING LIMITED ™

Dressings: Lime, Strawberry

SUMA WHOLEFOODS ™⊘✔

Vegannaise: Garlic, Plain

VEGANSTORE.CO.UK ☺™❶✔⊘

Yakso Mayoneze

WALKERS SNACK FOODS LTD ⊘

Dippas: Hot Salsa, Mild Salsa, Sweet & Zesty

EGG REPLACERS

LIFESTYLE HEALTHCARE LTD ™⊘

Allergycare Vegan Egg Replacer

ORGRAN ⊘

No Egg - egg replacer (Gluten-Free)

VEGANSTORE.CO.UK ☺™❶✔⊘

Orgran No Egg

GRAVIES & STOCKS

BISTO ⊘

Granules: Chip Shop Curry Sauce, Gravy for Every Meal Occasion, Onion Gravy, Vegetarian Dishes Gravy; Gravy Powder

JUST WHOLEFOODS ☺⊘

Instant Gravy Granules, Vegetarian Stock Powder

KALLO FOODS ⊘

Just Bouillon: Vegetable Gravy Powder, Vegetable Stock Cubes; *Stock Cubes:* **French Onion**, **Garlic & Herb**, **Low Salt Vegetable**, **Tomato & Herb**, **Vegetable**, Healthy Eating Yeast Free; **Vegetable Stock Powder**

KNORR

Herb Cubes: Mixed Herbs (Basil & Thyme), Parsley & Garlic; Pilau Seasoning Cubes for Rice, *Stock Cubes:* **Organic Vegetable**, Vegetable

LIFESTYLE HEALTHCARE LTD ™⊘

Allergycare Gluten-free Gravy Mix

LITTLE SALKELD MILL ☺✿⊘

Vegan Bouillon Powder

MARIGOLD HEALTH FOODS ❶⊘

Marigold Swiss Vegan Bouillon Powder: **Organic**, Original, Reduced Salt

McDOUGALLS FOODS ⊘

Thickening Granules

NESTLE UK LTD

Gravy Browning

ORGRAN ⊘

Gluten-Free Gravy Mix

VECON ✔⊘

Stock Paste

VEGANSTORE.CO.UK ☺™❶✔⊘

Marigold Vegan Bouillon, Orgran Gravy

'ICE CREAMS', SORBETS ETC

ALPRO (UK) LTD ⊘

Ice Cream: Chocolate, Strawberry, Vanilla

CALYPSO SOFT DRINKS ⊘

Cool Calypso Freeze Drinks w Juice, *Freezepops:* Calypso, Safari, Simpsons

FAYREFIELD FOODS LTD

Swedish Glace: Chocolate, Mocha, Pear, Raspberry, Strawberry, Vanilla

FIRST FOODS ☺⊘

First Glace Ice-Creams: Chocolate, Chocolate Fudge Swirl, Classic Vanilla, Strawberry

HEMP SHOP LTD ❶ ✔ ⊘

Hemp Ice-Cream: Mint Choc-Chip, **Strawberry**, **Vanilla**

MOTHER HEMP LTD. ™ ✔ ⊘

Hemp Ice: Mint Chocolate Chip, Strawberry, Vanilla

NESTLE UK LTD

102 Dalmations, *Mr Men Water Ice:* Blackcurrant, Orange; Traffic Cone

SOYA HEALTH FOODS LTD ☺❶⊘

Sunrise: Carob Ices, Ice-Dream

TOFUTTI UK LTD ⊘

Rock & Roll: Cakes, Cones; *Supreme Ice Cream:* Better Pecan, Chocolate Cookies, Madagascan, Strawberry, Vanilla

MARGARINES, FATS, OILS ETC

ANGLIA OILS LTD ⊘

Bread Dipping Oil: Balsamic Vinegar, Garlic & Chilli; *Collection Prestige:* Groundnut, Stirfry, Toasted Sesame, Walnut; *Cooking Oils:* Again & Again, Harry Ramsdens Traditional Tasting; *Extra Virgin Olive Oil Vinegar Dressing w:* Balsamic, White Wine; *Infused Olive Oil:* Basil, Chilli, Garlic, Lemon; *Spray n*

Cook: Olive Mist, Vegetable Spray

BREWHURST HEALTHFOOD SUPPLIES ™⊘

Vitaquell Margarine: **Organic**, Cuisine, Extra, Omega 3

CLEARSPRING ☺™❶⊘

Organic Oils: **Extra Virgin Olive**, **Hazelnut**, **Safflower**, **Sesame**, **Soybean**, **Sunflower**, **Sunflower Frying**, **Toasted Pumpkin Seed**, **Toasted Sesame**, **Walnut**; *Sesame Oil:* Spicy Toasted, Toasted

COOKEEN

White Fat

CRISP 'N' DRY

Vegetable Oil: Solid, Spry

FIRST ⊘

Cold Pressed Organic Oils: **Hazelnut**, **Peanut**, **Pumpkin Seed**, **Rapeseed**, **Safflower**, **Soyabean**, **Walnut**

FLORA MARGARINES

White Flora

FRY-LIGHT ™⊘

Non-stick Cooking Oil Spray

GR LANE ✔ ⊘

Wheat Germ Oil

GRANOSE ⊘

Margarines: Soya, Sunflower, Vegetable

KOBASHI ☺™✔👁⊘

Hempseed Oil

MATTHEWS FOODS ™⊘

Spreads: **Pure Organic Reduced Fat**, Calvia Calcium Enriched, Pure Soya, Pure Sunflower

MOTHER HEMP LTD. ™✔⊘

Bottled Hempseed Oil, Hempseed Oil

PLANTATION TRADING LIMITED ™

Avocado Oil, Macadamia Nut Butter, Macadamia Nut Oil

RAKUSEN'S ™

Tomor Margarines: 250g Block, 500g Sunflower Tub

SMILDE ™⊘

Sunflower Spread

SUMA WHOLEFOODS ™⊘✔

Suma Spreads: **Organic Sunflower**, 100% Sunflower, Low Fat, Soya

PICKLES, SAUCES, VINEGARS ETC

ANDUTRA LTD ⊘

Cholula Mexican Hot Sauce

ANGLIA OILS LTD ⊘

Chalice Tapenade: Green Olive, Kalamata Olive, Sun Dried Tomato, Sweet Red Pepper; **Midsummer Organic Balsamic Vinegar**

ASPALL ✔⊘

Organic Vinegar: **Balsamic**, **Cyder**, **White Wine**; *Vinegar:* Apple Balsamic, Cyder, White Wine

BAXTERS OF SPEYSIDE LTD ⊘

Beetroot in Redcurrant Jelly, Beetroot Pickle, *Chutney:* Albert's Victorian, Ena's Mulled Plum, Mango w Ginger, Mediterranean, Spiced Fruit, Tomato w Red Pepper; *Jelly:* Cranberry, Mint, Redcurrant, Wild Rowan; *Sauce:* Apple, Cranberry, Mint, Nick Nairn Hot & Sour Red Pepper

BERTOLLI

Pasta Sauces w Olive Oil: Chargrilled Vegetables, Chilli & Onion, Red Wine & Shallots, Roasted Garlic & Mushroom, Sun-ripened Tomato & Basil, Tomato

BRANSTON

Branston Rich & Fruity Sauce, *Pickle:* Original, Sandwich, Tomato

CALEDONIAN CURRY CO. ™⊘

Chilli Relish: Apricot & Fig, Beetroot, Hot Rhubarb, Red Pepper, Tomato

CHICKEN TONIGHT

Jamaican Jerk Stir It Up, *Sauces:*

Brazilian, Creamy Southern Louisiana, Italian Tomato Feast, Mexican Tomato & Sweetcorn, Oriental Sweet & Sour, Spanish Chicken; *Sizzle 'N' Stir Sauces:* Balti, Bhuna, Black Bean, Fruity Sweet & Sour, Hot Chilli Con Carne, Jalfrezi, Medium Chilli Con Carne, Spicy Sweet & Sour, Thai Sweet Chilli

CLEARSPRING ☺™❶⊘

Natto Miso Chutney, **Organic 'Bolognaise' Sauce: Seitan, Tofu**; **Organic Vinegars: Apple Balsamic**, **Balsamic**, **Balsamic - Vintage Aged**, **Brown Rice**, **Red Wine**, **White Wine**; *Shoyu:* **Organic Kagisa**, Johsen

COLMAN'S

Dry Sauce Mix: Shepherd's Pie Casserole, Sweet & Sour Pour Over; Fresh Garden Mint in Vinegar, *Mustards:* English, English Powder, Horseradish, Peppercorn, Wholegrain; *Sauces:* Bramley Apple, Classic Mint, Redcurrant; Sweet Mint Jelly

DIPAK FOODS LTD ™⊘

Curry Sauces: Sunder, Vegetable

ENJOY ORGANIC CO LTD ✿⊘

Mediterranean Sweet Red Pepper Sauce, Spicy Sicilian Tomato Sauce

FLORENTINO ™☺

Pesto: Basil, Red

GO ORGANIC LTD ✿⊘

Italian Tomato Pasta Sauce w:

Aubergine, Black Olive, Red Chilli, Sweet Basil, Sweet Pepper

GRANOVITA UK LTD ⊘

Organic Brown Sauce, Organic Tomato Ketchup

H J HEINZ ™⊘

Apple Sauce: Can, Jar; Exotic Sauce, Mediterranean Olive Sauce, **Organic Tomato Ketchup,** *Pickles:* Mild Mustard, Piccalilli, Ploughman's, Tangy Sandwich, Tangy Tomato; Tomato Frito, Tomato Ketchup, *Vinegars:* Balsamic, Distilled Malt, Malt, Red Wine, Salad, White Wine

HARBOURNE VINEYARD ☺✔⊘

Cider Vinegar

HEMP SHOP LTD ❶✔⊘

Red Vegan Hemp Pesto

KNORR

Fransheok Fruity Curry Sauce

LEEORA VEGETARIAN FOOD ™⊘

Salsa Sauce

LOYD GROSSMAN ⊘

Curry Sauces: Balti, Jalfrezi, Rogan Josh; *Sauces:* Bolognese, Primavera, Sweet Red Pepper, Tomato & Basil, Tomato & Chilli, Tomato & Wild Mushroom

MOTHER HEMP LTD. ™✔⊘

Hemp Pesto - Red Vegan, Hempso

NESTLE UK LTD

Dufrais Bistro Chef: All; *Sarson's Vinegars:* All; Soy Sauce

ORGANICO ⊘

Sauces: Basil, **Spicy Hot**, **Spicy Olive**, **Sweet Pepper**

PATAKS FOODS LTD ⊘

Chutneys: Ginger & Lime, Hot Mango, Mango, Premium Mango; *Cooking Sauces in Cans:* Balti (medium hot, mild), Delhi, Goan Pineapple, Madras, Rogan Josh, Vindaloo; *Cooking Sauces in Jars:* Balti, Goan Pineapple, Jalfrezi, Madras, Rogan Josh, Vindaloo; *Pickles:* Brinjal, Chilli, Garlic, Lime (hot, medium), Mango (hot, medium), Mixed Pickle

RAGU

Pasta Sauces: Basil & Oregano, Country Mushroom, Onions & Garlic, Original Sauce for Bolognese, Red Wine & Herbs, Tomato Lasagne Sauce, Traditional Recipe

SANCHI ⊘

Furikake, *Sauces:* **Organic Shoyu**, **Organic Tamari**, Mirin, Ponzu, Shoyu, Tamari, Teriyaki; *Vinegars:* **Organic Brown Rice**, Ume Su Plum

SEEDS OF CHANGE ✿ ⊘

Cooking sauces: Chilli w Jalapeno Peppers, **Sweet & Sour**; *Pasta Sauce:* Bolognese, Spicy Roast

Garlic, **Tomato & Basil**, **Wild Mushroom & Herb**; *Stir & Serve Sauces For Pasta:* **Roasted Peppers**, **Sundried Tomato & Basil**

SHARWOOD & COMPANY LTD, J.A. ⊘

Balti Curry Pastes: Hot, Medium, Mild; *Canned Cooking Sauces:* Dhansak, Madras, Rogan Josh; *Chilli Sauces:* Hot Chilli, Sweet; *Chutneys:* Apricot, Bengal Hot, Green Label Mango, Indian Curried Fruit, Major Grey, Mango & Apple, Mango & Lime, Peach; *Curry Pastes:* Extra Hot, Hot, Medium, Mild, Tandoori, Tikka; *Dipping Sauces:* Hoi-Sin, Peking Dip, Plum; *Hot Sauces:* Madras Spicy, Vindaloo Extra; Indian Lime Pickle, *Jalfrezi:* Fruity Hot, Hot, Mild, Mini Jar; Rezala; *Soy Sauce:* Light, Rich; *Spice Blends:* Balti, Kerala, Tikka; *Stir-Fry Sauces:* Black Bean, Chop Suey, Hoi-Sin & Spring Onion, Rajmahal Balti, Sweet & Sour, Szechuan Spicy, Tamarind Sweet & Sour, Teriyaki, Yellow Bean; *Stir-Fry Sauces w Vegetables:* Black Bean & Three Mushroom, Chop Suey, Hoi-Sin & Plum, Sweet & Sour, Sweet Chilli & Coriander, Szechuan; *Stir-In Noodle Sauces:* Black Bean & Roasted Pepper, Sweet Chilli & Garlic; *Table Sauces:* Curry, Green Label Chutney

SIMPLY ORGANIC ✿ ⊘

Pasta Sauces: Spicy Tomato, **Tomato & Basil**, **Tomato & Red Pepper**

SUMA WHOLEFOODS ™⃠✔

Organic Pesto: **Green, Red**; *Pasta Sauces:* Affumicata, Arrosta, Romana, Rustica

TASTEE FOODS LTD. ™

Ethnic Vegetable / Fruit Pickles: Carrot & Chilli, Hot Mango, Lime, Mild Mango, Sweet Mango

THE BUTEFUL SAUCE COMPANY ☺™⃠

The Original Buteful Sauce

VEGANSTORE.CO.UK ☺™❶✔⃠

Liquid Smoke, **Organic Dairy free Pesto,** *Sauce Mixes:* Alfedo, Cheese NOT!; Worcestershire Sauce

WHOLE EARTH FOODS LTD ✿⃠

Organic Tomato Ketchup

PIES & PASTIES

AMBROSIAN VEGETARIAN FOODS ☺™⃠

Organic Pasties: Cheez 'n' Chive, **Cheezy Bean**; Tomato & Garlic Sosage Rolls

GET REAL ORGANIC FOODS ✿⃠

Sutaki Pies

NATURAL FEAST CORPORATION ™⃠

Pie Shells

PAUL'S TOFU ™

Organic Mushroom & Tofu Pie, *Tofu Pasties:* Arame, Vegetable

ZEDZ FOODS ⃠

Savoury Muffins: Olive & Oregano, Sundried Tomato & Oregano; *Savoury Pasties:* 'Pizza', Coconut Curry

SAVOURIES — CANNED/BOTTLED

CHESSWOOD ⃠

Chili No Carne, *Organic Vegetable:* **Chili, Curry, Hot Pot**; Vegetable Balti Curry, Vegetable Casserole & Dumplings

CLEARSPRING ☺™❶⃠

Organic Lentils & Smoked Tofu w Vegetables, Organic Ratatouille, *Organic Ravioli:* **Seitan, Tofu**

GRANOSE ⃠

Lentil & Vegetable Casserole, Meatless Mince & Onion, Mock Duck, Nuttolene, Sausalatas

GRANOVITA UK LTD ⃠

Nut Luncheon, Vegetable Hotpot

H J HEINZ ™⃠

Baked Beans In Tomato Sauce: **Organic**, Barbecue, Curried, Healthy Balance, Standard; Meat Free Spaghetti

Bolognese, *Pasta Shapes In Tomato Sauce:* Barbie, Manchester Utd, Noddy, Pokemon, Rugrats, Teletubbies, Thomas The Tank Engine, Tweenies; *Spaghetti In Tomato Sauce:* **Organic**, Hoops, Standard, w Parsley

ORGRAN ⊘

Gluten-Free Tinned Spaghetti

PATAKS FOODS LTD ⊘

Canned Vegetable Curries: Black-eyed Bean Dhal, Bombay Potato, Chickpea Dhal, Lemon Dhal, Lentil Dhal, Mixed Vegetable, Potato & Pea Vegetable

WHOLE EARTH FOODS LTD ✿⊘

Organic Baked Beans

SAVOURIES — CHILLED / FRESH

CALEDONIAN CURRY CO. ™⊘

Aloo Choley, Baigan Nariyal, Baigan Tamatar, Bhindi Mirchiwal, Bombay Potato, Caledonian Chickpea, Channa Dhal Masala, Do Piaza Khumb, Highland Beetroot, Mushroom Bhaji, Palak Choley, Saag Aloo, Tarka Dal

CAULDRON FOODS LTD ⊘

Falafel, Nut Cutlets, ***Organic:* Falafel, Mexican Bondegas, Spicy Vegetable Koftas**

DIPAK FOODS LTD ™⊘

Bhaji: Onion, Spinach; Dal kachori, Peas Kachori, Peas Petis, Spinach Pakora

ECO-ZONE ☺ ◢ ⊘

Fresh Seaweed Punnet, Seaweed Tartare

LEEORA VEGETARIAN FOOD ™⊘

Blintzes, Chef's Special Pasta w Yemenite Roast Tofu, Felafel Balls, Japanese Seaweed Salad, Mejadra Rice w Thai Curry Tofu, Mushroom Rice w Hungarian Soya Goulash, Pasta w Sweet & Sour Tofu Goulash, *Quiche:* Malaysian, Mauritius Carrot & Coriander, Mushroom; Rice w African Koobbe, Rice w Italian Ragu Style Tofu, Teboula, Tuscan Pasta w Sun Dried Tomato and African Koobbe, Wild Rice w Soya Balls in Tomato Sauce

MacSWEEN OF EDINBURGH ⊘

Vegetarian Haggis

NATURE'S PLATE ™✿⊘

Jacket Spuds, Mixed Veg Curry & Rice, Salad, Buckwheat & Quinoa Vegetable Bake

PAUL'S TOFU ™

Mushroom & Nut Parcels, **Organic Nut Roast,** Tofu & Vegetable Samosa

REAL SAMOSA COMPANY ™

Indian Meals w Rice, Samosas, Sandwiches & Baguettes

FOOD

TAIFUN ☺✿⃠

Falafel, _Tofu Rice Cutlets:_ Corn-Pepper, **Curry-Pineapple**

TASTEE FOODS LTD. ™

Cocktail Pappadums & Samosas

WICKEN FEN ⃠

Cakes: Bangkok Noodle, Bubble & Squeak Potato, North African Cous Cous

SAVOURIES — DRIED

CLEARSPRING ☺™❶⃠

Noodles: Soba 100% Buckwheat, Soba 40% Buckwheat, Udon - Brown Rice, Udon - Wholewheat; **_Organic Noodles:_ Brown Rice Udon, Lomein, Soba, Soba - 100% Buckwheat , Soba - Jinenjo, Udon; Organic Udon - Wholewheat,** Ramen - Brown Rice, Ramen - Buckwheat

ECO-ZONE ☺⃠⃠

Dry Seaweed: Dulse, Kombu, Nori, Ocean Flakes, Ocean Salad, Sea Lettuce, Sea Spaghetti, Wakame; **_Organic Seaweed Pasta:_ Kombu Tagliatelle, Spirulina Tagliatelle, Wild**

FIRST QUALITY FOODS ☺⃠

Sammy's Couscous: Indian, Moroccan,
Roast Garlic & Olive Oil, Salad, Sundried Tomato, Wild Mushroom; Sammy's Falafel Mix

GRANOSE ⃠

Roast: Cashew, Cashew Mix, Nut, Nut Mix, Sunflower & Sesame Mix

H J HEINZ ™⃠

Noodles: Beef Flavour, Chicken Flavour, Curry Flavour, Spicy Thai Flavour

HEMP SHOP LTD ❶⃠⃠

Tagliatelle, Rigatelli & Fusilli Pasta

JUST WHOLEFOODS ☺⃠

Mixes: Biriyani, Chow Mein, Cous Cous & Lentils, Falafel, Hummus, Pillau

KNORR

Chow Mein Flavour Micro Noodles

MOTHER HEMP LTD. ™⃠⃠

Hemp / Spelt Pasta

ORGANIC

Snack Meals: Beef & Tomato, Chicken & Mushroom, Spicy Curry

ORGRAN ⃠

Falafel Mix

POT NOODLE

Hot Chicken Curry Flavour, Sweet & Sour Flavour

SANCHI ⃠

Organic Ramen Noodles: **Brown Rice**, **Mushroom**, **Seaweed**; *Seaweed:* Arame, Hijiki, Kombu, Nori, Sushi Nori, Wakame; *Soba Noodles:* 100% Buckwheat, 40% Buckwheat; *Udon Noodles:* Brown Rice (Genmai), Quinoa

SHARWOOD & COMPANY LTD, J.A. ⃠

Stir-Fry Rice Noodles

TRUFREE ™⃠

Pasta Penne, Pasta Shells, *Quicksnack:* Potato & Vegetable, Rice / Lentil; Spaghetti

VEGANSTORE.CO.UK ☺™❶✓⃠

Chow Mein or Biriani, JW Ready Meals, Shells N chRreese

SAVOURIES — FROZEN

BIRDS EYE WALLS LTD ⃠

<3% Fat Vegetable Jalfrezi, Alphabytes, Enjoy! Vegetable Biryani, *Waffles:* Barbeque, Potato

DALOON FOODS (UK) LTD ⃠

Indian Classics - 2 mixed-vegetable samosas & 4 onion bhajis, Indian Classics - 4 mixed-vegetable samosas, Oriental Classics - 4 spring rolls

DELHI KUTS ⃠

Vegetable Cutlets

DIPAK FOODS LTD ™⃠

Mixed Vegetable Springrolls, *Somosas:* Mixed Vegetable, Soya; Soya chunks Curry, Soya Mince Curry

DRAGONFLY FOODS ✿⃠

Original Organic Tatty

GOODLIFE FOODS ⃠

Falafel Catering Pack (No Yoghurt), Nut Cutlets

McCAIN FOODS GB LTD ⃠

Chippy Chips, Chunky Wedges, *French Fries:* Crispy, Gold Standard Crinkle Cut / Straight; Hash Browns, *Home Fries:* Crinkle Cut, Jacket Oven Chips, Straight Cut; *Micro Chips:* Crinkle Cut, Mega, Straight Cut, Wedges in Sauce BBQ; *Oven:* Crinkle Cut, Straight Cut; Rosti, *Savoury:* Southern Fries, Wedges; Smiles, Stringfellows Oven Fries, *Supervalue:* Chunky Chips, Crinkle Cut, Fast Food Fries, Straight Cut Chips

TASTEE FOODS LTD. ™

Frozen Samosas: Soya Mince, Vegetable

WAYFARER ⃠

Golden Vegetables in Dumplings, Potato & Bean in Tomato Sauce, Vegetable Curry

SEASONAL FOODS

DR HADWEN TRUST ☺ ⚑ ⊘

Animal-Free Christmas Pudding

GREEN & BLACKS ✿ ⊘

Organic Fairtrade Maya Gold Easter Egg

LYONS ⊘

Mince Lattice Tart, Mince Pies

MR KIPLING ⊘

Mince Slices, Minced Parcels

PAUL'S TOFU ™

Christmas Cake: **Organic**, Gluten free; *Christmas Pudding:* **Organic**, Gluten Free; *Mince Pies:* **2 Organic Gluten-Free w Miso & Kuzu, Organic w Miso & Kuzu,** Gluten free; **Organic hot x buns**

SNACKS — SAVOURY

CLEARSPRING ☺ ™ ❶ ⊘

Black Sesame Snacks: Brown Rice, Brown Rice Whole, Quinoa; Brown Rice Sea Vegetable Snacks, Brown Rice Whole Sesame Snacks, Roasted Pumpkin Seeds, Roasted Snack Mix

CRAZY JACKS ⊘

Bombay Mix

ENJOY ORGANIC CO LTD ✿ ⊘

Chilli Tortilla Chips

GOLDEN WONDER ⊘

Crisps: Murphy's Original Salted, Quite Hot Curry, Ready Salted, Steak & Onion, Worcester Sauce; Dry Roasted Peanuts, *Salt & Vinegar:* Crunchy Fries, Wheat Crunchies; Scruples Original

GREENCITY WHOLEFOODS ❶ ⊘

Bombay Mix, Chickpea Noodles, Garlic Sticks, **Organic Bombay Mix,** Osumi Crackers

HEMP SHOP LTD ❶ ⚑ ⊘

Hemp Seeds: **Soft, Toasted**

JONATHAN CRISP ⊘

Crisps: Jalapeno Pepper, Lightly Salted, Sea Salt & Black Pepper, Sea Salt & Malt Vinegar, Sundried Tomato & Basil

JORDAN (CEREALS) LTD ⊘

Paprika Snacks, Sun Dried Tomato & Herb Snacks

KETTLE FOODS ❶ ⊘

Kettle Chips: Lightly Salted, Natural Reds Lightly Salted Specials, Salsa w Mesquite, Sea Salt Rosemary & Garlic, Sea Salt w Balsamic Vinegar, Sea Salt w Crushed Black Peppercorns; *Kettle*

Organics Handcooked Chips: **Lightly Salted**, **Sea salt w Crushed Black Peppercorns**; *Kettle Tortillas:* Louisiana Hot Sauce, Sea Salt Coriander & Garlic; *Peak Baked Crisps:* Lightly Salted, Sea Salt & Balsamic Vinegar, Vegetable Medley Vegetable Crisps

KP FOODS ⊘

Discos: Pickled Onion, Salt & Vinegar; *Frisps:* Ready Salted, Salt & Vinegar Flavour; *Hula Hoops:* Original, Original Minis, Salt & Vinegar; *Hula Hoops Shoks:* Bigtime Saucy, Full-On Onion; *KP Crisps:* Beef Flavour, Ready Salted, Salt & Vinegar, Worcester Sauce; *KP Peanuts:* Brannigans Dry Roasted, Chilli Flavour Nutsters, Dry Roasted, Salt & Vinegar, Spicey Chilli Flavour; *McCoys Potato Chips:* Rock Salt, Salt & Malt Vinegar, Spiced Chilli; *Mini Chips:* Beef Flavour, Ready Salted, Salt & Vinegar; *Phileas Fogg Tortillas:* Classic Mexican, Spicy Habanero

MOTHER HEMP LTD. ™◢⊘

Hemp Seed: Hulled, Plain, Toasted

SANCHI ⊘

Chips: Brown Rice, Hot & Spicy Wasabi, Sea Vegetable; Sanchi Nippers (Seasoned Nori Snack)

SEABROOK POTATO CRISPS LTD ⊘

Crisps: Canadian Ham Crinkle Cut, Original Crinkle Cut, Original Ripples, Original Straight Cut

SUMA WHOLEFOODS ™⊘◢

Bhusu, Bombay Mix, Dehli Mix, Garlic Sticks, **Organic Bombay Mix,** Spiced Roast Chick Peas, Spicy Noodles, Spicy Sticks

TAIFUN ☺✿⊘

Thai Sticks

TASTEE FOODS LTD. ™

Pappadums

THE STAMP COLLECTION ⊘

Sweet Potato Chips, Vegetable Chips

VEGANSTORE.CO.UK ☺™❶◢⊘

Beanits, Chilli Nacho Cheese Protein Chips, Soya Rocks

WALKERS SNACK FOODS LTD ⊘

Crisps: Beef & Onion, Pickled Onion, Prawn Cocktail, Ready Salted, Salt & Vinegar, Worcester Sauce; *Doritos Dippas Dipping Chips, French Fries:* Ready Salted, Salt & Vinegar; *MAX:* Chip Shop Curry, Naked, Salt & Vinegar; Ready Salted Squares, Salt & Vinegar Quavers, Sea Salt & Malt Vinegar Flavour Sensations

SOUPS

BAXTERS OF SPEYSIDE LTD ⊘

Fresh: Classic Minestrone, Mediterranean Tomato; *Healthy Choice:*

FOOD

Carrot, Italian Bean & Pasta, Onion & Chickpea; *Organic:* **Bean & Pasta, Carrot, Parsnip & Nutmeg, Tomato & Vegetable, Vegetable**; *Traditional:* French Onion, Minestrone, Potato & Leek; *Vegetarian:* Mediterranean Tomato, Tomato & Butterbean

CAMPBELL'S GROCERY PRODUCTS LTD ⊘

Blends: Condensed Mediterranean Tomato, Hearty Vegetable; *Condensed Classics:* Lentil, Vegetable

CHIMAN'S ☺™⊘

Organic Spicy Vegetable, Spicy Vegetable

CLEARSPRING ☺™❶⊘

Miso Soup: **Organic Instant**, Red (Sea Vegetables), White (Tofu)

GO ORGANIC LTD ✿⊘

Italian Tomato & Basil, Warming Spicy Parsnip

H J HEINZ ™⊘

Carrot & Orange, Carrot Potato & Coriander, Country Vegetable, French Onion, Lentil, Mediterranean Tomato & Vegetable, Split Pea & Lentil, Tomato & Lentil, Tomato & Red Pepper, Vegetable Condensed, Winter Vegetable

JUST WHOLEFOODS ☺⊘

Instant Soup Mixes: **Carrot & Coriander, Cous Cous, Leek & Potato,**

Minestrone, Tomato, Vegetable

KNORR

Florida Spring Vegetable, Provencale Vegetable

REAL SOUP COMPANY ⊘

Cottage Lentil, Country Vegetable w Lentils, Low Cal Vegetable w Tomato, Minestrone, Oriental BBQ, Red Onion Marmalade, Spicy Salsa, Sun Dried Tomato & Sweet Red Peppers, Tomato & Basil w Green Peppers

SANCHI ⊘

Miso Soup: **Organic, Organic w Mushroom,** Instant w Seaweed

SEEDS OF CHANGE ✿⊘

Minestrone, Spicy Lentil, Three Bean

SIMPLY ORGANIC ✿⊘

Lentil & Parsley, Mediterranean Tomato, Yellow Split Pea

SUMA WHOLEFOODS ™⊘✔

Broth Mix, *Organic Soups:* **Carrot & Coriander, Minestrone, Pea, Spicy Lentil, Tomato, Tomato & Red Pepper**

WHITWORTHS LTD ⊘

Soup & Broth Mix

SOYA AND OTHER 'MILKS'

ALPRO (UK) LTD ⊘

Organic Soya Fruity: **Apple / Pear, Orange, Pineapple & Apricot;** *Organic Soya Milk:* **No Added Sugar or Salt, Sweetened, Vanilla Flavour;** *OY! Flavoured Soya Milk:* Banana, Chocolate, Strawberry; Rice Drink, Soya Cereal, *Soya Milk:* Sweetened w Apple Juice, Unsweetened, w Calcium, w Calcium & Vitamins

BREWHURST HEALTHFOOD SUPPLIES ™⊘

Vitaquell Organic Soya Drink: **Calci Plus, Chocolate Delight, Creamy Original, Vanilla Delight**

CLEARSPRING ☺™❶⊘

Rice Dream: **Organic Original,** Original - Calcium Enriched, Vanilla

ECOMIL ⊘

Organic Nut & Soya Drinks: **Almond, Hazelnut, Sum;** *Powders:* Almond, Hazelnut, Soya

FIRST FOODS ☺⊘

First Milk

GRANOSE ⊘

Organic Non-Dairy Shakes: **Banana, Chocolate, Strawberry;** *Soya 'Milk':* **Organic,** Calcium Enriched, Calcium Enriched Sweetened

GRANOVITA UK LTD ⊘

Soya Drink: **Organic Sugar Free,** Calcium Enriched

H J HEINZ ™⊘

Calcium Enriched Soya Milk, *Organic Soya Milk:* **Sweetened & Chilled, Unsweetened, Unsweetened & Chilled, Vanilla, Vanilla & Chilled;** *Soya Drink:* Banana, Chocolate

IMAGINE ⊘

Rice Dream Rice Milk: Carob, Chocolate Enriched, Original, Original Enriched, Vanilla, Vanilla Enriched

KALLO FOODS ⊘

Rice Drink: **Chocolate, Natural**

ORGANIC SUPPLIES ☺✿⊘

Bio Avena Oat Drink, *Bio Rice Drink:* **Almonds, Natural, Toasted Barley, Vanilla**

Plamil ☺™❶⊘

Non-Dairy Alternative to Milk: Concentrated Soya Sugar Free, Pea White-Sun w Apple, Soya Sugar Free, Soya w Apple

PRITCHITT FOODS ™⊘

"Soya Maid" Minipots

SANCHI ⊘

"Bonsoy" Soya Milk

SANITARIUM HEALTH FOOD CO (UK) ⊘

So Good Soya Milk: Chocolate, Regular, Vanilla

SARC HEALTH FOODS ™☑⊘

The Soy Milker

SOYA HEALTH FOODS LTD ☺❶⊘

Soya Milk 'Sunrise': **Organic Sweetened**, **Organic Unsweetened**, Calcium & Vitamin Enriched

VEGANSTORE.CO.UK ☺™❶☑⊘

Moo NOT! Soy Milk Powder

WHITEWAVE ⊘

White Wave: Calcium Enriched – Sweetened, No Added Sugar

SPICES

CHIMAN'S ☺™⊘

Aloo Gobi, Balti Pasta, Bean Curry, Bombay Potatoes, Dal, *Organic:* **Allo Gobi**, **Bean Curry**, **Bombay Potatoes**, **Dal**, **Spicy Chick Peas**; Spicy Chick Peas

PATAKS FOODS LTD ⊘

Curry Pastes: Balti, Bhuna, Biryani, Extra Hot Curry, Garam Masala, Jalfrezi, Kashmiri Masala, Korma, Madras, Mild Curry, Rogan Josh, Tikka, Tikka Masala, Vindaloo

SPREADS — SAVOURY

CAULDRON FOODS LTD ⊘

Chickpea & Black Olive Paté, *Vegetable Paté w:* Herbs, Mushrooms

GR LANE ☑⊘

Natex: Yeast Extract, Yeast Extract Reduced Salt; **Tartex Organic Pate,** *Tartex Vegetarian Pates:* All; *Vessen Pates:* All

GRANOVITA UK LTD ⊘

Organic Ready Spready: **Garlic & Herb**, **Herb**, **Mushroom**, **Original**; *Pateole:* Herb Provencal, Mushroom, Olive; *Ready Spready:* Herb Provence, Mushroom, Original; **Tangy Tomato Pate (Yeast free)**

LEEORA VEGETARIAN FOOD ™⊘

Paté: Green Lentil, Soya

MARMITE

Yeast Extract

NATÈ⊘

Paté: **Carrot / Paprika**, **Garlic / Basil**, **Hazelnut**, **Prov. Herbs**, **Shii-také Mushroom**

REDWOOD WHOLEFOOD COMPANY
☺™❶⊘

Cheatin' Paté: de Campagne, Forestier, Provencal

SUMA WHOLEFOODS ™⊘✔

Organic Pate: **Herb**, **Mushroom**; *Organic Peanut Butter:* **Crunchy**, **Crunchy - no salt**, **Smooth**; **Organic Tomato Paste**, *Pate:* Herb, Mushroom, Vegetable; *Peanut Butter:* Crunchy, Crunchy - no salt, Smooth, Smooth - No Salt

SUN PAT

Peanut Butter: American Style, Crunchy, Smooth, Wholenut

VEGANSTORE.CO.UK ☺™❶✔⊘

Granovita Pate in Tubes

WHOLE EARTH FOODS LTD ✿⊘

Nut Butters: **All**

SPREADS — SWEET

BAXTERS OF SPEYSIDE LTD ⊘

Scotch Orange Reduced Sugar Marmalade

CLEARSPRING ☺™❶⊘

Organic Fruit Spreads: **Apricot**, **Blueberry**, **Orange**, **Prune**, **Sour Cherry**, **Strawberry**

EQUAL EXCHANGE TRADING ⊘

Organic Cashew Butter

Plamil ☺™❶⊘

Carob Spread Sweetened or Sugar-free

TREE-HARVEST ✔⊘

Arctic Forest Jams & Jellies: Angelica, Bilberry & Crowberry, Ligonberry, Rowanberry

TOFU, TEMPEH, MISO ETC

CAULDRON FOODS LTD ⊘

Tofu: **Organic**, **Organic Original**, **Organic Smoked**, Marinated, Marinated Pieces, Naturally Smoked, Original

CLEARSPRING ☺™❶⊘

Hatcho Miso, *Organic Miso:* **Danival Barley**, **Danival Brown Rice**, **Johsen Genmai (Brown Rice)**, **Makura (Sweet White)**, **Onozaki Mugi (Barley)**; **Organic Tempeh**, Snow Dried Tofu

DRAGONFLY FOODS ✿⊘

Organic Tofu: **Deep-Fried**, **Natural**, **Smoked**

LEAFCYCLE ☺™⊘

Leaf Curd (Pure Organic Leaf Curd),

LEAFU (Organic Tofu w Leaf Curd)

LEEORA VEGETARIAN FOOD ™⊘

Carrot Cottage Tofu

MARIGOLD HEALTH FOODS ❶⊘

Braised Tofu

PAUL'S TOFU ™

Ganmodoki Tofu Mock Goose, *Tofu:* Abura Age Marinated, Nigari

PHYTOFOODS ☺⊘

Tempeh Kits - including starter culture and full instruction/recipe book.

RR TOFU ☺❶⊘

Organic Tofu: **Deep Fried, Marinated, Organic, Sea Cakes, Sesame Rissoles, Smoky**; Regular Tofu

SANCHI ⊘

Miso: **Organic Mugi (Barley); Organic Unpasteurised Barley (Mugi)**; Genmai (Brown Rice), Hatcho (Soya Bean), Mugi (Barley), Shiro

SOTO TOFU ⊘

Organic Tofu: **4 Seasons Terrine, Fresh Herbs, Fried Hazelnut, Pure Fresh, Smoked, Smoked / Mushrooom**

SOYA HEALTH FOODS LTD ☺❶⊘

Sunrise Tofu

TAIFUN ☺✿⊘

Tofu: **Plain, Plain "Demeter", Silken, Smoked, Smoked "Demeter", Smoked w Almonds & Sesame Seeds**; *Tofu Terrine:* **Barock, Country-Style, Graffiti, India**

'YOGHURTS'

ALPRO (UK) LTD ⊘

Organic Yofu: **Natural, Peach / Mango, Red Cherry**; *Yofu:* Junior, Strawberry & Peach

GRANOVITA UK LTD ⊘

Deluxe Soyage: Banana, Black Cherry, Mango, Peach & Apricot, Plain, Raspberry, Strawberry, Tropical; *Organic Soyage:* **Fruits of the Forest, Peach & Apricot, Strawberry**

SO GOOD ⊘

Black Cherry, Peach & Passion Fruit, Pineapple, Plain, Strawberry

NOTES

■ **banana chips** May be dipped in honey.

■ **bread** A few pre-packed loaves contain either skimmed milk powder or vitamin D3. Most large producers use vegetable-based emulsifiers (E471, E472 etc). Check with local bakers re ingredients and type of fat used to grease tins.

■ **cereals** The vitamin D in fortified cereals is often the animal-derived D3.

■ **chocolate** Do not assume that plain chocolate is always animal-free. For UK-produced chocolate, reading the ingredients listing is not always sufficient. Continental plain chocolate is less likely to contain animal substances. All of the chocolate products listed here have been made without animal-derived ingredients or processing aids. However, many have been produced on the same lines as milk chocolate products, so although machines are cleaned thoroughly between different products (to meet health and hygiene and product quality requirements), there is a very slight, theoretical, risk of contamination, meaning that they may not be suitable for dairy intolerants. Note that this is the case for *all* products except those made by companies which produce nothing but vegan products.

■ **crisps** Whey, lactose or other animal-derived processing aids may be used as a flavour carrier. There is no statutory requirement for them to be listed as an ingredient.

■ **di-calcium phosphate** May be sourced from bone and may be used as a growth medium for yeast used to manufacture bread. However, the most common yeast food used in the UK baking industry is calcium sulphate (animal-free).

■ **fruit** May be glazed with animal (commonly beeswax or shellac), vegetable (usually carnauba — cheaper than shellac) or mineral waxes. Contact manufacturers for further details as information changes regularly (according to season, supplier, etc).

■ **gelatine carrier** Beta-carotene & vitamin D2 may be 'carried' in gelatine to maintain stability. As a *general* rule powdered forms of these vitamins are gelatine-derived. In the case of beta-carotene, vegetable oil carriers are available and are generally animal-free, however, when sold as a supplement it is typically encased in capsules made of gelatine.

■ **jams, jellies, conserves, marmalade and preserves** Have been omitted as being obviously vegan unless they contain additional ingredients e.g. alcohol.

■ **masterfoods** (incorporating Mars, Uncle Bens, Dolmio, and Suzi-Wan) chose not to be listed as their products frequently change - they prefer to provide product information themselves and are happy to respond to customer enquiries. Phone their customer care department on 0800 000000 or visit their website www.masterfoods.co.uk

■ **processing aids** May be animal derived. There is no statutory requirement for these to be listed on products.

■ **salt** Most salt is vegan except some low salts which contain a milk derivative. Centura Foods produce a variety of different types of salt which are vegan including Iodised Salt which would be useful for the vegan diet (which *may* be low in iodine).

■ **sugar** Bone char is sometimes used as a decolourant in sugar production. However, the largest suppliers of sugar to companies in the UK — British Sugar, Tate & Lyle and Billington — do not use any animal-derived ingredients (except for Tate & Lyle Traditional Royal Icing which contains dried egg white powder). Billington supplies Sainsbury's, Tesco, Safeway and Waitrose with their own label unrefined sugars. Whitworths no longer use animal derivatives in the processing of their sugars. Merryfield supplies Aldi supermarkets and its demerara and granulated sugars are suitable for vegans.

■ **vinegar** Although malt and spirit vinegars (mainly used in pickles, relishes etc) are generally animal-free, the production of wine, cider and sherry vinegars may involve the use of a fining agent of animal origin.

DRINK

BEERS

BASS ⊘

Grolsch

BLACK SHEEP BREWERY PLC ⏚ ⊘

Bottled Ales: Blacksheep (4.4%), Monty
Python's Holy Grail (4.7%), Riggwelter
Strong Yorkshire (5.7%), Yorkshire
Square (5%)

BRAKSPEAR & SONS PLC ⏚ ⊘

**Brakspear Live Organic Ale,
Naturale Organic Lager**

BROUGHTON ALES ™⏚ ⊘

Waitrose: **Organic Bitter**, IPA

DR HADWEN TRUST ☺⏚ ⊘

**Bucher Organic Pilsner Case,
Golden Promise Bitter, Mixed Beer
& Lager Case, Riedenburger Weisse
Wheatbeer, Samuel Smiths Organic
Ale**

GEORGE BATEMAN & SON ™⏚ ⊘

Bottled Beers: **Yella Belly Organic
Beer**, Combined Harvest Multigrain
Beer, Rosey Nosey Premium Ale, Victory
Ale, XXXB Classic Bitter

INTERBREW ⏚ ⊘

Heineken Export, Hoegaarden, Rolling
Rock

LINFIT BREWERY ⏚ ⊘

Dark Mild 3.0%, English Guineas 5.3%
Stout

ORGANIC WINE COMPANY ⊘ ☼

**Bateman's Organic "Yella Belly" Ale,
Broughton Brewery: Angel Organic
Lager, Border Gold Organic Ale;
Bucher Pilsner, Golden promise
Bitter, Live Organic Ale –
Brakspear's Brewery, *Samuel
Smith's:* Best Organic Ale, Organic
Lager**

PITFIELD BREWERY ☺™☼ ⏚ ⊘

**Black Eagle, East Kent Goldings, Eco
Warrior, Hoxton Heavy, Pitfield
Original**

SAMUEL SMITH ™⏚ ⊘

Ale: **Organic Best**, India, Nut Brown,
Old Brewery Pale, Winter Welcome;
Lagers: **Organic**, Pure Brewed; *Stout:*
Celebrated Oatmeal, Imperial

SCOTTISH COURAGE LTD ⊘

Beck's, Holsten Pils

VINCEREMOS ⏚ ⊘

***Broughton Ales:* Angel Lager,
Border Gold; *Pinkus:* Hefe Weizen,
Original Obergarrig, Original
Obergarrig, Pils, Special Lager,
Special Lager; *Sam Smiths:* Organic
Ale, Organic Lager**

VINTAGE ROOTS ☼ ⊘

Black Isle Brewery Black Isle Porter, Brakspear Live Organic, Bücher Organic Pilsner, Caledonian Brewery Golden Promise Bitter, Dupetit Cannabia, Freedom Organic Pilsener, O'Hanlons Brewing Co Organic Rye Beer, *Pinkus:* **Amber Beer, Lager, Wheatbeer;** *Riedenburger:* **Organic Lager (Helles), Weisse Wheatbeer;** *Tadcaster Brewery Samuel Smiths:* **Organic Best Ale, Organic Lager;** *Vintage Roots:* **Organic Beer, Organic Lager**

VIVA! ☺❶✔⊘

Beers: All

WOLVERHAMPTON & DUDLEY BREWERIES PLC ✔⊘

Marston's "Low C"

CHAMPAGNE

ANIMAL AID ☺❶✔⊘⚖76

Champagne Case

DUVAL-LEROY

Vegan Champagne

ORGANIC WINE COMPANY ⊘☼

Champagne – Carte d'Or Brut – Jose Ardinat

PURE WINE COMPANY ☼✔⊘

Jose Ardinat Non-Vintage Carte d'Or Brut

VINCEREMOS ✔⊘

José Ardinat (France): **Brut Cuvée Spèciale, Brut, Carte d'Or, Brut, Carte d'Or (half bottle), Demi Sec, Carte d'Or, Millesime 1995, Rosè, Carte d'Or**

VINTAGE ROOTS ☼⊘ è

Fleury Champagne: **Blanc de Blancs 1990/94, Carte Rouge, Carte Rouge, Fleur de l'Europe, Rosè Brut, Vintage 1992 'Cuvée 2000 et un 1992, Vintage 1993/1996; Fleury - NV Champagne Fleur de l'Europe, Georges Laval Champagne Premier Cru Reserve Special Brut,** *Serge Faust Champagne:* **Carte d'Or, Cuvée Reserve**

VIVA! ☺❶✔⊘

Champagnes: All

CIDERS & PERRIES

ASPALL ✔⊘

Suffolk Cyder: **Organic**, Dry, Medium

BULMER LTD ✔⊘

Bulmers Original, Bulmers Traditional (keg), Strongbow, Symonds Scrumpy Jack, White Lightning, Woodpecker Cider

DUNKERTON'S CIDER COMPANY ☺☐⊘

Ciders: Black Fox Sparkling Medium Dry, Premium Organic Sparkling, Kingston Black; **Perries: Sparkling, Still; Still Blended Ciders: Dry, Med, Med Sweet, Sweet**

MATTHEW CLARK PLC

Perry: Country Manor, Pink Lady Sparkling

ORGANIC WINE COMPANY ⊘✲

Weston's Organic Cider

SEDLESCOMBE ORGANIC VINEYARD ™✲☐⊘

Dry Cider

VINTAGE ROOTS ✲⊘

Domaine des Cinq Autels Normandy Cider, Dunkertons: Premium Organic Cider, Traditional Dry Organic Cider; *Eric Bordelet:* **Poirè Granit, Sydre Argelette, Sydre Brut Tendre;** *Westons:* **Organic Cider**

VIVA! ☺❶☐⊘

Ciders: All

WESTON & SONS LTD ⊘

Henry Weston's Vintage Reserve, Marcle Millennium, *Oak Conditioned Cider:* Medium Sweet, Strong Medium Dry; **Organic: Cider, Perry, Spritzer, Vintage Cider**; Scrumpy Supreme, *Stowford Press Cider:* Dry, LA, Medium Dry, Medium Sweet

'HOT'

BAKEBEST ⊘

Prewetts Instant Drink: **Organic Chicory,** Chicory

CLEARSPRING ☺™❶⊘

Mate Tea: Mandarine-Orange, Original, Strawberry-Vanilla; **Organic Teas: Bancha (Hojicha), Genmaicha, Genmaicha Green, Genmaicha Green, Hojicha Roasted Bancha Leaf, Hojicha Roasted Bancha Leaf, Kukicha (Bancha) Twig, Sencha Green, Sencha Green**; *Teas:* Brown Rice, Kukicha Twig, Mu - 16 Herbs, Roasted Brown Rice, Sencha Green

GREEN & BLACKS ✲⊘

Organic Hot Chocolate

HEMP SHOP LTD ❶☐⊘

Hemp Tea

NESTLE UK LTD

Caro: Extra, Instant

ORGANICO ⊘

Drinking Chocolate

RIDPATH PEK LTD ☺⊘

Barleycup: **Organic,** Granules, Powder Instant Cereal Drink

VEGANSTORE.CO.UK ☺™❶✔⊘

Gourmet Organic Drinking Chocolate

WHOLE EARTH FOODS LTD ✿⊘

Organic: **Nocaf, Wakecup**

SOFT

BIONADE

Beanie's Health Foods

Organic Isotonic Fruit Drinks: **All**

CALYPSO SOFT DRINKS ⊘

Cup Drinks: Sugar-Free, Tip-Top, Tom & Jerry; *Flavoured Natural Mineral Water:* Sparkling, Still; *Juice Drinks:* Cartoon Network, Orange, Rugrats, Simpsons

ELLA DRINKS ⊘

Bouvrage Raspberry Drink

FENTIMANS LTD ☺⊘

Curiosity Cola, Seville Orange jigger, **Traditional Ginger Beer,** Victorian Lemonade

HEMP SHOP LTD ❶✔⊘

Cannacola, Swiss Cannabis Lemonade

INNOCENT ⊘

Innocent Pure Fruit Smoothies: Blackberries & Blueberries, Cranberries & Raspberries, Mangoes & Passionfruits, Oranges, Bananas & Pineapples, Strawberries & Bananas; *Innocent Really Lovely Juices:* Apples, Blackcurrants & Elderflowers, Oranges, Mangoes & Lime, Pink Grapefruit, Pineapples & Lime

LIPTON

Ice Tea: Lemon, Peach

MOULIN DE VALDONNE ⊘

Organic Cordials: **Blackcurrant, Grenadine, Lemon, Mixed Berries, Orange**

NESTLE UK LTD

Nesquik Powder

RED BULL CO.

Red Bull

ROCKS ORGANIC CORDIALS

Bella Blackcurrant Juice Drink, *Organic Cordials:* **Blackcurrant, Christmas, Cranberry, Elderflower, Ginger, Lemon, Lime, Pineapple, Pink Grapefruit**

SEDLESCOMBE ORGANIC VINEYARD ™❶✔⊘

Juice: **Apple, Blackberry & Apple, Bramley Apple, Cox Apple, Pear**

THORNCROFT ☺⊘

Mist Elderflower Drink

VINTAGE ROOTS ✿⊘

Organize

VIVA! ☺❶◊ ⊘

Cordials: All; *Juices:* All

WESTON & SONS LTD ⊘

Organize: Apple, Cranberry, Lemon

WHOLE EARTH FOODS LTD ✿⊘

Organic Soft Drinks: Cola, Cranberry, Lemonade, Orange

SPIRITS & APÈRITIFS

ALLIED DOMECQ SPIRITS AND WINES LTD ◊⊘

Ballantine's: Gold Seal Scotch, Scotch; Beefeater Gin, *Courvoisier Cognacs:* All; Domecq La Ina Sherry, *Harvey's Sherry:* All; Hawker's Sloe Gin, *Mixed Doubles:* Borzoi Vodka & Lemonade, Borzoi Vodka & Tonic, Lamb's White Rum & Cola, Teacher's Whisky & Lemonade; *Phillips of Bristol Alcoholic Cordials:* Aniseed, Green Peppermint, Grenadine, Lovage, Pink Cloves, Shrub, White Peppermint; *Rums:* Black Heart, Lamb's Navy, Lemon Hart Golden; *Tequila Sauza:* Blanco, Conmemorativo, Extra Gold, Hornitos; *Whisky:* Canadian Club, Laphroaig Old Scotch, Laphroaig Single Islay Malt Scotch, Maker's Mark Bourbon, Scapa Single Orkney Malt Scotch, Stewarts Cream of the Barley blended Scotch, Teacher's Scotch, The Glendronach 12 Year Old Scotch, Tullamore Dew Irish

BACARDI-MARTINI

Bacardi Breezers: All; Bacardi Rum, Bombay Gin, Dewars Whisky, Eristoff Vodka, Jack Daniels Whisky

ORGANIC WINE COMPANY ⊘

Alain Verdet: Crème de Cassis de Bourgogne, Crème de Framboise, Crème de Mure, Crème de Pêche; *Gabriel Gomez Sierra Morena Port:* Vino Dorado Seco, Vino Palido Seco; *Guy & Georges Pinard:* Cognac Foussignac – V.S.O.P., Cognac – Foussignac – Napoleon; *Jacques & Dany Brard Blanchard:* Cognac, Cognac – V.S.O.P., Estival – , Pineau des Charentes – Blanc, Pineau des Charentes – Rosè; Juniper Green Organic London Dry Gin, Utkins UK5 Vodka

SAMUEL SMITH ™◊⊘

Famous Taddy Porter

SEDLESCOMBE ORGANIC VINEYARD ™✿◊⊘

Liqueurs: Blackberry, White grape

VINCEREMOS ◊⊘

Organic Spirits Company: Juniper Green Organic London Dry Gin, Papagayo Organic Single Estate White Rum, Utkins UK5 Organic Vodka; *Roland Seguin:* Cafè Cognac, Cassis au Cognac, Cognac Napolean, Cognac VSOP, Cognac XXX VS, Delice d'Orange, Pineau des

Characters Blanc, Pineau des Characters Rose

VINTAGE ROOTS ☼ ⊘

Casal dos Jordoes: Tawny Port, Vintage Character Port; Clos St Martin - 1999 AOC Muscat de Rivesaltes 1999, *François Clot:* Cerise (Cherry), Vinoix (Walnut); Jacques & Dany Brard Blanchard AOC Pineau des Charentes

VIVA! ☺❶✔⊘

Fortified Wines & Ports: All

WESTON & SONS LTD ⊘

Organize: Apple & White Rum, Cranberry & Vodka, Lemon & Gin

WINES – RED

ANIMAL AID ☺❶✔⊘⚗–76

Wines: All

DAVENPORT VINEYARDS ☼✔⊘

Wines: All

DR HADWEN TRUST ☺✔⊘

Mixed Cases

HARBOURNE VINEYARD ☺✔⊘

English Wines

MATTHEW CLARK PLC

Stowells of Chelsea Merlot

ORGANIC WINE COMPANY ⊘✿

Australia: Cabernet Sauvignon 1994 – Thistle Hill, Clare Valley Red 1999 – Penfolds, Shiraz 1997 – Botobolar Vineyard – Kevin and Trina Karstrom, Shiraz/Cabernet Sauvignon 1998 – Robinvale Vineyards; *Beaujolais:* Domaine de Buis-Rond – Beaujolais AC 1999/2000 – Thierry & Sophie Harel, Domaine de Buis-Rond – Beaujolais Villages AC 1999 – Thierry & Sophie Harel; *Bordeaux:* Chateau Cotes des Caris – Bordeaux AC 2000 – Christian Guichard, Chateau Côtes des Caris – Bordeaux Supérieur AC 1997 – Christian Guichard, Chateau Moulin Saint-Magne – Côtes de Castillon AAAC 1997/8 – Jean-Gabriel Yon, Clos de la Perichére – Graves AC 1995/6 – Gabriel Guerin; *Bourgogne:* Bourgogne Cote Chalonnaise AC 1999 – D'Heilly & Huberdeau, Bourgogne Passetoutgrain AC 1999 – D'Heilly & Huberdeau; *Corbieres:* Chateau Pech-Latt – Corbieres A.C. 2000 – Tradition – S.C. Pech-Latt, Chateau Pech-Latt – Corbieres A.C. – Selection Vieilles Vignes 1998; *Côtes du Rhône:* Chatelaine Stephanie – Côtes du Ventoux AC 1999 – Olivier Azan, Clos du Joncuas – Gigondas AC 1998 – Fernand Chastan, Crozes Hermitage AC 1998 – "Clos de Grives" – Domaine Combier, Domaine la Garanciere – Côtes du Rhône Séguret AC 1998 – Fernand

Chastan, Domaine Saint-Apollinaire – Côtes du Rhône AC 1997 – "Cuvée d'Apolline" S.C.A. Daumas, Domaine Saint-Apollinaire – Côtes du Rhône AC 1998 – "Cuvée Préstige" S.C.A. Daumas, Domaine Saint-Apollinaire – Côtes du Rhône AC 1998 – "La Quintessence" S.C.A. Daumas, Domaine Terres de Solence – Côtes du Ventoux AC 1998 – "Les Trois Peres" Anne Marie & Jean Luc Isnard, Domaine Terres de Solence – Côtes du Ventoux AC 1999/2000 – "Le Prieure" Anne Marie & Jean Luc Isnard, Vacqueyras AC 1998 – "La Font de Papier" – Fernand Chastan; Natum – Montepulciano d'Abruzzo DOC 1999/2000 – Agriverde, Organic Red Wine – Vin de Pays de l'Herault – Olivier Azan, *Penedes:* Caballero de Mesasrrubias – La mancha D.O. '99/2000 – Parra Jimenez Bodega, Parra Jimenez Tinta Barrica – La Mancha DO 1999 – Parra Jimenez Bodega, Rioja DO 1999/2000 – "Noemus" – Domaine Navarrsotillo, Senorio de Elda – Alicante DO 1999 – Bodegas Bocopa; *Piedmont:* Barbera – Colline Novarese DOC 1999 – Bianchi, Gattinara DOC 1999 – Bianchi, Gattinara – "Vigneto Valferana" DOC 1994 – Bianchi, Ghemme DOC 1995 – Bianchi, Nebbiolo – "Vigneto Valfre" – Colline Novarese DOC 1998 – Bianchi, Primo Sole Rosso – Vino da Tavola 1998 – Bianchi, Sizzano DOC 1995 – Bianchi, Spanna Nebbiolo – Colline Novarese DOC

1998/9 – Bianchi; Richmond Plains (New Zealand) Nelson Pinot Noir 1998/9, Selvato – Vino da Tavola 1999 – Azienda Agricola "Nuova Murgia", *The Loire:* Pinot Noir A.A.C. 1998/9 – AndrÈ Stentz, Vin de Pays du Jardin de France – Cépage Cabernet – Guy Bossard; *Toscana:* Chianti D.O.C.G. 1998 – Il Casale, Lignano Rosso – "Unico" – Vino da Tavola – Podere Lignano, Pinot Nero Rosso – IGT 1998 – Il Termine, Sangiovese – Rosso dei Colli della Toscana Centrale 1999 – VdT – Il Casale; *Veneto:* Bainsizza Rosso - Lison Pramaggiore DOC 1998 - Vino Barricato - Arnaldo Savian, Cabernet Franc – Lison Pramaggiore DOC 1998 – Arnaldo Savian, EcoVite Cabernet Sauvignon - Lison Pramaggiore DOC 2000 – Tenuta Santa Anna, EcoVite Merlot - Lison Pramaggiore DOC 2000 – Tenuta Santa Anna, Merlot – Lison Pramaggiore DOC 1999 – Arnaldo Savian, Refosco del Peduncolo Rosso - Lison Pramaggiore DOC 1999 – Arnaldo Savian; Vin de Pays: Albaric – Vin de Pays du Gard – Hoirie Albaric, Domaine de Petit Roubié - Vin de Pays de l'Herault – Olivier Azan, Domaine la Grangette – Vin de Pays D'Oc 1997/8 – Syrah – Emmanuelle Mur-Gomar, Domaine la Grangette – Vin de Pays D'Oc – Tradition - Emmanuelle Mur-Gomar

PURE WINE COMPANY ☼ ◢ ⊘

Badger Mountain (USA): Cabernet

Franc / Merlot, Cabernet Sauvignon; *Cantina Pizzolato (Italy):* Cabernet Piave DOC, Il Vacanziere IGT - Rosso Da Tavola, Merlot del Piave DOC, Merlot del Veneto IGT - Vigneto Rosso; *Castello Di Arcania (Italy):* Cabernet DOC, Merlot DOC; Chateau Barrail des Graves (France) St Emillion AC, Chateau de Boisfranc (France) Beaujolais Superior AC, Coltiva (Italy) Lambrusco di Modena Rosso IGT Frizzante, *Domaine De Balazut (France):* Cabernet Sauvignon AC, Merlot AC, Syrah AC; *Era (Italy):* Nero d'avola IGT, Sangiovese IGT; J. & F. Lurton (France) Terra Sana Red, Jacques Frelin (France) Crozes Hermitage AC 1999 / 2000, Jasci (Italy) Montepulciano d'abruzzo, rosso, *Michael Bettili (Italy):* Merlot DOC, Serenel - Rosso da Tavola, Valpolicella DOC; Ottomarzo (Italy) Bardolino Classico DOC, Parra Jiminez (Spain) Caballero de Mesarrubias DOC, *Robinvale Vineyards (Australia):* Cabernet Sauvignon, Shiraz; Sonop Wine Farm (South Africa) Pinotage

SEDLESCOMBE ORGANIC VINEYARD ™ ☼ ◢ ◌

Dry Red: English Wine, Regent

SOLANO TRADING ™ ◢ ◌

Domaine de Farlet, Meze, France: Cabernet Sauvignon, Merlot; *Michel Delecroix, Theziers, France:* Cabernet, Côtes de Rhône

VINCEREMOS ◢ ◌

Albet i Noya (Spain): Can Vendrell Tinto, Lignum Negre, Tempranillo d'Anyada; *Bagordi (Spain):* Rioja, Rioja Crianza; *Barjac (France):* Merlot, Vin de Pays de l'Herault, Vin de Pays du Gard; *Couston (France):* Côtes du Rhône Villages, Valréas Domaine de la Grande Bellane, *Domaine Richeaume (France):* Cabernet Sauvignon, Côtes de Provence, Carignan, Côtes de Provence, Cuvée Columelle, Côtes de Provence, Syrah, Côtes de Provence, Tradition, Côtes de Provence; *Domaine St. Michel (France):* Cabernet Sauvignon, Vin de Pays d'Oc, Merlot, Vin de Pays d'Oc, Syrah-Malbec, Vin de Pays d'Oc; *Jacques Frelin (France):* Ar-Men Cabernet Boisé, Vin de Pays d'Oc, Cabardes , Cabernet Sauvignon, Vin de Pays d'Oc, Chateau Barrail des Graves, St ...milion , Chateau du Moulin De Peyronin Cuvée Capucine, Bordeaux , Chateau Laborie Fouisseau, Faugeres, Cordouan, Coteaux Languedoc, Côtes du Rhône, Côtes du Rhône Villages, Côtes du Ventoux, Crozes Hermitage, Cuvée de Marouette Merlot, Vin de Pays d'Oc, Domaine de Clairac Joubio, Vin de Pays l'Herault, Domaine de Savignac, Vin de Pays de l'Herault, French Organic Red, Vin de Pays l'Herault, Oaked Merlot, Vin de Pays d'Oc, Syrah, Vin de Pays de l'Herault, Vin de Pays d'Oc (50cl),

Vin de Pays du Gard; *La Nature:* Barbera, Argentina, Cabernet Sauvignon, Vin de Pays d'Oc , Merlot, Vin de Pays d'Oc, Rhone Valley Red, Shiraz/Cabernet Sauvignon, Australia, Vin de Pays Rouge; *Los Pinos (Spain):* Crianza, Dominio los Pinos Barrica, Seleccion Tinto; *Ottomarzo (Italy):* Bardolino Classico, Schaffer (Italy) Barbera 'Solo per Laura, Valpolicella Classico; *Paul Giboulot (France): Bourgogne Roug , Hautes Côtes de Nuits; Perlage (Italy):* Cabernet del Veneto, Corte del Giano, Merlot del Veneto, Solatio Rosso; *Richmond Plains (New Zealand):* Escapade, Nelson, Pinot Noir, Nelson, Reserve Pinot Noir, Nelson; *San Michele (Italy):* Chanti Classico Riserva, Chianti Classico, Chianti Colli Fiorentini; *San Vito (Italy):* Chianti, Chianti Vigna la Reina, Fior di Selva Barrique; *Vignoble Saint Frédéric (France):* Gigondas, Seguret, Vacqueyras; *Volpi (Italy):* Era Montepuiciano d'Abruzzo, Era Nero d'Avola, Era Sangiovese; *Wilhelm Zahringer (Germany):* Spütburgunder Spatlese, Baden, Spütburgunder, Baden

VINTAGE ROOTS ☼⊘

Albaric Vin de Pays du Gard 2000/2001, *Albet i Noya:* DO Penedés 'Nuria' 1999, DO Penedes Can Vendrell Cabernet Sauvign 2000, DO Penedes Lignum 1999, DO Penedes Reserva Marti 1997/1998,

DO Penedes Tempranillo Co.lecciu 1998/1999, DO Penedes Tempranillo d'Anyada 1999/2000, DO Penedes-Cabernet Sauvignon Col.lecciu 1999, DO Penedes-Syrah Col.lecciu 1998/1999; *Bettili:* IGT Organic Rosso; DOC Lison Pramaggiore - Cabernet Franc 2000, DOC Lison Pramaggiore - Merlot 2000, DOC Valpolicella 2000; Bodegas Irjimpa DO La Mancha - 'Caballero de Mesarrubbia 2000/2001, Bodegas Palmera DO Utiel-Requeoa Bobal y Tempranillo 2000, Bodegas Ruiz Jimenez DO Rioja - Perseus 2000, Botobolar Vineyard Shiraz 1997/2000, *Buondonno:* DOC Chianti Classico 1998/1999, DOC Chianti Classico Riserva 1997; Casale Mattia IGT Lazio - Merlot 2000, Chateau Coursou AOC Bordeaux Supérieur 1999/2000, *Chateau de Bastet:* AOC Côtes du Rhone - Cuvée Sainte Nelly 2000, AOC Côtes du Rhône - Cuvée Spéciale 2000; Chateau de Roubia AOC Minervois 1999, Chateau des Hautes Combes AOC Bordeaux - Organic Claret 2000, *Chateau Falfas:* AOC Côtes de Bourg 'Le Chevalier' 1996/1998, AOC Côtes de Bourg 1998/1999; Chateau Haut Mallet AOC Bordeaux Supérieur - Chateau Haut Ma 1999, Chateau Haut-Nouchet AOC Pessac Leognan 1998, Chateau Jacques Blanc AOC St Emilion Grand Cru 'Cuvée du Maôtr 1998/1999, Chateau La Grave AOC Fronsac 1998/1999, Chateau Le Rait AOC

Bordeaux Supérieur 1999/2000, Chateau Pech-Latt AOC Corbiéres Selection Vielles Vignes 1998/99, *Chateau Richard:* AOC Bergerac - Half Bottle 1999/2000, AOC Bergerac 1999/2000; Chateau Romanin AOC Les Baux de Provence 1997/1998, Chiusa Grande Montepulciano d'Abruzzo Terre Di Casali 2000, Christian Ducroux AOC Regnie 2000, *Clos de Joncuas:* AOC Gigondas 1998, AOC Vacqueras 'La Font de Papier' 1999; Clos St Martin AOC CÙtes du Roussillon 1999 / 2000, *Di Filippo:* Vino da Tavola Rosso dell'Umbria 2000, Vino da Tavola-Rosso dell'Umbria 'Terre San Nicola 1998/1999; Domaine Combier AOC Crozes Hermitage 2000, *Domaine de Brau:* AOC Cabardes 2000/2001, VDP d'Oc Cuvée Gabriel - Merlot 2000, VDQS Cabardees 'Cuvée Exquise' 1999, Vin de Pays de l'Aude 2000/2001; Domaine de Buis-Rond AOC Beaujolais 2000, *Domaine de Soulié:* AOC St Chinian 1999/2000, VDP de Monts de la Grage - Cuvée Remy 2000/2001, VDP des Monts de la Grage - 'La Folie' 1997; Domaine des Frogeres AOC Saumur Champigny 2000, Domaine du Jas d'Esclans AOC Côtes de Provence Cru Classé 1998, Domaine Mestre Grotti Vin de Pays d'Oc 1999/2000, Domaine St Nicolas VDQS Fiefs Véndeens - Biodynamic Rouge 2000, Domaine Terres Blanches AOC Les Baux de Provence 'Cuvée Aurelia' 1995, Domaine

VacquiÈre AOC 'Organic Cotes du RhÙne' 1999/2000, Dominique & Catherine Derain AOC St Aubin 'Le Ban' 1999, *Emilien d'Albret:* Vin de Pays d'Oc - Organic Cabernet Sauv 2000, Vin de Pays d'Oc - Organic Syrah 2000, Vin de Pays d'Oc Organic Merlot 2000, Vin de Pays de l'Hérault - Organic Roots 1999/2000; Fasoli Gino IGT La Calle - Merlot Rosso 2000, Fetzer Vineyards Zinfandel - Bonterra Mendocino 1998/1999, Jean Claude Rateau AOC Beaune Premier Cru 1999, *Les Pradelles:* VDP de l'Hérault - Les Pradelles Rouge 2 2000/2001, Vin de Pays de l'Herault 2000/2001; *Mas Igneus:* DO Priorato FA112 1997/1999, DO Priorato FA206 1999/2000; Mcntalbano Vino da Tavola Rosso -Terre Montalbano 2000/2001, *Ottomarzo:* DOC Valpolicella Amarone Classico 1997/1998, DOC Valpolicella Classico 'La Grola' 1999; Penfolds Merlot/Shiraz/Cabernet Sauvignon - Clare Valley 1999, Pepe DOC Montepulciano d'Abruzzo 1997/1998, *Pierre André:* AOC Chateauneuf du Pape 1995, AOC Chateauneuf du Pape 1998; Quinta da Esteveira DOC Douro 1998/1999, *Robinvale Vineyards:* Barrique Shiraz / Cabernet Sauvignon, Cabernets 1998, Shiraz / Cabernet Sauvignon - Victoria 1999; Solatio I Casciane DOCG Chianti 2000, *Sonop Wine Farm:* Merlot - Organic Terroir 2001, Pinotage - Organic

DRINK

Terroir 2001, Shiraz - Organic Terroir 2001; *Viberti:* Barolo Bricco Viole 1996, Barolo La Volta 1996, DOC Barbera d'Alba 1998/1999, DOC Barolo 1998, DOC Dolcetto d'Alba 1998; *Vintage Roots:* DO La Mancha - Organic Tinto, Vin de Pays des Côtes de Thongue - Organ 2000/2001

VIVA! ☺❶ ⓘ ⊘

Red Wines: All

WINES - FRUIT

AVALON VINEYARDS ⊘

Organic: Apple, Ginger, Gooseberry, Raspberry, Tayberry; Plum

BROUGHTON PASTURES ORGANIC FRUIT WINE

Blackberry, Blackcurrant, Elderberry, Elderflower, Ginger, Sparkling Elderflower

ORGANIC WINE COMPANY ⊘ ✧

Organic Wines: Blackcurrant – 10.5% alc., Elderberry – 13%, Elderflower - 10.5% Alc., Ginger – 13% alc.

SEDLESCOMBE ORGANIC VINEYARD ™ ✧ ⓘ ⊘

Black Cherry, Golden Apple, Plum

WINES – ROSÈ

DAVENPORT VINEYARDS ✧ ⓘ ⊘

Wines: All

HARBOURNE VINEYARD ☺ ⓘ ⊘

English Wines

ORGANIC WINE COMPANY ⊘

Les Domaines de Petit Roubié– Vin de Pays de l'Herault – Olivier Azan

PURE WINE COMPANY ✧ ⓘ ⊘

Cantina Pizzolato (Italy): Il Vacanziere IGT - Rosato de Tavola, Rossato del Veneto IGT Frizzante; Jasci (Italy) Montepulciano D'abruzzo Cerasuolo

SOLANO TRADING ™ ⓘ ⊘

Michel Delecroix, Theziers, France

VINTAGE ROOTS ✧ ⊘

Albet i Noya DO Penedes Pinot Noir/Merlot d'Anyada 2000/2001, Domaine de Brau VDP de L'Aude - Brau Rosé 2000/2001, Domaine du Jas d'Esclans AOC Côtes de Provence Cru Classé Rosé 2000/2001

WINES — SPARKLING

ANIMAL AID ☺❶✔️ ⊘ ⚒ 76

Celebration Fizz

DAVENPORT VINEYARDS ✿✔️⊘

Wines: All

ORGANIC WINE COMPANY ⊘✿

Achard Vincent: Clairette de Die
A.C. – Demi-Sec – "Tradition"
G.A.E.C, Cremant de Die A.C. – Brut
– Methode Traditionelle G.A.E.C ;
Bernard Delmas: Blanquette de
Limoux A.C , Cremant de Limoux
A.C; Cremant D'Alsace AAC – Andre
Stentz, Cremant de Bourgogne AC –
Veuve Ambal, Cuvée de la Boissiere
– Brut – Jacques & Dany Brard
Blanchard, Cuvee Ludwig Hahn –
Vin Mousseux Methode
Traditionelle – Guy Bossard,
Prosecco di Valdobbiadene DOC –
Arnaldo Savian, Saumur Brut A.C.
1989 – Gerard Leroux, Sedlescombe
Brut – Traditional Method – Roy
Cook, Spumante – Brut DOC –
Erbaluce "Incontro" – Giuseppe
Bianchi, Spumante Brut – IGT –
Arnaldo Savian

SEDLESCOMBE ORGANIC VINEYARD
™✿✔️⊘

*Cuveé Bodiam Brut English
Sparkling Wine: 2000, 2001; Cuveé
Pinto Noir Brut Rose Sparkling*

English Wine: 2000, 2001

VINCEREMOS✔️⊘

Achard Vincent (France): Clairette
de Die Brut, Clairette de Die
Tradition; *Albet i Noya (Spain):* Cava
Brut 21, Can Vendrell, Cava, Can
Vendrell; *Domaine du Jas (France):*
Blanquette de Limoux, Cremant de
Limoux; *Perlage (Italy):* Prosecco
Frizzante, Prosecco Spumante de
Valdobiaddene

VINTAGE ROOTS ✿⊘

Achard Vincent AOC Clairette de
Die 'Tradition', *Albet i Noya DO
Cava:* Barrica 21, Brut 21, Brut
Reserva, Can Vendrell, Rosé
Reserva; Bosco del Merlo Prosecco,
D'Heilly-Huberdeau AOC Crémant
de Bourgogne, Delmas AOC
Blanquette de Limoux

WINES — WHITE

ANIMAL AID ☺❶✔️ ⊘ ⚒ 76

Wines: All

AVALON VINEYARDS ⊘

Organic English Table Wine: 3
varieties

DAVENPORT VINEYARDS ✿✔️⊘

Wines: All

DR HADWEN TRUST ☺ ✔ ⊘

Mixed cases

HARBOURNE VINEYARD ☺ ✔ ⊘

English Wines

MATTHEW CLARK PLC

Stowells of Chelsea Muscadet

ORGANIC WINE COMPANY ⊘ ✿

Abruzzo: Natum – Trebbiano d'Abruzzo DOC 2000 – Agriverde, Riseis - Trebbiano d'Abruzzo DOC 1997 – Agriverde, Tresor – Chardonnay Colline teatine IGT 1998 – Agriverde; *Bergerac:* Chateau le Barradis – Monbazillac A.C. 1995 – Labasse-Gazzini, Gewurztraminer A.A.C. 1998/1999 – André Stentz, Muscat A.A.C. 1998 - André Stentz, Riesling A.A.C. 1998/2000 – André Stentz, Sylvaner A.A.C. 1999/2000 – André Stentz, Tokay Pinot Gris A.A.C. 1998/1999 – André Stentz; *Botobolar Vineyard (Australia):* Chardonnay 1998, Marsanne 1998; Bourgogne Aligoté AC 1999 – D'Heilly & Huberdeau, *Côtes du Rhône:* Domaine Saint-Apollinaire – Côtes du Rhône AC 1998 – "Blanc de Blancs" Frederic Daumas, Domaine Saint-Apollinaire – Côtes du Rhône AC 1998 – "l'Exceptionnelle" Viognier - Frederic Daumas, Domaine Terres de Solence – Leonides – Côtes du Ventoux AC 1999/2000 Anne Marie & Jean Luc Isnard; Erbaceo – Vino

da Tavola 1997/2000 – Azienda agricola "Nuova Murgia", Languedoc: Cuvée Petit Roubie – Vin de Pays de l'Herault – Olivier Azan, Domaine de Petit Roubié – Vin de Pays de l'Herault – Olivier Azan, Domaine de Petite Roubié - Vin de Pays de l'Herault – Cepage Marsanne – Azan, Domaine la Batteuse – Vin de Pays d'Oc – Chardonnay – Bernard Delmas, Domaine la Batteuse – Vin de Pays d'Oc – Mauzac – Bernard Delmas, Domaine la Grangette – Vin de Pays d'Oc – Sauvignon – "Boreale" – E Mur-Gomar; *Le Midi:* Chateau Côtes des Caris – Bordeaux Blanc sec AC '99/2000 – Christian Guichard, Chateau Côtes des Caris – Bordeaux Blanc sec AC 1997 – Christian Guichard, Chateau la Croix Simon – Entre-Deux-Mers AC – 2000 – Jean Gabriel Yon, Chateau Pech-Latt – Corbieres AC 2000 – S.C Pech-Latt, Chateau Petit Roubié – Picpoul de Pinet – Coteaux de Languedoc A.C. 1998/2000 – Olivier Azan, Clos de la Perichere – Graves AC 1998 – Gabriel Guerin; *Loire:* Gros Plant du Pays Nantais V.D.Q.S. 1999/2000 sur lie – Guy Bossard, Le Haut Liey – Vouvray sec AC 1993 – S A Huet, Muscadet de Sevre et Maine A.C. 1997 sur lie "Hermine d'Or" – Guy Bossard, Muscadet de Sevre et Maine A.C. 2000 sur lie – Domaine de la ParentiÈre, Muscadet de Sevre et Maine A.C. 2000 sur lie – Guy Bossard , Sancerre A.C. 1999 – Nicole et Christian Dauny; *New*

Zealand: Gisborne Chardonnay 1999
– The Millton Vineyard, Millton
Vineyard Chenin Blanc – Barrel
Fermented 1999 – The Millton
Vineyard, Nelson Chardonnay 1999
– Richmond Plains; Organic White
Wine – Bordeaux blanc sec AC
1999/2000 – Christian Guichard,
Piedmont: Chardonnay – Langhe
DOC 1999/2000 – Punset, Eloise
Bianco – Vino da Tavola 1999 –
Bianchi, Erbaluce – Colline Novarese
DOC 1998/9 – Bianchi; Robinvale
Vineyard (Australia) Chardonnay
1998, *Sauternes:* Chateau la
Garenne – Sauternes AC 1996/1999
– Nicole & Christian Ferbos, Chateau
la Garenne – Sauternes AC
1997/1999 – N & C Ferbos;
Sedlescombe (England) Late Harvest
2000 – English Table Wine – Roy
Cook, *Tuscany:* Il Fiore di Lignano
1997 – Vino da Tavola – Podere
Lignano, Lignano Bianco 1998 –
Vino da tavola – Podere Lignano,
Trebbiano – Bianco dei Colli Della
Toscana Centrale – Vino da Tavola
1999 – Casale; *Veneto:* Bainsizza
Bianco - Lison Pramaggiore DOC
1998 – Vino Barricato - Arnaldo
Savian, Chardonnay – Lison
Pramaggiore DOC 1998 – Arnaldo
Savian, EcoVite Pinot Grigio - Lison
Pramaggiore DOC 1999 – Tenuta
Santa Anna, Pinot Grigio - Lison
Pramaggiore DOC 1999 – Arnaldo
Savian, Verduzzo – Lison
Pramaggiore DOC 1999 – Arnaldo
Savian

PURE WINE COMPANY ☼ ⚄ ⊘

Albet I Noya (Spain) Cava Can
Vandrell, Badger Mountain (USA)
Chardonnay, Bernard Delmas
(France) Cremant de Limoux AC,
Cantina Pizzolato (Italy):
Chardonnay Charmat, Il Vacanziere
IGT - Bianco De Tavola, Prosecco
Charmat, Spumante Frederik DOC,
Spumante Stefany DOC, Verduzzo
del Veneto IGT - Vigneto Bianco;
Cantine Foraci (Italy) Sollatio Blanco
IGT, Casale Mattia (Italy) Frascati
Superiore DOC, *Castello Di Arcania
(Italy):* Pinot Grigio DOC, Sauvignon
DOC; Christian & Nicole Dauny
(France) Sancerre AC, Domaine De
Balazut (France) Blanc de Blanc AC,
Domaine de Petit Roubie (France)
Picpoul de Pinet AOC, *Domaine
Philippe & Jean Goulley (France):*
Chablis AOC, Chablis Premiere Cru
Montmains 1999 / 2000, Petit
Chablis AOC; Guy Bossard (France)
Muscadet de Sevre Et Main Sur Lie
AC, J & F Lurton (France) Terra Sana
White, Jasci (Italy) Trebbiano
D'abruzzo, Bianco, *Michael Bettili
(Italy):* Pino Grigio DOC, Serenel -
Bianco Da Tavola, Soave Classico
DOC, Soave DOC; *Robinvale
Vineyards (Australia):* Chardonnay,
Chenin Blanc, Sauvignon Blanc;
Sonop Wine Farm (South Africa):
Chardonnay, Sauvignon Blanc

SEDLESCOMBE ORGANIC VINEYARD
™ ☼ ⚄ ⊘

English Wine: Chardonnay, Dry

White, Late Harvest, Reserve

SOLANO TRADING ™⏴✓ ⊘

Domaine de Farlet, Meze, France: Chardonnay, Voignier; Michel Delecroix, Theziers, France Blanc vin de Pays

VINCEREMOS ⏴✓ ⊘

Albet i Noya (Spain): Can Vendrell Blanco, Lignum Blanc; *Bonterra (USA):* Chardonnay, Muscat , Roussanne, Viognier; *Ch de Barradis (France):* La Balance, Bergerac, Monbazillac; *Clos St Martin (France):* Muscat de Rivesaltes, Muscat Sec, Vin de Pays des Pyrenés Orientales; *Dom Garreliere (France):* Chenin Blanc, Touraine, Sauvignon Blanc, Cuvée Cendrillon, Touraine, Sauvignon Blanc, Touraine; *Domaine de Farlet (France):* Chardonnay, Vin de Pays des Collines de la Moure, Viognier, Vin de Pays des Collines de la Moure; *Domaine Richeaume (France):* Blanc de Blanc, Côtes de Provence, Viognier, Côtes de Provence; Domaine St. Michel (France): Chardonnay, Vin de Pays d'Oc, Entre Deux Mers, Sauvignon Blanc, Vin de Pays d'Oc; *Eugene Meyer (France):* Gewurztraminer, Pinot Blanc, Sylvaner; *Frick (France):* Gewurztraminer Cuvée Precieuse, Pinot Blanc Cuvée Classique, Pinot Blanc Cuvée Precieuse, Pinot Gris Cuvée Precieuse, Sylvaner Cuvée Classique; *Guy Bossard (France):* Domaine de la Parentiere Muscadet de Servre et Maine Sur Lie, Gros Plant Sur Lie, Vin de Pays Nantais, Hermine d'Or, Muscadet de Servre et Maine Sur Lie; *Jacques Frelin (France):* Chateau Petit Roubie, Picpoul de Pinet, Cuvée de Marouette Sauvignon Blanc, Vin de Pays de l'Aude, Domaine de Petit Roubie, Vin de Pays des Côtes de Thau, Joubio Blanc Domaine de Clairac, Vin de Pays l'Herault, Marsanne, Vin de Pays de l'Herault; *Jean Goulley (France):* Chablis, Petit Chablis; *Klaus Knobloch (Germany):* Bacchus Kabinett, Rheinhessen, Ortega Spatlese, Rheinhessen; *La Nature:* Chardonnay, Vin de Pays d'Oc, Chardonnay/Sauvignon Blanc, Australia, La Mancha Blanco, Spain, Sauvignon Blanc, Vin de Pays d'Oc, Torrontes, Argentina; *Millton (New Zealand):* Viognier Tietjen, Gisborne, Chardonnay, Barrel Fermented, Gisborne, Chardonnay, Gisborne, Chenin Blanc Barrel Fermented, Gisborne, Opou Reisling, Gisborne; *Paul Giboulot (France):* Bourgogne, Hautes Côtes de Nuits; *Perlage (Italy):* Chardonnay, Solatio Bianco; *Podere Canneta (Italy):* La Luna e Le Torri, Vernaccia di San Gimignano; *Richmond Plains (New Zealand):* Chardonnay, Nelson, Sauvignon Blanc, Nelson; *San Vito (Italy):* Bianco Colli dell'Etruria Centrale, Verdiglio, Vin Santo; *Volcanic Hills (Hungary):* Dry White, Neszmély, Irsai Oliver, Neszmély

VINTAGE ROOTS ☼ ⊘

Albet i Noya: DO Penedes - 'Lignum' Blanco -Albet I No 1999/2000, DO Penedes - Can Vendrell Chardonnay/Xa 2000/2001, DO Penedes - Chardonnay Colleccio 1999, DO Penedes - Xarello d'Anyada 1999/2000; *Andre Stentz:* AOC Alsace - Pinot Blanc 1999/2000, AOC Alsace Gewrztraminer 1999/2000, AOC Tokay d'Alsace 1999/2000; *Bettili:* DOC Lison Pramaggiore - Pinot Grigio 2000/2001, Serenel Frizzante 2000/2001; Bodegas Fabril Alto Verde Chardonnay - Buenas Ondas 2001, Casale Mattia - Frascati Superiore - 2000/2001, *Chateau La Canorgue:* AOC Côtes du Luberon 2000/2001, VDP de Vaucluse - Viognier 1999/2000; Chateau La Garenne AOC Sauternes 1996/1997, Chateau Le Barradis AOC Monbazillac 1997, Chateau Petit Roc AOC Bordeaux Sec - Petit Roc 1999/2000, Chateau Pouchard Larquey AOC Entre-Deux-Mers 1999/2000, *Chateau Richard:* AOC Bergerac Sec 2000/2001, AOC Saussignac - Coup de Coeur 1997/1998, AOC Saussignac - Tradition1998/1999; Christian Dauny AOC Sancerre 2000/2001, Coop Jesus del Perdon DO La Mancha - Organic Blanco 2000/2001, Di Filippo DOC Grechetto dei Colli Martani 'Terre S 1999/2000, Domaine Bassac VDP des Côtes de Thongue - Muscat MoÎlle 2000/2001, *Domaine de Brau:* VDP d'Oc - Cuvée Nina 2000/2001, VDP de l'Aude - Chardonnay Finement Bois 1999; Domaine de Farlet VDP des Collines de la Moure - Chardonna 2000/2001, Domaine de Jas D'Esclans AOC Côtes de Provence Cru Classé 2000/2001, Domaine de la Parentiere AOC Muscadet de Sévre et Maine sur Lie 2000/2001, *Domaine Jean Goulley:* AOC Chablis 2000, AOC Chablis Premier Cru Fourchaume 1999, AOC Chablis Premier Cru Montmains 1999, AOC Petit Chablis 1999/2000; Domaine Petit Roubie VDP de l'Hérault - Marsanne 2000/01, Domaine Spiropoulos VQPRD Mantinia 'Orino' 2000/2001, Domaine St Nicolas VDQS Fiefs Vendéens - Biodynamic Blanc 2000/2001, *Dominique & Catherine Derain:* AOC St Aubin 1999/2000, AOC St Aubin Premier Cru 'En Remilly' 1999; *Emilien d'Albret:* VDP d'Oc - Organic Chardonnay 2000/2001, VDP d'Oc - Organic Sauvignon Blanc 1999/2000; *Fasoli Gino:* DOC Soave Superiore 2000/2001, DOC Soave Superiore Pieve Vecchia - Faso 1999/2000, San Zeno Recioto di Soave 1997/1998; Fetzer Vineyards Chardonnay - Bonterra Mendocino 1999/2000, Guy Bossard AOC Muscadet Sévre et Maine sur Lie - 'H 2000, Holmes Brothers Marlborough - Sauvignon Blanc 2000/2001, *Huet:* AOC Vouvray - Demi-Sec 1999, AOC Vouvray - MoÎlleux 1996, AOC Vouvray - Sec 1999; *Kawarau Estate:* Reserve

Chardonnay - Cromwell / Central 1999/2000, Sauvignon Blanc - Cromwell / Central Ota 2000/2001; *Klaus Knobloch:* Riesling Kabinett Trocken 1999/2000, Weisserburgunder Kabinett Trocken 1999/2000; *Les Pradelles:* VDP de l'Hérault - Les Pradelles Blanc 2 2000, VDP de L'Hérault- Les Pradelles 2000/2001; *Montalbano:* DOC Fruili Grave - Pinot Grigio 2000/2001, DOC Fruili Grave - Sauvignon Blanc 2000/2001, IGT Terre Montalbano Bianco - Fruili Gra 2000/2001; Nuova Cappelletta DOC Piemonte Chardonnay 2000, Pierre André AOC Chateauneuf du Pape 1998/2000, Podere Canneta DOCG Vernaccia di San Gimignano 2000/2001, *Richmond Plains:* Chardonnay - Nelson 2000/2001, Sauvignon Blanc - Nelson 2000/2001; *Robinvale Vineyards:* Chardonnay / Chenin Blanc / Sauvignon Bl 1999/2000, Chardonnay 1998/1999; Sedlescombe Dry White 1999/2000, *Sonop Wine Farm:* Sauvignon Blanc - Organic Terroir 2001, Chardonnay - Cape Soleil 2001; St Ursula Weinkellerei Qba St Ursula -Organic 2000, Viberti DOC Piemonte Chardonnay 1998 / 1999, *Vintage Roots:* IGT Organic Bianco 2000/2001, AOC Bordeaux - Organic Blanc 2000/2001, IGT Sicilia - Sollatio Bianco 2001, VDP d'Oc - Cuvée Bernard -Bernard Delmas 2000/2001

VIVA! ☺❶✔⊘

White Wines: All

NOTES

■ **beers** As a general rule traditional, cask-conditioned beers ('real ales') are usually clarified (cleared) with isinglass finings (see page 273 Glossary of Animal Substances). The addition of the finings speeds up a process that would otherwise occur naturally. Keg, canned, beersphere and some bottled beers are usually filtered without the use of animal substances. Lagers are generally chill-filtered but a *few* may involve the use of isinglass. Animal-derived finings continue to be used in all Guinness-, Scottish & Newcastle- (except Holsten Pils and Beck's) and Bass (except Grolsch) *produced* beers.

■ **soft drinks** Be alert to the possible presence of animal-derived colourants, such as cochineal. Orange coloured drinks may contain beta-carotene held in a gelatine suspension (see **gelatine carrier**, page 95).

■ **spirits** The production of spirits does not appear to involve the use of animal substances.

■ **water** That supplied by Yorkshire Water to the villages of Marsett, Stalling Busk, Boltby, Buckden, Chapel-le-Dale, Oughtershaw, Scar House, Starbotton, Hawkswick, Airton, Fossdale and Barden House (and possibly Aysgarth, Crumma, Newsholme near Skipton, Coalsgarth

and Rudland) has been filtered through 'Brimac' – a substance manufactured from carbonised cattle bones by Tate & Lyle Process Technology. In addition, North West water use carbonised cattle bones as a filter in one site in North East Cumbria that serves around 150 people.

■ **wines** Most wines on sale in off-licences and supermarkets have been fined using one of the following: blood, bone marrow, chitin, egg albumen, fish oil, gelatine, isinglass, milk or milk casein. Non-animal alternatives include limestone, bentonite, kaolin and kieslguhr (clays), plant casein, silica gel, and vegetable plaques. Co-op now label those wines that are suitable for vegans and declare all processing aids used in their manufacture. Several major off-licences now have vegan lists available so do ask.

TOILETRIES
& COSMETICS

BATH & SHOWER

ABSOLUTE AROMAS LTD ✔ ⊘

Ord River Bath & Shower Gel

AMPHORA AROMATICS LTD ✔ ⊘

Aromatherapy Bath Fizz Bombes:
Grapefruit, Juniper, Lavender,
Mandarin, Meroli, Ylang Ylang; *Bath
Oils:* Anti-Cellulite, Athletic, Fresh Feet,
Invigorating, PMT, Pure Pleasure,
Relaxing, Sensuous, Skin Nourishing;
Bath & Shower Gel: Aromatherapy
Base, Energising, Genetleman's, Gym &
Swim, Relaxing, Sensual; *Cocoa Butter
Aromatherapy Bath Bars:* Lavender,
Mandarin, May Chang, Ylang Ylang;
Goodnight Sleeptight Bubble Bath w
Lavender & Chamomile, Moisturising
Bath Soak, Relaxing Bath Soak

ANIMAL AID ☺ ❶ ✔ ⊘ ⅄ 76

English Rose Moisturising Shower Gel,
Tropical Shower Gel, Vanilla & Passion
Flower Foam Bath, Violet & Almond
Foaming Bath Oil

ANNE-MARIE BORLIND ❶ ✔ ⊘

Bodyvital Body Creme Scrub, *Shower
Gel:* Body Lind, Body Lind Sportiv

ARBONNE ❶ ✔ ⊘

Awaken: Bath & Shower Gel, Sea Salt
Scrub; *Unwind:* Bath & Shower Gel,
Bath Salts

BAREFOOT BOTANICALS ™ ✔ ⊘

SOS Bath Oil

BAY HOUSE AROMATICS ✔ ⊘ ⅄ 78

Bubble Bath / Shower Gel, Dispersing
Bath Oil, Lavender Bath Milk, Luxury
Bath Milk, *The Bay House Blue Range
Bath Oils:* Exotic, Refreshing, Relaxing;
The Bay House Blue Range Body Scrub:
Grapefruit & Lime, Lavender Relaxing,
Rosemary & Fennel

BEAUCAIRE ☺ ✔ ⊘

Shower Balm

BEAUTY THROUGH HERBS ☺ ✔ ⊘ 👁

Galeno Gold Body Scrub, Out Of Africa
Bath Essence

BIOCOSMETICS

Starflower Bath Oil

BODY REFORM (UK) LTD ❶ ✔ ⊘ 👁

Bath / Shower Gel: Aloe Vera,
Invigorating, Men's Reform, Reviving,
Skin Friendly, Tea Tree, White musk;
Bath Soak: Aromatherapy, Pain
Relieving; Men's Reform Body Splash,
Skin Friendly Foam Bath, White Musk
Body Scrub

CAMILLA HEPPER LTD ✔ ⊘ ⅄ 87

Bath Oil: Herbal, Lemon Mint,
Marigold; *Bath & Shower Gel:* Cocktail
Shower Shaker No 2, Jasmin, Lavender,
Lemon Verbena, Rose, Seaweed, White
Musk; *Foam / Bubble Bath:* Avocado,

Caribbean, Fruity, Orange Blossom

CHIKPE ✔ ⊘

Bath Buns: Lazy Lavender, Sea Salsa, Stress Release; *Bath & Shower Gel:* Apple & Sandalwood, Ginger & Ylang Ylang, Mandarine, Strawberry & Papaya; *Bubble Cakes:* Bubbilicious, Strawberry Soother; *Fragrance Bath Bombs:* Recharger, Strawberry Fields Forever, Stress Buster; *Glitter Bombs:* Glitterbomb, Pink Sparkler, Sky @ Night; *Miniature Pearl Bath Bombs:* Blue, Orange, Princess; *Sea Salt Bombs:* Citrus Grenade, Ocean Tonic, Sea Salt Soother

DOLMA ☺™✔ ⊛ ⊘

Aromatic Body Shampoos: Antiseptic, Deep Relaxing, Invigorating, Relaxing, Relaxing & Refreshing; Ho-Leaf & Orange Moisturising Body Wash

DR HADWEN TRUST ☺ ✔ ⊘

Aromatherapy Nature Power Bath Range: Anti-stress Foam, PMT Foam, Sleepytime Splash, Vitalising Splash; *Foam Bath:* Lavender Geranium & Ylang Ylang, Mixed Fruits, Oriental Musk, Strawberry Sundae, Tropical Palm; Rose Foaming Bath Oil, *Shower Gel:* Apple, Cherry

ESCENTIAL BOTANICALS LTD.™✔ ⊘ ⊛

Foam Bath: Refreshing, Relaxing, Soothing, Stimulating; Fruit Range Bath & Shower Gel, Invigorating Body Tonic

ESSENTIALLY YOURS ™✔ ⊘

Natural Elements: Bath Oil, Hair & Body Shampoo; *Natural Elements Shower Gel:* Anti-Fatigue, Anti-Stress

FAITH PRODUCTS LTD ❶✔ ⊘ ⊛ ⅄ 78

Foam Bath / Shower Gel: Aloe Vera & Ylang Ylang , Lavender & Geranium, Organic Chocolate, Seaweed, Tea Tree

GREEN PEOPLE CO. ™✔ ⊘

Gentle Polish (Body Scrub), *Men's Range Hair & Body Wash:* Cool Style, Vita Min Boost; *Shower Gel:* Aloe Vera, Rosemary & Pink Clay; Vita Min Fix Shower Wash

HEALTHQUEST LIMITED ™✔ ⊘

Body Scrub, Shower Gel

HEMP UNION ™✔ ⊘

Hemp Oil: Bubble Bath, Foam Bath, Shower Gel

HIGHER NATURE ✔ ⊘

Bath Remedies: Alka-bathe Powder, Alka-clear V-caps / Powder, Special Sea Soak salts

HONESTY COSMETICS LTD ☺❶✔ ⊘ ⊛ ⅄ 76

Foam Bath: Geranium & Lavender, Orange, Tangerine & Vanilla; *Shower Gel:* Apple & Sandalwood, Ginger & Ylang Ylang, Hair & Body Shampoo, Mandarine, Strawberry & Papaya, Sun & Sport

HUMANE RESEARCH TRUST ☺❶✔⦸

Norfolk Lavender Bath Fizzer: Lavender, Men's; *Norfolk Lavender Bath & Shower Gel:* Ladies', Men's Luxury

JOPHIEL ☺❶✔⦸

Bath Oils: All

JURLIQUE ✔⦸

Bath Oil: Romance, Tranquil, Vibrance; *Bath Salts:* Lavender, Lemongrass, Orange & Cinnamon, Rose, Rosemary & Mandarin, Ylang Ylang & Patchiouli; *Body Bar:* Lavender, Lemongrass, Orange & Cinnamon, Rose, Ylang Ylang; Lavender Shower Gel

KENT COSMETICS ☺✔👁⦸

Australian Organics: Bath / Shower Gel, Exfoliating Body Wash, Shower Gel

KISS MY FACE ✔

Bath: Active Athletic Muscle Relaxant, Anti-Stress, Cold & Flu, Early to Bed Moisture, Early to Rise, Peaceful Patchouli Moisture, Romance; *Shower Gel:* Rough Thyme, Silky Soft

KOBASHI ☺™✔👁⦸

Fragrance Free Bath Base, Refreshing Fruit Bath, Relaxing Bath, Wild Flower Shower Gel

LITTLE MIRACLES / APHRODITE'S ROSE ✔⦸

Rosy Glow Body Scrub

LUSH ✔⦸

Bath Ballistics: Avobath, Big Blue, Butterball, Fairy Jasmine, Fizzy O'Therapy, Hot Java, Ickle Baby Baff, Jills Daisy, Karma Sutra, Lush Bath Bomb, Prince of Bathness, Softy, Summer Blues, The Sicilian, Tisty Tosty, Uluru, Waving Not Drowning, World Piece; *Bubble Bar Slices:* Amandopondo, Aura Suavis, Bathos, Blue Skies & Fluffy White Clouds, Creamy Candy Bath, Happy, Psychodelic; *Fresh More than Mortal Body Scrub, Luxury Bath Melts:* Aqua, Ceridwen's Cauldron, Dreamtime, Floating, Island, Karma, Mirabilis; *Shower Gel:* Narcotick, Tramp; *Smoothies:* Creamed Almond & Coconut, Gumback Express, Whitewash

MARTHA HILL ❶✔⦸

Bath Oil: Citrus Refreshing, Lavender Relaxing, Rose Geranium Harmonising, Seaweed Therapeutic; *Body Wash:* Citrus Refreshing, Lavender Relaxing, Rose Geranium Harmonising, Seaweed Therapeutic; *Gently Exfoliating Seaweed Body Scrub, Pure & Simple Bath Grains:* Citrus, Lavender, Rose Geranium

MEADOWSWEET ☺™✔👁⦸

Bath Oils: Comfrey & Chickweed Foaming, Herbal Aromatic Relaxing, Rose Foaming; *Foam Bath:* Aloe Vera, Alpine, Easy Breathe, Mixed Fruits, Nature Power Anti Stress, Nature Power PMT, Oriental Musk, Tropical Palm,

Ylang Ylang; Herbal Relaxing Bath Soak, Lavender / Geranium / Ylang-Ylang Bath, *Nature Power Splash:* Sleepytime, Vitalising; *Shower Gels:* Apple, Cherry, Evening Primrose, Fragrance Free

MODERN ORGANIC PRODUCTS ✔ ⊘

Body Wash: Basil-Lime, Cranberry-Kiwi, Oatmeal-Coconut, Pear

MOLTON BROWN COSMETICS ✔ ⊘

Bath & Shower Gel: Heavenly Gingerlily Moisture, Invigorating Ginseng, Revuvenating Artic Birch, Seamoss Energising Therapy, Vitamin A B & C, Warming Eucalyptus; *Bathing Milk:* Purifying Grapeseed Anti-Oxidant, Rejuvenating Marine, Relaxing Zhan Zhi, Sensual Orchid; *Hair & Body Sport Wash,* Moisture Rich Aloe & Palm Body Bar, Re-Charge Black Pepper Body Wash, Relaxing Yuan Zhi Bathing Gel, Seamoss Stress Relieving Soak Therapy, Sensual Foaming Bath, Travel Reviving Shampoo & Shower Gel

MOTHER HEMP LTD. ™ ✔ ⊘

Bubble Bath, Shower Gel

NATIONAL TRUST ENTERPRISES ✔ ⊘ ⚶ 98

English Lavender Foam Bath

NATURAL COLLECTION ✔ ⊘

Bath & Massage Oils: 7th Heaven, Lotus, Tantra, Zen; *Bath Salts:* 7th Heaven, Lotus, Seaweed, Tantra, Zen;

Bubble Bath: 7th Heaven, Lotus, Seaweed, Tantra, Zen; *Exfoliating Body Scrub:* 7th Heaven, Lotus, Tantra, Zen; Rosemary & Pink Clay Shower Gel

NATURE KNOWS BEST ✔ ⊘

Bath Essence: Pine, Seaweed

NATUREWATCH ☺ ✔ ⊘ 👁 ⚶ 76

Clearly Compassionate Shower Gel: Mandarin & Lemongrass Invigorating, Rosemary Pine & Lemon; Lavender & Geranium Relaxing Bath Soak

NEAL'S YARD REMEDIES ✔ ⊘

Aromatic Foaming Bath, Baseline 100 Gel

NEW SEASONS ✔ ⊘

Neutral Base: Bath Milk, Foam Bath, Shower Gel

ORD RIVER TEA TREE OIL ™

Bath & Shower Gel

ORIGINAL SOURCE ™

Bath Foam: Orange & Almond, Pure Lime, Pure Spice, Tea Tree & Lavender, Tea Tree & Mint; *Moisturising Body Wash:* Almond & Orange, Tea Tree & Lavender, Tea Tree & Mint; *Shower:* Orange & Grapefruit, Pure Lemon, Pure Lime, Spearmint, Tea Tree & Lemon, Tea Tree & Mint, Tea Tree & Orange

POTIONS AND POSSIBILITIES ✔ ⊘

Bath & Shower Gel: Anti-Fatigue, Relax

& Unwind, Serenity, Traditional Lavender; *Luxury Aromatherapy Bath Oil:* Executive Stress Relief, Happy Birthday Blend, Someone Special, Special People Range, Ultra Relaxing; *Luxury Bath Sizzlers:* All

PURPLE FLAME AROMATHERAPY

Foam Bath, Shower Gel

SCENT BY NATURE ☺🆔🚫

Dispensable Vegetable Bath Oil Base

SHANTI HEALTH & BEAUTY PRODUCTS ☺❶🆔🚫

Aromatic Bath Oil

TARA TOILETRIES ☺❶🆔🚫

Bath Crystals, Shower Gel

THURSDAY PLANTATION 🆔🚫✂-95

Tea Tree Herbal Skin Wash

TLC COLLECTION 🆔👁🚫

Nougat Nourishing Cream Bath

TREE-HARVEST 🆔🚫

Ylang Ylang Foaming Bath Oil

VEGANSTORE.CO.UK ☺™❶🆔🚫

Cariad Bath Milks, Cariad Dead Sea Salts, Escential Botanicals Shower & Bath Gel, Faith In Nature Bubble Bath, Jason Organic Satin Shower & Bath Wash

VINDOTCO UK LTD ☺🆔🚫

Body Shampoo

VITA YOUTH 🆔🚫

Tea Tree Oil Shampoo & Body Wash

WELEDA 🆔🚫👁✂-85

Bath Milk: Citrus, Lavender, Rosemary

YOUR BODY ™🆔👁🚫

Apricot Bath Oil, *Aromatherapy Shower & Bath Gel:* Lavender & Bergamot, Orange & Lemon, Rosemary & Cedarwood; *Foam Bath:* Aromatherapy Luxury, Seaweed; Musk Bubble Bath, *Shower & Bath Gel:* Aloe Vera, Cellulite Control De-Tox For All Skin Types, Coconut, Kontiki, Lime, Men's Range Sage, Musk, Peach, Strawberry, Vitamin E

BRUSHES ETC

BLACKMORES 🆔🚫

Body Bar Loofah

CAMILLA HEPPER LTD 🆔🚫✂-87

Hands & Feet Pumice Sponge

NEAL'S YARD REMEDIES 🆔🚫

Body Mitt, Loofah

YOUR BODY ™🆔👁🚫

Natural Bath Collection Accessories: Body Tone, Foot Care, Hair care, Loofah, Sisal, Soap Dishes

CONDITIONERS & HAIR CARE

ABSOLUTE AROMAS LTD ✔ ⊘

Ord River Conditioner

AMPHORA AROMATICS LTD ✔ ⊘

Aromatherapy Conditioner Base

ANIMAL AID ☺❶✔⊘⅄–76

Coconut Conditioner

ANNE-MARIE BORLIND ❶✔⊘

Ceramide Cream Rinse, Vital Hair Care Fluid

ARBONNE ❶✔⊘

Conditioning Mist, Moisturizing Rinse, Protein Pak

BAY HOUSE AROMATICS ✔⊘⅄–78

Hair Conditioner

BEAUCAIRE ☺✔⊘

Hair Conditioner

BEAUTY THROUGH HERBS ☺✔⊘👁

Cryotermol Hair Lotion, Hair Masque, Hair Repair Conditioner, Hair Repair Conditioner w Cryotermol

BIOCOSMETICS

Starflower Scalp & Hair Oil

BIORGANIC HAIR THERAPY LTD

Biomin Protein Vitamin Spray, Natural Body Hair Volumiser, Rebuild Intensive Protein Treatment, Remoist Moisturising Conditioner, Right Now Leave-In Conditioner

BLACKMORES ✔⊘

Hair Moisturiser, Treatment Conditioner - Henna & Jojoba

BODY REFORM (UK) LTD ❶✔⊘👁

Conditioner: Skin Friendly, Tea Tree, White Musk

CAMILLA HEPPER LTD ✔⊘⅄–87

Avacado Treatment Wax, *Conditioner:* Herbal Protein, Natural Orange, Raspberry, Rosemary Scalp, Seaweed

CAPITELLI OILS ™✔⊘

Testa Fresca

CHIKPE ✔⊘

Coconut & Avocado, Jojoba & Peach, Rosemary & Lavender

DANIEL FIELD ☺✔⅄–76

Conditioners: Body Builder Detangling, Curl Enhancing, First Aid, Intensive Therapy 5 Spa, Revitalising Mineral, Smooth & Shine, Volumising; Mineral Hair Repair Masque, Plant Remoisturising Treatment

DOLMA ☺™✔👁⊘

Hair Conditioners: Cedarwood &

Cypress, Lavender & Jojoba; Rosemary, Nettle & Marigold Hair Lotion

DR HADWEN TRUST ☺✔⊘

Conditioner: Banana & Vanilla, Chamomile, Coconut Frequency, Comfrey Plus Care Intensive, Mango & Apricot

ESCENTIAL BOTANICALS LTD. ™✔⊘☻

Revitalising Conditioner, *Scalp Conditioning Oil:* Dry, Normal / Oily

ESSENTIALLY YOURS ™✔⊘

Natural Elements: Anti-Tangle Spray, Hair & Scalp Fluid, Hair Oil

FAITH PRODUCTS LTD ❶✔⊘☻⚭78

Conditioner: Ginkgo Biloba, Hemp & Meadowfoam, Jojoba w Panthenol, Lavender & Geranium, Organic Aloe Vera, Organic Chocolate, Rosemary, Saw Palmetto, Seaweed, Tea Tree

GR LANE ✔⊘

Tea Tree Conditioner

GREEN PEOPLE CO. ™✔⊘

Conditioners: Aloe Vera, Itch Away, Rosemary, Vita Min Fix; Men's Cool Style Condition & Style

HEALTHQUEST LIMITED ™✔⊘

Conditioner

HEMP UNION ™✔⊘

Hemp Oil: Conditioner, Hair Oil

HERB UK LTD ✔⊘

Nature's Essential: Conditioner, Intensive Treatment, Seal & Shine

HERBS HANDS HEALING ✔⊘

Earth & Wind Conditioner, Morning Rain Hair Water

HONESTY COSMETICS LTD ☺❶✔⊘☻⚭76

Conditioner: Coconut & Avocado, Jojoba & Peach

JOPHIEL ☺❶✔⊘

Conditioner: All

JURLIQUE ✔⊘

Hair Revitaliser Balm

KENT COSMETICS ☺✔☻⊘

Australian Organics Conditioner

KISS MY FACE ✔

Obsessively Natural: Conditioned Response, Light Weight Conditioner, Upper Management

LUSH ✔⊘

Veganese Conditioner

MARTHA HILL ❶✔⊘

Deep Moisturising Conditioner

MEADOWSWEET ☺™✔☻⊘

Conditioners: Aloe Vera, Banana & Vanilla, Chamomile, Coconut, Comfrey

& Cade Intensive, Kiwi & Lemon Balm, Mandarin & Papaya, Mango & Apricot, Nettle; *Men's Range Conditioners:* Cologne, Sandalwood

MODERN ORGANIC PRODUCTS ✔ ⊘

Conditioner: Daily Rinse, Glisten, Leave-In, Mixed Greens; Extreme Moisture, Extreme Protein, Pear Detangler

MOLTON BROWN COSMETICS ✔ ⊘

Instant Conditioner, Ultra Light Bai Ji Hydrator

MOTHER HEMP LTD. ™ ✔ ⊘

Conditioner

NAPIERS DISPENSARY ✔

Hair Lotion: Eucalyptus, No. 2, Rosemary

NATURAL COLLECTION ✔ ⊘

Conditioner: Aloe Vera, Hemp, Naked Hemp, Rosemary

NATURE'S DREAM ✔ ⊘

Naturtint Rosemary Hair Shield

NATUREWATCH ☺ ✔ ⊘ ◉ ⚘ 76

Jojoba & Lavender Intensive Conditioner

NEAL'S YARD REMEDIES ✔ ⊘

Chamomile & Jojoba Conditioner, Rosemary & Cedarwood Hair Treatment

ORD RIVER TEA TREE OIL ™

Conditioner

ORIGINAL SOURCE ™

Conditioners: Extra Strong Mint, Refreshing, Lemon & Mint, Balancing, Mint & Balsam, Enriching, Mint & Green Tea, Protecting, Orange & Almond, Enriching, Orange & Grapefruit, Volumising, Orange & Lemon, Balancing, Orange & Tea Tree, Protecting, Tea Tree & Mint, Volumising

QUINESSENCE AROMATHERAPY ☺ ❶ ✔ ⊘ ◉

Protein Conditioner Base

SHANTI HEALTH & BEAUTY PRODUCTS ☺ ❶ ✔ ⊘

Hair Oil, Hair Tonic

SUMA WHOLEFOODS

Conditioners: Aloe Vera, Tea Tree

THURSDAY PLANTATION ✔ ⊘ ⚘ 95

Tea Tree Conditioner

TIGI ✔

Conditioner: Deep Reconstruct, Instant, Moisture & Shine, Thickening Paste; Peppermint Treatment, Protein Spray

TIKI ✔ ⊘

Hair Conditioner, Vitamin E High Potency Oil

TOILETRIES & COSMETICS

URTEKRAM ⊘✔

Conditioner: Aloe Vera, Camomile, Children, Lavender, Rose, Tea Tree

VEGANSTORE.CO.UK ☺™❶✔⊘

Conditioner: Extra Rich Natural Sea Kelp System, Moisturising; Hair Polish, Jason Natural Aloe Vera 84% System, Spritz

WELEDA ✔⊘👁⚖85

Bottled Conditioner: Calendula, Lemon Balm, Rosemary; Rosemary Hair Lotion

YIN YANG BEAUTY CARE ☺✔⊘

Conditioning Hair care

YOAH

Hemp Oil Conditioner

YOUR BODY ™✔👁⊘

Conditioners: Aloe Vera, Chamomile, Marigold, Musk, Red Apple, Rosemary, Seaweed, Tea Tree, Vitamin E

DEODORANTS & ANTIPERSPIRANTS

AMPHORA AROMATICS LTD ✔⊘

Thai Deodorant Stones

ANIMAL AID ☺❶✔⊘⚖76

White Musk Deodorant

ANNE-MARIE BORLIND ❶✔⊘

Bodyvital Deo Balm, *Deodorant Spray:* Body Lind, Body Lind Sportiv

BEAUCAIRE ☺✔⊘

Deocream

BODY REFORM (UK) LTD ❶✔⊘👁

Antiperspirant: Aloe Vera, Skin Friendly, White Musk; *Body Spray:* Men's Reform Deodorant, White Musk; Sports Range Deocristal

CAMILLA HEPPER LTD ✔⊘⚖87

Watercress Deodorant

CHIKPE ✔⊘

Deodorant Stone

DEODORANT STONE (UK) LTD ☺✔⊘

Deodorant Stone, *Roll-On Stone:* Aloe & Cucumber, Herbal Spice, Tea Tree, Unscented; *Spray-On Stone:* Aloe & Cucumber, Herbal Spice, Tea-Tree, Unscented

DOLMA ☺™✔👁⊘

Roll-On Deodorant

GREEN PEOPLE CO. ™✔⊘

Deodorant: Deokrystal, No Scent, Rosemary; *Men's Deodorant:* Stay Cool, Stay Fresh

HEMP UNION ™✔⊘

Hemp Oil Deodorant

128

HOLLYTREES ✔ ⊘

Herbal Deodorant

KISS MY FACE ✔

Active Enzyme Stick Deodorant:
Lavender, Natural Fragrance Free,
Natural Scented; *Liquid Rock Roll-On:*
Fragrance Free, Lavender, Patchouli,
Scented

LAFE ☺ ✔ ⊘

Aloe Vera & MSM Natural Crystal Spray,
Natural Crystal Hemp Oil Roll-On:
Active, Lavender, Power, Unscented

LUSH ✔ ⊘

Solid Deodorants: Aromaco,
Aromarant, Fuwari, Krysztal, Lavender,
T'eo

MARTHA HILL ❶ ✔ ⊘

Deodorant: Herbal, Pure

MEADOWSWEET ☺™ ✔ ⊜ ⊘

Body Sprays: White Musk, Wild Dewberry

NATURAL COLLECTION, THE ✔ ⊘

Deodorant Sprays, Deodorant Stone,
Natural Deodorant: Push-up Crystal,
Ylang Kava

NEAL'S YARD REMEDIES ✔ ⊘

Deodorant Stone, Lemon & Coriander
Deodorant

ORIGINAL SOURCE ™

Antiperspirant: Tea Tree & Lemon, Tea
Tree & Mint, Tea Tree & Orange; *Roll-
On Deodorant:* Tea Tree & Lavender, Tea
Tree & Lemon, Tea Tree & Mint

PITROK LTD ✔ ⊘

Crystal Deodorant: Original, Push-up;
Spray Deodorant: Fragrance, Natural

PURPLE FLAME AROMATHERAPY ✔ ⊘

Deodorant Chrystal: Roll-On, Salt

SHANTI HEALTH & BEAUTY PRODUCTS ☺❶ ✔ ⊘

Deodorant Lotion

THURSDAY PLANTATION ✔ ⊘ ⚘95

Tea Tree: Antiperspirant Floral,
Antiperspirant Sport, Roll-On
Deodorant

TOM'S OF MAINE ✔ ⊘

Natural Anti-Perspirant & Deodorant,
Natural Deodorant Gentle Formula:
Calendula, Woodspice; *Natural
Deodorant Original Formula:*
Honeysuckle Rose, Unscented

VEGANSTORE.CO.UK ☺™❶ ✔ ⊘

Jason Natural Organic Tea Tree Stick,
Tom's Of Maine Deodorant Sticks

WELEDA ✔ ⊘ ⊜ ⚘85

Deodorant: Citrus, Herbal

XYNERGY HEALTH PRODUCTS ✔ ⊘

Aloe & Cucumber Roll-On Deodorant, Deodorant Stone

YOUR BODY ™ ✔ ◉ ⊘

For Men Deodorant, *Musk:* Body Spray, Deodorant

ESSENTIAL OILS & MASSAGE PRODUCTS

AMPHORA AROMATICS LTD ✔ ⊘

Essential Oils: All; *Massage Oils:* Anti-Cellulite, Athletic, Fresh Feet, Invigorating, PMT, Pure Pleasure, Relaxing, Sensual, Sensuous, Skin Nourishing; *Moisturising Body Oil:* for Daily Use, Massage, Relaxing, Sensual *Organic Essential Oils:* All

ARBONNE ❶ ✔ ⊘

Unwind Massage Oil

ARKOPHARMA (UK) LTD ☺ ✔ ⊘

Massage Gels: Litelegs, Phytorhuma

BAY HOUSE AROMATICS ✔ ⊘ ⚹ 78

Essential / Carrier / Vegetable Oils: All; *The Bay House Blue Range Massage Oils:* Exotic, Refreshing, Relaxing

BEAUTY THROUGH HERBS ☺ ✔ ⊘ ◉

Complementary, Carrier & Massage

Oils: All; *Essential Oils:* All

BODY REFORM (UK) LTD ❶ ✔ ◉ ⊘

Essential & Carrier Oils: All; *Massage Oils / Lotions / Creams:* All

CAMILLA HEPPER LTD ✔ ⊘ ⚹ 87

Aromatherapy Muscular Massage, *Essential Oils:* All

CAPITELLI OILS ™ ✔ ⊘

Dormi Bene, Invigorante, Primia, Versatilita

CHIKPE ✔ ⊘

Solid Massage Bars: Juniper-Relaxing, Mars-Fun, Neptune Invigorating

COTSWOLD HEALTH PRODUCTS ☺⊘

Essential Oils: All

DOLMA ☺™ ✔ ◉ ⊘

Massage Oil: Anti-Cellulite, Invigorating, Relaxing, Soothing

DR HADWEN TRUST ☺ ✔ ⊘

Comfrey After Sports Massage Oil

ESCENTIAL BOTANICALS LTD. ™ ✔ ⊘ ◉

Massage Oil

ESSENTIAL OIL COMPANY ☺ ✔ ⊘ ◉

Pure Essential Oils: All; *Vegetable & Nut oils:* All

ESSENTIALLY YOURS ™ ✔ ⊘

For Play Creams: Anticipation Penis,

Discovery; *For Play Gels:* Divine Nipple, Everlasting, Interplay Lubricating; *For Play Oils:* Fantasy Massage, Yin-Yang Lubricating; *Natural Elements Massage Oils:* Facial, Refreshing, Relaxing

FAITH PRODUCTS LTD ❶⌀⊘👁⚹78

Essential Body Massage Oil

HEALTHQUEST LIMITED ™⌀⊘

Essential Oils: Eucalyptus, Geranium, Lavender, Lemon, Lemongrass, Peppermint, Rosemary, Sweet Orange, Tea Tree, Ylang Ylang; *Massage Oils:* Muscle Rub, Relaxing, Sensual; *Mood Blends:* Easy Breathe, Energising, Meditation, Relaxing, Restful Night, Sensual

HERBS HANDS HEALING ⌀⊘

Essential Oils: All; *Massage & Base Oils:* All

HERMITAGE OILS ☺❶⌀⊘

Absolute Oils: All; *Essential Oils:* All; *Fixed Oils:* All

JOPHIEL ☺❶⌀⊘

Blended Essential Oils: All; *Carrier Oils:* All; *Essential Oils:* All; *Massage Oils:* All

JURLIQUE ⌀⊘

Essential Oils: All

KOBASHI ☺™⌀👁⊘

Aromatherapy Poster, *Blended Massage Oils:* Anti-Cellulite, Relaxing, Sensual,

Sports; Burner-Vapourisers, Carrier Oils, Essential Oils, Starter Baskets

LUSH ⌀⊘

Massage Bars: Amazonian, Bewitched, Black Magic, Fever, Into Thin Air, Iridescent Glitterbug, Snake Oil Bar, Therapy, Wiccy Magic Muscles

MEADOWSWEET ☺™⌀👁⊘

Carrier Oils: Avocado, Carrot, Evening Primrose, Grapeseed, Jojoba, Peach Kernel, Sweet Almond, Wheatgerm; *Massage Oils:* Herbal Aromatic Relaxing, Men's Range Comfrey After Sports, Nature Power Body Firming Contouring, Nature Power Cellulite Thigh Intensive; *Pure Essential Oils:* Basil, Bergamot, Black Pepper, Camphor, Cedarwood, Chamomile (Roman), Citronella, Clary Sage, Clove, Cypress, Eucalyptus, Frankincense, Geranium, Ginger, Grapefruit, Juniper, Lavender (High Altitude), Lemon, Lemon Grass, Lime, Mandarin, Manuka, Marjoram (Sweet), Myrrh, Niaouli, Orange, Patchouli, Peppermint, Petitgrain, Pine, Red Thyme, Rosemary, Rosewood, Sandalwood, Sweet Fennel, Tea Tree, Vetivert, Ylang-Ylang

MICHELINE ARCIER AROMATHERAPY ⌀⊘

Essential Oils: All

MOTHER HEMP LTD. ™⌀⊘

Massage Oil

NAPIERS DISPENSARY ✔

Essential & Massage Oils: All; *Organic Essential Oils:* All

NEW SEASONS ✔ ⊘

Absolute Oils: All; *Carrier Oils:* All; *Essential Oils:* All; *Organic Oils:* All

ORD RIVER TEA TREE OIL ™

Pure Tea Tree Oil: 10 ml & 25 ml

POTIONS AND POSSIBILITIES ✔ ⊘

Essential Oil Blends: Energise, Party, Relaxation, Sleep; *Massage Blends:* Joint & Muscle Relief, Relaxation; *Pure Essential Oils:* All

PURPLE FLAME AROMATHERAPY ✔ ⊘

Essential Oils: All

QUINESSENCE AROMATHERAPY ☺❶✔⊘👁

Essential Oils: All; *Massage Oils:* Athletic, Cellulite, Invigorating, Joint Mobility, Muscle Ease, Relaxing, Stress, Stretch Marks; *Organic Oils:* All

ROMANY ✔ ⊘

Aromatherapy Oils: All

SCENT BY NATURE ☺✔⊘

Essential oils: All; Frankincense Tree Resin, Lavender Essential Oil Sleep Stones

SCOTTISH HERBAL SUPPLIES

Organic & Non-Organic Essential Oils, Vegetable Oils

SHANTI HEALTH & BEAUTY PRODUCTS ☺❶✔⊘

Body Rub, Facial Massage Oil

TREE-HARVEST ✔ ⊘

Essential Oils: All

VEGANSTORE.CO.UK ☺™❶✔⊘

Cariad Aromaballs, Pure Plant Massage Oil

YOUR BODY ™✔👁⊘

Aromatherapy Body Massage Oil

EYE PRODUCTS

ANNE-MARIE BORLIND ❶✔⊘

Eye Make Up Remover, Kohl Crayons, Powder Eye Shadow, Pura Soft Q10 Eye Area Care

ARBONNE ❶✔⊘

Bio-Hydria Eye Cream, *Global Color Eye Pencils:* All; *Global Color Eye Shadows:* All; Lash Colour, Snap! 2 in 1 Eye Make Up Remover Pads, Thick-It Lash Enhancer

BARRY M COSMETICS ✔👁✂85

Dazzle Dust, *Kohl Pencils:* All

BEAUCAIRE ☺✔⊘

Eye Cream, Eye gel

BEAUTY THROUGH HERBS ☺✔️⊘👁

Galeno Gold Nourishing Eye Cream Gel, Phyto Marine Eye Contour Gel

BLACKMORES ✔️⊘

Eye Balm - Cornflower, Eye Make Up Remover, Eye Nourish - Angelica

BODY REFORM (UK) LTD ❶✔️⊘👁

Eye Contour Cream, Night Repair Eye Balm

CAMILLA HEPPER LTD ✔️⊘⅄87

Cucumber Eye Gel, Eye Make-Up Remover Lotion, Herbal Eye Cream

DANY BERNARD ✔️⊘

Herbal Eye Sachet

DOLMA ☺™✔️👁⊘

Aloe Vera Eye Gel, Camomile & Aloe Vera Eye Cream, Camomile & Fennel Eye Make-Up Remover

DR HADWEN TRUST ☺✔️⊘

Comfrey Plus Cucumber Eye Gel, Eye Make-up Remover Cream

ESCENTIAL BOTANICALS LTD. ™✔️⊘👁

Classic Cleansing Eye Cream

ESSENTIALLY YOURS ™✔️⊘

Natural Elements Eye: & Neck Gel, Cleansing Liquid, Cream, Firming Serum

FAITH PRODUCTS LTD ❶✔️⊘👁⅄78

Aloe Vera Eye Gel

GREEN PEOPLE CO. ™✔️⊘ Eye

Cream (Night), Eye Gel (Day)

HERBS HANDS HEALING ✔️⊘

Eyebright & Goldenseal Eyewash

HONESTY COSMETICS LTD ☺❶✔️⊘👁⅄76

Beauty Without Cruelty Soft Kohl Eye Pencils

KISS MY FACE ✔️

A C & E Eye Opener, Eye Witness Eye Creme, Shea Butter Eye Makeup Remover

MARTHA HILL ❶✔️⊘

Elderflower Eye Contour Gel, Eye Contour Balm, *Gentle Cleansing for Eyes:* Gel, Lotion

MEADOWSWEET ☺™✔️👁⊘

Eye Gels: Comfrey & Cucumber, Elderflower, Fragrance Free; Eye-Make-Up Remover Cream

MOLTON BROWN COSMETICS ✔️

Eye Wear Soft Powder Shadows, Eyes Right Soft Powder Pencil, Finishing Line – Long Last Liner, Molton Brown Eye Rescue, Recover Eyes, Take Cover – Eyes

MONTAGNE JEUNESSE ✔ ⊚ ⊘

Moisturising Soothing Eye Gel

POTIONS AND POSSIBILITIES ✔ ⊘

Firming Eye Gel

SAUFLON PHARMACEUTICALS ✔ ⊘

Contact Lens Solutions: All in One Light, ComfortVue, Delta Cleaner, Delta Plus, Multi, Trizyme

STARGAZER ✔ ⊘

Eyedust, Eyeshadow

TREE-HARVEST ✔ ⊘

Eye Gel

VEGANSTORE.CO.UK ☺™❶ ✔ ⊘

Anne Marie Borlind: Gentle Eye Make Up Remover, Khol Crayons, Powder Eye Shadow Duos

YOUR BODY ™ ✔ ⊚ ⊘

Elderflower Eye Gel, *Eye Make-up Remover:* Aloe Vera, Eyebright, Vitamin E; Wheatgerm Oil Eye Cream

FEMININE HYGIENE

ARKOPHARMA (UK) LTD ☺ ✔ ⊘

Phyto Soya: Feminine Wash, Vaginal Gel

LUNAPADS ✔ ⊘

Washable Organic Sanitary Towels

NATRACARE ✔ ⊘

Organic Applicator Tampons: Regular, Super; *Organic Digital Tampons:* Regular, Super, Super+; *Pads:* Panty Shields , Regular, Slender, Super, Ultra+Wings

NATURE'S MOTHER ✔ ⊘

Feminine Hygiene Wash

VEGANSTORE.CO.UK ☺™❶ ✔ ⊘

Natracare: Organic Tampons, Pads, Panty Shields, Ultra Pads w Wings

FOOT & LEG CARE

AMPHORA AROMATICS LTD ✔ ⊘

Herbal Relaxing Foot Spray

ANIMAL AID ☺❶ ✔ ⊘⅃76

Cool Mint Foot Lotion, Peppermint Foot Powder

ARBONNE ❶ ✔ ⊘

Herbal Foot Care

BAY HOUSE AROMATICS ✔ ⊘⅃78

Peppermint & Aloe Vera Foot Lotion

BEAUCAIRE ☺ ✔ ⊘

Foot Cream Tea Tree

BEAUTY THROUGH HERBS ☺✓⊘👁

Phyto Care: Footbalm Herbal Cream, Legtonic

BETTERWARE ✓🏃2000

Toenail Softener

BODY REFORM (UK) LTD ❶✓⊘👁

Body Sculpture Thigh Cream, Tea Tree Foot Lotion

CAMILLA HEPPER LTD ✓⊘🏃87

Aloe Vera Foot Lotion

CHIKPE ✓⊘

Peppermint Foot Lotion

CHRISTY ✓👁

Feet Treats Foot Sachet: Conditioning Lotion, Cooling Liquid Talc, Revitalising Scrub, Revitalising Soak; *Feet Treats Foot Tube:* Conditioning Lotion, Cooling Liquid Talc, Revitalising Scrub, Revitalising Soak; *Sole Mates Foot Care:* Coconut & Passionflower Rescue Balm, Green Tea & Lime Crushed Salt Scrub, Jojoba & Spearmint Deodorising Moisturiser, Peppermint & Marine Extracts Deo Spritz, Spa Foot Soak

DEODORANT STONE (UK) LTD ☺✓⊘

Peppermint Foot Spray-On Stone

DOLMA ☺™✓👁⊘

Aromatic Foot Shampoo: w Lemongrass & Cypress, w Tea Tree & Thyme; Peppermint Foot Cream

DR HADWEN TRUST ☺✓⊘

Athlete's Foot Oil, Body-firming Contouring Massage Oil, Cellulite & Thigh Massage, Deodorising Foot Spray, Herbal Foot Soak, Leg & Vein Cream, Peppermint Foot Cream

ESCENTIAL BOTANICALS LTD. ™✓⊘👁

Cooling Foot Balm

ESSENTIALLY YOURS ™✓⊘

Natural Elements Anti-microbial Foot: Cream, Soak, Spray; *Natural Elements Foot Massage Cream, Natural Elements Refreshing Foot:* Scrub, Soak; *Natural Elements Warming Foot:* Cream, Soak

FAITH PRODUCTS LTD ❶✓⊘👁🏃78

Essential Foot Lotion

JURLIQUE ✓⊘

Foot & Leg Tonic

LAVINIA ✓⊘

Foot Bath Concentrate, Foot Bath Salts, Foot & Leg Lotion, Foot Powder w Essential Oils, Herbal Foot Cream

LUSH ✓⊘

Fresh Volcano Foot Mask, Pied de Pepper

MARTHA HILL ❶✓⊘

Energising Leg Gel, Moisturising Foot Balm

TOILETRIES & COSMETICS

MEADOWSWEET ☺™🐰👁⊘

Creams: Comfrey & Peppermint Foot, Leg & Vein, Peppermint Foot; Deodorising Foot Spray, Herbal Foot Soak, Nature Power Athletes Foot Oil

MONTAGNE JEUNESSE 🐰👁⊘

Iced Blueberry & Balm Mint Deodorising Foot Cooler, Morello Cherry & Balm Mint Tired Leg Gel, Watermelon & Balm Mint Deodorising Foot Scrub

NEAL'S YARD REMEDIES 🐰⊘

Lavender & Tea Tree Foot Salts, Pumice Foot Scrub

POTIONS AND POSSIBILITIES 🐰⊘

Finger & Heel Relief, Foot Relief Cream

POWER HEALTH PRODUCTS 🐰⊘

Leg & Vein Balm

PURPLE FLAME AROMATHERAPY 🐰⊘

Sweet Feet Reflexology Wipes

QUINESSENCE AROMATHERAPY ☺❶🐰⊘👁

Foot Balm

THURSDAY PLANTATION 🐰⊘⚡-95

Tea Tree: Anti-Fungal Gel, Foot Powder, Foot Spray

VEGANSTORE.CO.UK ☺™❶🐰⊘

Cariad Peppermint Foot Gel, Tisserand Foot Lotion

YOUR BODY ™🐰👁⊘

Peppermint Foot: Bath, Lotion, Powder, Spray

GIFT BOXES & PACKS

GREEN PEOPLE CO. ™🐰⊘

Organic Face Pamper Pack

LUSH 🐰⊘

Fancy Three: Bed of Roses, Blue Lagoon, Bombsadaisy, Sea, Sun & Sicilian; *Gift Boxes:* Anything But Ordinary, Bottle Of Bubbly, Bunty, Buttercup, Counting Sheep, Dreamwash, Karma Collection, Pink Caroline, Pyjamarama, Red Rooster Wrapped, Sea Vegetable Wrapped, Serenity, Shimmy Shimmy Glitterbug, Smile B Happy, Spellbound, Super Deluxe Bath Box, The Return of the Bubble Bath

MARTHA HILL ❶🐰⊘

Camomile Skin Care Set

NATIONAL TRUST ENTERPRISES 🐰⊘⚡-98

English Lavender Gift Set

POTIONS AND POSSIBILITIES 🐰⊘

Collections: Bath Oil Unwind, Energising Bath & Body, Relief Balm, Themed Luxury Bath Salts, Ultimate;

Cracker Gift Pack Luxury Bath Sizzlers: Energising, Relaxing; *Relaxation Selections:* Evening, Lavender

SCENT BY NATURE ☺ ⅟ ⊘

Gift Selection Packs, Themed Gift Packs

SEVEN WIVES

3 Soaps Gift Set: care range, castille range

HAIR DYES

CAMILLA HEPPER LTD ⅟ ⊘ ⅜ 87

Natural Henna Hair Colours: Black, Chestnut Brown, Copper Gold, Natural Auburn

CHIKPE ⅟ ⊘

Henna: Black, Blonde, Chestnut, Copper / Auburn, Fiery Red, Light Red, Mahogany, Neutral

COTSWOLD HEALTH PRODUCTS ☺⊘

Henna: Chestnut Brown, Indian Red, Neutral, Sahara Blonde; *Henna powder:* Black, Red

DANIEL FIELD

Semi-Permanent Plant Remoisturising Colour: Hazelnut, Palm Nut Brown, Saffron Gold, Walnut; *Water Colours:* All

HERB UK LTD ⅟ ⊘

Changes Semi Permanent Hair Colour: Allamanda, Dianthus, Felicia, Genista, Inula, Jasminum, Kalmia, Morina, Nerine; *Tints of Nature Permanent Hair Colour:* Black, Dark Blonde, Dark Brown, Dark Henna Red, Darkest Brown, Light Blonde, Light Brown, Light Golden Brown, Light Henna Red, Medium Blonde, Medium Brown, Medium Golden Blonde, Medium Mahogany Blonde, Medium Mahogany Brown, Medium Red Copper, Platinum Blonde, Rich Copper Brown, Soft Copper Blonde

LUSH ⅟ ⊘

Les Cacas: Brun, Marron, Noir, Rouge

NATURE'S DREAM ⅟ ⊘

Naturtint: Permanent Hair Colorant, Reflex Shine on Colour Rinse

NEAL'S YARD REMEDIES ⅟ ⊘

Henna

STARGAZER ⅟ ⊘

Hair Colour, *Hair Gell:* Glitter, Neon; Hair Jewellery

WORLDS END TRADING ☺❶ ⅟ ⊘

Henna: Black, Blonde, Chestnut, Copper, Fiery Red, Light Red, Mahogany, Neutral

HAIR SPRAYS, GELS ETC

BIORGANIC HAIR THERAPY LTD

Biogel Nutritional Styling Gel, Profile Styling Serum, Stylelock Finishing Spray

CAMILLA HEPPER LTD ◀ ⊘ ⚹-87

Jojoba Hair Gel

DANIEL FIELD ☺ ◀ ⚹-76

Cactus Sap Styling Gel, Curl Enhancing Spritz, Curl, Hold & Shine, Define & Texture Paste, Glossing Gel, Polishing Wax, Pump up the Volume!, *Serum:* Anti-Frizz, Mirror Finish, Smooth & Shine; *Spray:* Anti-Frizz Miracle, Anti Frizz Protector, Body Builder; Straighten & Smooth Balm, Style & Shape Cream, Styling Wax, Volumising Air-O-Foam

GREEN PEOPLE Co. ™◀ ⊘

Aloe Vera & Rosemary Styling Gel

MARTHA HILL ❶◀ ⊘

Natural Style Conditioning Hair Gel

MODERN ORGANIC PRODUCTS ◀ ⊘

Cream: Defining, Molding; D-Curl, *Form Foaming Gel:* for Heavy Hold, for Light Hold; *Gel:* Heavy Hold, Light Hold; Glisten Shine Drops, *Hairspray:* Eco-firm, Eco-light; High Shine Pomade, Pomade, *Spray:* Volumising, Weightless Shine; Styling Tonic

MOLTON BROWN COSMETICS ◀ ⊘

Soft Control Hair Gel

TIGI ◀

Curl Jam, Hold & Gloss, Molding Gel, Pure Gloss, Spray Shine, Straight Talk, Strong Glaze, Texturising Pomade, Thickening Creme

HAND & NAIL PRODUCTS

ANIMAL AID ☺❶◀ ⊘⚹-76

Marigold & Marshmallow Hand Cream

ANNE-MARIE BORLIND ❶◀ ⊘

Hand Balm

ARBONNE ❶◀ ⊘

Hand Cream

BARRY M COSMETICS ◀ ◉⚹-85

Nail Paints: All

BAY HOUSE AROMATICS ◀ ⊘⚹-78

Hand Cream: for Gardeners w Sandalwood & Benzoin, Jojoba Base, Luxury w Rose Oils

BEAUCAIRE ☺◀ ⊘

Hand Cream

BEAUTY THROUGH HERBS ☺ ✔ ⊘ 👁

Phyto Care Nail Restore Herbal Cream

BIO-D CO. LTD.

'Squeaky' Natural Hand Cleaner, 'Working Hands' Skin Repair Cream

BLACKMORES ✔ ⊘

Body Care Calendula Hand Creme

BODY REFORM (UK) LTD ❶ ✔ ⊘ 👁

Nail Paints: All; Safe Hands Environmental Protection Hand Cream, Strawberry & Papaya Hand & Nail Complex

CAMILLA HEPPER LTD ✔ ⊘ 🐾 87

Evening Primrose Hand Cream

CAPITELLI OILS ™ ✔ ⊘

Crema Mani

CELLANDE MIDLANDS ☺ ✔ ⊘

Hand Cleaner: Coconut, Lavender & Avocado Oil, Pine

CHIKPE ✔ ⊘

Coconut Fibre Nail Brush, Hand Cream w Comfrey

CHRISTY ✔ 👁

Hand Maiden Hand Care: Anti-Aging Hand Cream, Overnight Rescue Balm, Pamper Therapy Pack

DOLMA ☺ ™ ✔ 👁 ⊘

Hand Cream: Lemongrass, Wild Poppy; Nail & Cuticle Oil

DR HADWEN TRUST ☺ ✔

Hand Cream: Peach & Apricot, Rich Rose, Rose & Glycerine

ESCENTIAL BOTANICALS LTD. ™ ✔ ⊘ 👁

Classic Hand Cream

ESSENTIALLY YOURS ™ ✔ ⊘

Natural Elements Extra Rich Hand Cream

FAITH PRODUCTS LTD ❶ ✔ ⊘ 🐾 78

Hand Wash: Lavender & Geranium, Tea Tree

FOOD SAFE LTD ☺ ❶ ✔ ⊘

Safe Hands

GR LANE ✔ ⊘

Tea Tree Hand Wash

GREEN PEOPLE CO. ™ ✔ ⊘

Help at Hand Cream

GROOMERS LTD ✔ ⊘

Germaway Hand Disinfectant

HEMP SHOP LTD ❶ ✔ ⊘

Squeaky Hand Cleaner

HONESTY COSMETICS LTD
☺❶✔️◌👁️⊘✈76

Hand Cream w Comfrey

JURLIQUE ✔️⊘

Nail Oil

KENT COSMETICS ☺✔️👁️⊘

Australian Organics Hand Cream

LIBERON WAXES LTD

Liquid Glove

MARTHA HILL ❶✔️⊘

Cuticle Cream: Gentle, Nourishing; Evening Primrose Moisturising Hand Cream, Nourishing Nail Oil, Skin Smoothing Hand Scrub

MEADOWSWEET ☺™✔️👁️⊘

Hand Creams: Peach & Apricot, Rich Rose; Lemon & Hawthorn Barrier Cream, Nature Power Antiseptic Hand Wash Cleanser, Rose & Glycerine Hand Lotion

MOLTON BROWN COSMETICS ✔️⊘

Fine Liquid Hand Wash, Soothing Hand Lotion

NATUREWATCH ☺✔️⊘👁️✈76

Lavender & Lemon Hand & Nail Cream

NEAL'S YARD REMEDIES ✔️⊘

Citrus Hand Wash

NEW SEASONS ✔️⊘

Neutral Base Hand Cream

ORIGINAL SOURCE ™

Hand Wash: Pure Lime, Tea Tree & Lavender, Tea Tree & Lemon, Tea Tree & Mint

POTIONS AND POSSIBILITIES ✔️⊘

Finger & Heel Relief

PURPLE FLAME AROMATHERAPY ✔️⊘

Hand Cream w Comfrey

QUINESSENCE AROMATHERAPY ☺❶✔️⊘👁️

Hand Cream Base, Nourishing Hand Cream

SCENT BY NATURE ☺✔️⊘

Calendula & Chamomile Hand Cream

STARGAZER ✔️⊘

Nail Art Pen, Nail Polish

TLC COLLECTION ✔️👁️⊘

Nougat Nurturing Hand Cream

VEGANSTORE.CO.UK ☺™❶✔️⊘

Cariad Lavender Hand Cream, Tisserand Hand & Nail Cream

VINDOTCO UK LTD ☺✔️⊘

Hand Cleaner

VITA YOUTH ✔ ⊘

Tea Tree Oil Hand Cream

YOUR BODY ™ ✔ 👁 ⊘

Marigold Hand Lotion

LIP PRODUCTS

ANNE-MARIE BORLIND ❶ ✔ ⊘

Lip Liner

ARBONNE ❶ ✔ ⊘

Global Color Lip Pencils: All; *Global Color Lipsticks:* All; Sheer Shine

BARRY M COSMETICS ✔ 👁 ⚕85

Lip Liners: All

BIOCOSMETICS

Starflower Lip Balm

BODY REFORM (UK) LTD ❶ ✔ ⊘ 👁

Lipsticks: All

CAMILLA HEPPER LTD ✔ ⊘ ⚕87

Lip Smoothies: Banana, Mint, Passionfruit

DOLMA ☺™ ✔ 👁 ⊘

Lip Salves: Mandarin, Spearmint

DR HADWEN TRUST ☺ ✔ ⊘

Lip Balm: Banana, Coconut, Green Apple, Strawberry, Wild Dewberry

GREEN PEOPLE CO. ™ ✔ ⊘

Cool Lips (Mint), Fresh Lips (Citrus), Soft Lips ("No Scent")

HEMP SHOP LTD ❶ ✔ ⊘

Merry Hempster Lip Balm: Lemon & Lime, Orange (SPF 18), Peppermint (SPF18), Spearmint, Tangerine

HEMP UNION ™ ✔ ⊘

Hemp Oil Lip Balm

HONESTY COSMETICS LTD
☺❶ ✔ ⊘ 👁 ⚕76

Beauty Without Cruelty Lip Colours, Lip Balm

KISS MY FACE ✔

Organic: Hot Spots, Lip Balm, Lip Repair

MARTHA HILL ❶ ✔ ⊘

Aloe Vera Lip Balm

MEADOWSWEET ☺™ ✔ 👁 ⊘

Lip Balms: Banana, Coconut, Green Apple, Peppermint, Red Cherry, Rich Plum, Strawberry, Wild Dewberry

MOLTON BROWN COSMETICS ✔ ⊘

Lush Colour Glaze, Not Just Lips 3 In 1 Travel Stick, Perfect Lips – Stay Fast Definer, Super Long Last Formula, Vitamin Saver, Wet Clear Gloss, Wonder Booster

STARGAZER ✔️ ⊘

Glitter Lipstick, Lipstick

THURSDAY PLANTATION ✔️ ⊘ ⚷ 95

Tea Tree Lip Fix Cream

VEGANSTORE.CO.UK ☺™❶✔️⊘

Anne Marie Borlind Lip Pencils, Fruity Lip Balms, Jason Sunbrella SPF 20 Lip Protector

YOAH

Lip Balms: Coconut, Mango, Spearmint

YOUR BODY ™✔️👁⊘

Lip Balms: Apricot, Banana, Kiwi Fruit, Morello Cherry, Orange Mint, Strawberry

PERFUMES ETC

AMPHORA AROMATICS LTD ✔️ ⊘

Exotic Essential Oil Perfumes: Energising & Revitalising, Erotic & Exotic, Relaxing, Sensual, Tranquil & Calming

ARBONNE ❶✔️⊘

Glorious Forever Eau De Parfum

ASCENT ☺✔️⊘

Organic Perfume: All

BEAUTY THROUGH HERBS ☺✔️⊘👁

Out Of Africa: Cologne, Perfume

BODY REFORM (UK) LTD ❶✔️⊘👁

Men's Range Aftershaves / Colognes [Similar To]: Arome Epice [Kouros], Arome Frais [Farenheit], Fougere Citronee [Paco Robanne], Herbe Sauvage [Aramis], Jou Jou [Joop], L'eau Frais [Cool Water], Oree Du Bois [Jazz], Romantik [Romance], Toujours [Eternity]; White Musk Perfume Oil, *Women's Range Fragrance Sprays / Oils [Similar To]:* Accent [White Musk], Bouquet Rose [White Linen], Br One [Ck1], Classique [Beautiful], Coulis [Champagne], Dessey [L'eau Dissey], Esprit [Ysatis], Evasion [Escape], Feu Vert [Coco], Fleur Blanche [Anais Anais], Fleur Fruitee [Georgio], Foret Oriental [Sam Sara], Fusion [Paris], Jeune Fille [Tommy Girl], Orient [Opium], Persistence [Obession], Polar Pour Elle [Polo Sport], Printaniere [Lou Lou], Romantik [Romance], Sable [Dune], Sauvage [Safari], Toujours [Eternity], Tradition [Chanel No5]

CAMILLA HEPPER LTD ✔️⊘⚷87

Perfume Oils: Coel-Na-Mara, Honeysuckle, Hyacinth, Jasmin, Lavender, Lemon Verbena, Lily Of The Valley, Orange Blossom, Pot-Pourri, Rose, Sandalwood, White Musk

DOLMA ☺™✔️👁⊘

Amethyst Mist, Anahita, Calista, Cushie B, Prelude, Quintet, Raga, Sarabande, Sonata, Vegamusk

HUMANE RESEARCH TRUST ☺❶✔⊘

Norfolk Lavender Compassion Ladies' Perfume

JURLIQUE ✔⊘

Freesia: Eau De Toilette, Perfume

LUSH ✔⊘

Karma Fragrance

MEADOWSWEET ☺™✔👁⊘

Fragrances: Banana & Vanilla, Coconut Ice, Mango & Apricot, Rose & Cinnamon

MODERN ORGANIC PRODUCTS ✔⊘

Fragrance

MOLTON BROWN COSMETICS ✔⊘

Molton Brown Cool Fragrance

NATIONAL TRUST ENTERPRISES ✔⊘⚹~98

English Lavender Spray Cologne

PERFUMERS GUILD LTD ☺❶✔👁⊘

Anniversary Woman, Bespoke Signature Scents (Personalised Perfume), *Chypre Blends:* Christina, Margot; *Citrus Blends:* Louisa, Twenty One; *Country House Home Fragrances:* Christmas, English Rose, Flower Shop, Provence Lavender, Scent of Seville; Eau de Parfum for Women, *Floral Blends:* Alice, Gabriella, Lily of the Valley, Margaret, Provence Lavender; *For Men:*

Anniversary Man, Eau de Toilette for Men, Kensington, St John, Twenty One; Marine Blend - Diana, *Oriental Blends:* Amber, Georgina, Sophie; *Scents of Romance:* Original, St Valentine, Unforgettable, With Love; *The Rose Collection:* English, Heritage, Millennium, Society; The Scent of Flowers, The Scent of Friendship - Amitie

POTIONS AND POSSIBILITIES ✔⊘

Serenity Perfume

SHANTI HEALTH & BEAUTY PRODUCTS ☺❶✔⊘

Natural Perfume: Harmony, Inspiration, Kalynium, Oriental, Sleep-Easy, Tranquility

TREE-HARVEST ✔⊘

Tree Cologne: Birch, Cypress, Elder, Juniper, Mosses, Rowan

WELEDA ✔⊘👁⚹~85

Men's Eau de Cologne

YOUR BODY ™✔👁⊘

Alcohol Free Perfume Oil For All Skin Types Except Sensitive: Apple Blossom, Canterbury Rose, Country Garden, Dewberry, English Lavender, Honeysuckle, Lavender, Lotus, Rose, Sandalwood, Seville Orange, Strawberry, Tea Rose, Vanilla, White Musk, Wild Honeysuckle

SHAMPOOS

ABSOLUTE AROMAS LTD

Ord River Shampoo

AMPHORA AROMATICS LTD ✍ ⊘

Aromatherapy Base, Gym & Swim Conditioning, Strong Tea Tree

ANIMAL AID ☺❶✍⊘⤳76

Jojoba Orange & Rosemary Conditioning, Sea spray, Tea-tree & Coconut

ARBONNE ❶✍⊘

Hair Care

BANFI NATURELLE ✍⊘

Salon Range: Cucumber, Ginseng, Nettle & Wheatgerm, Rosemary, Scarborough Fair, Seaweed

BAY HOUSE AROMATICS ✍⊘⤳78

Cream Shampoo

BEAUCAIRE ☺✍⊘

Shampoo

BEAUTY THROUGH HERBS ☺✍⊘👁

Ginseng, Ginseng w Cryertomol

BIO-D CO. LTD. ™

Solid Shampoo Bars

BIORGANIC HAIR THERAPY LTD

Isobath Nutritional Balancing, Isonate Vegetable Mineral

BLACKMORES ✍⊘

Chamomile, Marshmallow, Wild Nettle

BODY REFORM (UK) LTD ❶✍⊘👁

Aloe Vera Jojoba, Men's Reform Conditioning, Skin Friendly, Tea Tree, White Musk

CAMILLA HEPPER LTD ✍⊘⤳87

Chamomile, Coconut Oil, Herbal, Jojoba Oil, Lavender & Sesame Oil, Men's Conditioning, Natural Orange, Rosemary, Seaweed, Ti-Tree & Thyme, Watercress

CAPITELLI OILS ™✍⊘

Bene, Invigorante Gentle

CHIKPE ✍⊘

Apple & Rosemary, Chamomile & Orange, Lemon & Vanilla, Peach & Coconut, *Shampoo Bar:* Chamomile, Lemon, Mint

DANNEX ✍⊘

Medicated Plus Conditioner, Vitamin & Orange

DOLMA ☺™✍👁⊘

Jojoba & Sandalwood Hair Shampoo, *Nettle & Pectin Hair Shampoos:* Bitter Orange & Tangerine, Cedarwood & Cypress, Lavender & Sage, Rosemary, Tea Tree & Thyme

DR HADWEN TRUST ☺✔⊘

Banana & Vanilla, Chamomile, Coconut frequency wash, Comfrey plus Nettle all-purpose, Herb & Protein deep conditioning, Lavender, Mango & Apricot, *Men's Hair & Body Shampoo:* Jaztec, Sandalwood; Ultra-mild formula, Wild Thyme & Mint

ESCENTIAL BOTANICALS LTD. ™✔⊘☻

Balancing, Fruit Range Everyday, Moisturising

ESSENTIAL OIL COMPANY ☺✔⊘☻

Base Shampoo & Conditioner

ESSENTIALLY YOURS ™✔⊘

Natural Elements Conditioning Shampoo

FAITH PRODUCTS LTD ❶✔⊘☻⚖78

Gingko Biloba, Hemp & Meadowfoam, Jojoba w Panthenol, Lavender & Geranium, Organic Aloe Vera, Organic Chocolate, Rosemary, Saw Palmetto, Seaweed, Tea Tree

FSC ✔⊘

Head High: Aloe Vera Shampoo & Revitaliser, Rosemary Frequent Use, Tea Tree Oil Dandruff

GR LANE ✔⊘

Tea Tree Shampoo

GREEN PEOPLE CO. ™✔⊘

Aloe Vera Herbal, Hair & Body Bar, Itch

Away, Rosemary Herbal, Vita Min Fix

HEALTHQUEST LIMITED ™✔⊘

Normal / Dry, Normal / Greasy

HEMP UNION ™✔⊘

Hemp Oil Shampoo

HERB UK LTD ✔⊘

Nature's Essential, Sulfate Free

HERBS HANDS HEALING ✔⊘

Bergamot & Orange, Chamomile, Head & Hair, Lavender & Ylang Ylang, Rosemary & Geranium

HONESTY COSMETICS LTD ☺❶✔⊘☻⚖76

Apple & Rosemary Conditioning, Chamomile & Orange, Hair & body, Lemon & Vanilla, Nettle & Lavender, Peach & Coconut

JOPHIEL ☺❶✔⊘

Shampoos: All

KENT COSMETICS ☺✔☻⊘

Australian Organics

KISS MY FACE ✔

Obsessively Natural Shampoo: Big Body, Miss Treated, Natural, SaHaira, Whenever

KOBASHI ☺™✔☻⊘

Fragrance Free Base, Wild Tea Tree & Mandarin, Wild Thyme & Lime

145

LUSH ✔ ⊘

Antiphilitron, Ibiza Party, *Shampoo Bars:* Dr. Peppermint, Featherweight Fruit Bar, Irresistible Bliss, Jumping Juniper, Soak & Float, Ultimate Shine; *Solid Shampoo:* Chamomile, Gentle Lentil, Lawn, Trichomania; Washday Greens

MARTHA HILL ❶ ✔ ⊘

Deep Moisturising, Gentle Balancing, Protein Enriched

MEADOWSWEET ☺™ ✔ 👁 ⊘

Aloe Vera, Banana & Vanilla, Chamomile, Coconut, Comfrey & Nettle All Purpose, Fragrance Free, Herb & Protein, Kiwi & Lemon Balm, Lavender / Geranium / Ylang-Ylang, Mandarin & Papaya, Mango & Apricot, *Men's Range:* Cologne, Jaztec, Sandalwood; Nettle, Seaweed, Ultra mild formula, Wild Thyme & Mint

MODERN ORGANIC PRODUCTS ✔ ⊘

Basil Mint, Glisten, Lemongrass, Mixed Greens, Pear

MOLTON BROWN COSMETICS ✔ ⊘

Triple Action Biao Hairwash

MOTHER HEMP LTD. ™ ✔ ⊘

Hemp Oil Shampoo

NAPIERS DISPENSARY ✔

Quassia, Tonic

NATURAL COLLECTION ✔ ⊘

Aloe Vera, Hemp, Naked Hemp, Rosemary

NATURE KNOWS BEST ✔ ⊘

Apricot

NATURE'S DREAM ✔ ⊘

Naturtint Shampoo: New Natural, Plant Extracts

NATUREWATCH ☺ ✔ ⊘ 👁 ⚕-76

Cypress & Tea Tree, Jojoba & Lavender Protein, Lemon & Ylang Ylang, Rosemary Bay & Cedarwood

NEAL'S YARD REMEDIES ✔ ⊘

Baseline, Calendula, Chamomile & Orange Flower, Coconut & Jojoba, Nettle & Sage, Rosemary & Thyme, Seaweed

NEW SEASONS ✔ ⊘

Neutral Base Conditioning Shampoo

NUTRITIONAL HEALTHCARE ✔ ⊘

Avtar Shampoo

ORD RIVER TEA TREE OIL ™

Shampoo

ORIGINAL SOURCE ™

Extra Strong Mint, Refreshing, Lemon & Mint, Balancing, Mint & Balsam, Enriching, Mint & Green Tea, Protecting, Orange & Almond,

Enriching, Orange & Grapefruit,
Volumising, Orange & Lemon,
Balancing, Orange & Tea Tree,
Protecting, Tea Tree & Mint, Volumising

PURPLE FLAME AROMATHERAPY ✔ ⊘

Base Shampoo, Tea Tree

QUINESSENCE AROMATHERAPY ☺❶✔⊘👁

Frequent, Mild Base, Tea Tree

SEVEN WIVES OF ST IVES SOAP CO ☺✔⊘

Shampoo Bars: Chamomile &
Geranium, Rosemary & Tea Tree

SHANTI HEALTH & BEAUTY PRODUCTS ☺❶✔⊘

Camomile, Coconut, Herbal, Lemon &
Orange, Rosemary

SIMPLY SOAPS ™✔⊘

Shampoo Bars: Chamomile, Eucalyptus
& Lavender, Rosemary & Lavender

SUMA WHOLEFOODS ™⊘✔

Cucumber, Mandarin, Pure, Tea Tree,
Tea Tree Promotion Pack

THURSDAY PLANTATION ✔⊘☃95

Tea Tree: Anti-Dandruff, Deep
Cleansing

TIGI ✔

Deep Cleanse, Gentle Cleanse,
Moisture & Shine, Scalp Cleanse,

Thickening, Treatment

TIKI ✔⊘

Camomile, Marigold, Nettle, Rosemary

TOM'S OF MAINE ✔⊘

Aloe & Almond, Honeysuckle

TREE-HARVEST ✔⊘

Shampoo Soap: Neem, Tropical
Coconut

URTEKRAM ⊘✔

Aloe Vera, Chamomile, *Curing
Shampoo w Rhassoul:* Blonde,
Chestnut, Dark Brown, Dark red henna,
Fiery Red Henna, Mahogany, Neutral
Henna, Red Henna, Rhassoul; *Hair &
Body Shampoo:* Lavender, Mandarin,
Rose; Hawthorn, Henna Neutral, Henna
Red, Herbal, Nettle Anti Dandruff,
Rhassoul, Rosemary, Sage, Seaweed,
Tea Tree, Thistle

VEGANSTORE.CO.UK ☺™❶✔⊘

Extra Rich Natural Sea Kelp System,
Hair & Scalp, Moisturising, Scalp
Conditioning

VITA YOUTH ✔⊘

Aloe Vera, Tea Tree Oil Shampoo &
Body Wash, Vitamin E

WELEDA ✔⊘👁☃85

Bottled Shampoo: Calendula, Lemon
Balm, Rosemary; Rosemary Tube
Shampoo

YOAH

Hemp Oil Shampoo

YOUR BODY ™ ✔ ☜ ⊘

Aloe Vera, *Aromatherapy Range:*
Aromatic Conditioning, Tea Tree Oil;
Chamomile, Chamomile Baby, Coconut
Conditioning, Marigold, *Men's Range:*
Jojoba Conditioning, Medicated; Musk,
Red Apple, Rosemary, Seaweed, Tea
Tree, Vitamin E

SHAVING PRODUCTS

ANIMAL AID ☺❶✔⊘⅄76

Aftershave Lotion, Coconut Shaving
Cream

ARBONNE ❶✔⊘

Skin Fitness for Men Soothing Shave
Gel

BODY REFORM (UK) LTD ❶✔⊘☜

Men's Reform: Aftershave Balm,
Shaving Cream

CAMILLA HEPPER LTD ✔⊘⅄87

Daen Depilatory Wax Strips, *Skin
Demands for Men:* AfterShave Balm,
Birch Shaving Cream, Face Protection,
Panther Aftershave

DOLMA ☺™✔☜⊘

Especially for Men: 'Sirius' Aftershave /

Cologne, De-Luxe Aftershave Balm,
Wet Shaving Fluid

DR HADWEN TRUST ☺✔⊘

Aloe Vera Aftershave, Pre-Wet Shave
Cream

ESSENTIALLY YOURS ™✔⊘

Natural Elements: Depilatory Shave Oil,
Easy Shave for Men

GREEN PEOPLE CO. ™✔⊘

Pre-Shave Face Wash, Shave Now
Shaving Gel

HEMP UNION ™✔⊘

Hemp Oil Shaving Oil

HERBS HANDS HEALING ✔⊘

Splash on Toner, Sunrise After Shave
Water

KISS MY FACE ✔

Obsessively Natural Moisture Shave:
Cool Mint, Fragrance Free, Jasmine, Key
Lime, Marine, Peaceful Patchouli,
Peaches & Creme, Summer Melon,
Vanilla Earth, Virgin Forest, Virgin Forest

MARTHA HILL ❶✔⊘

David Hill for Men: Cleansing & Shaving
Gel, Skin Calming Aftershave Balm,
Skin Calming Shaving Oil, Skin
Refreshing Aftershave Gel, Skin
Soothing Cream Shave

MEADOWSWEET ☺™✓👁⃠

Men's Range Aftershave: Aloe Vera Skin Gel, Cologne, Jaztec, Sandalwood; Men's Range Pre-Wet Shave Moisturising Cream

NATURAL COLLECTION ✓⃠

Shaving Oil: Men's, Women's

NEAL'S YARD REMEDIES ✓⃠

Lavender & Vitamin E Shaving Soap, Shaving Oil

ORIGINAL SOURCE ™

Shave Gel: Pure Lime, Tea Tree & Lemon, Tea Tree & Mint

QUINESSENCE AROMATHERAPY ☺❶✓⃠👁

Aftershave Balm

SUKAR ❶✓👁⃠

Hair Removal System, Strip-sugar, Sugaring Paste

TOM'S OF MAINE ✓⃠

Natural Shaving Cream: Gentle Honeysuckle, Refreshing Mint

TREE-HARVEST ✓⃠

Shaving Bowl: Bay, Juniper

VEGANSTORE.CO.UK ☺™❶✓⃠

Cariad Shaving Oil: Alternative, Original; Kiss My Face Moisture Shaves, Tom's of Maine Shaving Cream

VIVA! ☺❶✓⃠

Shaving Soap

WELEDA ✓⃠👁✂85

Shaving Lotion

YIN YANG BEAUTY CARE ☺✓⃠

Shaving Cream

YOUR BODY ™✓👁⃠

Men's Range: Aftershave Balms, Coconut Shaving Cream

SKIN CARE – MASKS, WRAPS, ETC

ANNE-MARIE BORLIND ❶✓⃠

Beauty Extras: Anti-Stress Mask, Exfoliating Peel; *LL Regeneration Series:* Moisturising Cream Mask, Vital Cream Mask

ARBONNE ❶✓⃠

Masque: Bio Hydria Alpha-Complex Hydrating, Extra strength, Mild

BEAUCAIRE ☺✓⃠

Masks: Cream, Face & Body Peeling, Gel

BEAUTY THROUGH HERBS ☺✓⃠👁

Galeno Gold Face Masque: Anti-Age, Purity

149

TOILETRIES & COSMETICS

BIOCOSMETICS

Aroma Gel Contour Wrap

BLACKMORES ✔ ⊘

Mask: Deep Cleanse Clay, Pure Chamomile

BODY REFORM (UK) LTD ❶ ✔ ⊘ 👁

Face Mask: Arnica, Peppermint

CAMILLA HEPPER LTD ✔ ⊘ ⚓-87

Mask: Herbal Clay, Oatmeal & Almond Oil

CHIKPE ✔ ⊘

Mask: Eastern Rejuvenator, Oriental Tonic, Sea Magic

CHRISTY ✔ 👁

Facemask Sachet: Avocado, Cucumber, Jasmine & Evening Primrose, Jojoba & Green Tea, Lemongrass & Witchhazel, Lime & Coriander, Sea Clay, Tea Tree, Wild Peach & Cranberry; *Facemask Tube:* Cucumber, Lime & Coriander, Sea Clay, Tea Tree

DOLMA ☺™ ✔ 👁 ⊘

Rosemary & Seaweed Facial Mask

DR HADWEN TRUST ☺ ✔ ⊘

Face Mask: Apple Blossom, Avocado & Cucumber, Comfrey plus Marshmallow

ESSENTIALLY YOURS ™ ✔ ⊘

Natural Elements Face Mask: Combination

/ Oily, Dry / Mature , Normal

GREEN PEOPLE CO. ™ ✔ ⊘

Vita Min Mask

HONESTY COSMETICS LTD ☺❶ ✔ ⊘ ⚓-76

Face Mask w Tea Tree & Lavender

KISS MY FACE ✔

Masque: Deep Pore Cleansing, Lemongrass Souffle, Scrub; Pore Shrink Deep Cleansing Mask

MARTHA HILL ❶ ✔ ⊘

Seaweed Peeling Mask

MEADOWSWEET ☺™ ✔ ⊘

Face Mask: Apple Blossom, Avocado & Cucumber, Comfrey & Marshmallow, Tropical Fruit

MONTAGNE JEUNESSE ✔ 👁 ⊘

Dead Sea: Black, Body Mud Mask, Salt Cellulite Mud Mask, Salt Firming Gel; *Masque:* Apricot & Almond Oil Hot, Cucumber Peel-Off, Hot Earth Sauna, Peach Kernel & Walnut Exfoliating, Red, Strawberry Gel

QUINESSENCE AROMATHERAPY ☺❶ ✔ 👁

Marine Clay Mask

WELEDA ✔ ⊘ ⚓-85

Almond Facial Masque, *Iris Masque:* Facial, Intensive Treatment

YIN YANG BEAUTY CARE ☺✔⊘

Precious Earth Face Mask

YOUR BODY ™✔👁⊘

Facial Masks: Almond Oil, Pineapple

SKIN CARE – MOISTURISERS & BODY LOTIONS

ABSOLUTE AROMAS LTD ✔⊘

Ord River Hand & Body Lotion

ANIMAL AID ☺❶✔⊘⚘–76

Apricot & Jojoba Moisturising Cream, Exotic Body Lotion, Vanilla & Macadamia Nourishing Cream

ANNE-MARIE BORLIND ❶✔⊘

Beauty Extras: Ceramide Vital Fluid, Facial Firming Gel, Intensive Care Capsules, Velvet Cream; *Bodyvital:* Body Cream, Caring Body Spray Lotion; Cellulite Gel, *LL Regeneration Series:* Concentrate Ampoules, Decoullete Cream, Liposome-Emulsion, Moisturising Ampoules; *Young Beauty:* Peach Series Facial Cream, U-Series Herbal Day Cream

ARBONNE ❶✔⊘

Bio-Hydria: Alpha-Complex Moisture for Day SPF 8, Extreme, Naturesomes; *Bio-*

Matte Oil-Free Moisture: for Day SPF 8, for Night; *Body Lotion:* Awaken, Body Care & Speciality, Unwind; Moisture Cream, *Natural Balancing Cream:* PhytoProlief, Prolief; Night Cream, NutraMin-C Moiture Repair Set, *NutraMin-C w Bio Hydria:* Body Finish, Body Primer, Lift, Night Cream, Night Serum; Rejuvenating Cream, *Rejuvenating Mist:* Awaken, Reactive, Unwind; Skin Conditioning Oil, Skin Fitness for Men Moisture Plus AHAs

ARKOPHARMA (UK) LTD ☺✔⊘

Phyto Soya Age Minimising Cream

BAREFOOT BOTANICALS ™✔⊘

Rosa Fina Intensive Radiance Face Oil, *Rosa Fina Nourishing Rejuvenation:* Body Lotion, Cream; SOS Intensive Skincare Rescue Cream

BAY HOUSE AROMATICS ✔⊘⚘–78

Avocado & Grapefruit Skin Cream, *Base Cream:* Calendula, Comfrey, Sweet Almond, Vitamin E; Carrot & Orange Skin Cream, Chamomile Cream, *Face & Body Gel:* Aloe Vera, Lavender, Tea Tree; Frankincense & Rosehip Face Cream, Lavender & Comfrey Healing Cream, Lemon & Rose Hand & Body Lotion, Lemon & Rose Revitalising Cream, Marigold & Vitamin E Rich Night Cream, Palmarosa & Almond Moisturising Cream, Tea Tree Antiseptic Skin Cream, Tea Tree & Lavender Hand & Body Lotion

BEAUCAIRE ☺ ✔ ⊘

Body Lotion, *Intensive:* Light, Lotion, Medium, Rich, Tea Tree; *Liposome:* Light, Medium, Super, Tea Tree; *Super Sensitive:* Light, Medium, Rich; Tonic Lotion

BEAUTY THROUGH HERBS ☺ ✔ ⊘ ◉

Galeno Gold: Anti-Cellulite Body Cream, Cell Renewal Serum, Firming Body Cream, Firming Gel, Hydrating Body Cream, Intensive Hydrating Cream, Intensive Hydrating Lotion, Ultimate Body Contour, Vitalising Day Cream; Out Of Africa Body Lotion, *Phyto Care:* Breast Tone, Calmskin Herbal Gel, Coolskin Herbal Gel; *Phyto Marine:* Intensive Nourishing Cream, Nourishing Cream, Vitalising Lotion

BENTLEY PEARL ☺⊘

Yvelle Therapy Naturelle Arnica Body Balm

BIOCOSMETICS

Gels: Aloe Vera, Aloe Vera (galvanic), Rosewater; *Starflower:* Body Lotion, Cream, Oil Blend

BLACKMORES ✔ ⊘

Apricot & Jojoba Body Oil, *Day Creme:* Apricot SPF8, Marshmallow; Evening Primrose Body Lotion, Moisturising Body Care, *Night Creme:* Avocado, Gentian; Oil Free Moisturiser

BODY REFORM (UK) LTD ❶ ✔ ⊘ ◉

Aloe Vera Gel, Anti-Ageing Serum, Body Contour Treatment, *Body Lotion:* Aloe Vera w Vitamin E, Skin Friendly; *Cream:* Aloe Vera Day, Aloe Vera Moisturising w UV Protection, Anti Wrinkle, Avocado Night Nourishing, Men's Reform Facial Moisturiser, Peppermint Day, Skin Friendly Facial Moisturising, St John's Wort Day, Tea Tree Treatment, Wheatgerm Night, White Musk Body; Neck Smoothing Complex, Pure Herbal Roll On Wrinkle Care, White Musk Body Moisturiser

CAMILLA HEPPER LTD ✔ ⊘ ⚘ 87

Anti-Wrinkle Oil, Azufre Lotion, *Body Lotion:* Jojoba Oil, Orange Blossom & Cocoa Butter, Rose; *Cream:* Avocado Moisture, Azufre, Camilla's Cleansing, Evening Primrose Night, Facial Wash, Regenerative, Rich Skin Food, T-Zone Moisturising Control, Wheatgerm & Marigold Moisture; Exfoliating Tropical Skin Polisher

CAPITELLI OILS ™ ✔ ⊘

Crema Peidi, *Lozione Per Il Corpo:* Body Lotion, Luxury Body Lotion; Pelle Grassa, Pelle Secca

CELESTIAL DESIGNS AROMATHERAPY ™

Face Cream

CHIKPE ✔ ⊘

Body Lotion: Cocoa Butter, Geranium &

Ylang Ylang, Peach & Vanilla;
Moisturising Cream: Lavender &
Sandalwood, w Vitamin E

DOLMA ☺™✔👁⊘

Aloe Vera Hand & Body Lotion, De-Luxe
Facial Oil, *Facial Oil For:* Dehydrated
Skin, Dry Skin, Mature Skin, Sensitive
Skin, Thread Veins; Geranium &
Evening Primrose, Night Cream,
Moisture Creams: Avocado & Ylang
Ylang, Carotene Enriched Fragrance
Free, Carotene, Ho-Leaf & Orange,
Evening Primrose & Marigold, heatgerm
& Lavender; *Moisture Lotions:*
Camomile, Fragrance free; Niamh De-
Luxe Body Lotion

DR HADWEN TRUST ☺✔⊘

Aloe Vera Repair Gel, Comfrey Plus
Cocoa Butter Lotion, *Cream:* Carrot Oil,
Comfrey Plus Carrot Night, Comfrey
Plus Vitamin E Moisturising, Evening
Primrose, Herbal Skin Soothing, Melon
& Carrot Day, Melon & Jojoba Night,
Vitamin E

ESCENTIAL BOTANICALS LTD. ™✔⊘👁

Body Lotion, *Classic Day Moisturiser:*
Dry, Normal / Oily; Classic Night
Replenishing Cream (Normal / Oily),
Essential Replenishing Oil (Normal /
Oily), Exotic Body Lotion

ESSENTIAL OIL COMPANY ☺✔👁

Aloe & Seaweed Gel, Base Creams &
Lotions

ESSENTIALLY YOURS ™✔⊘

Natural Elements: Body Lotion, Extra
Rich Barrier Cream, Firming Gel, Hand
& Body Lotion, Moisturising Oil; *Natural
Elements for Combination / Oily Skin:*
Moisturiser, Night Gel, Serum Gel;
Natural Elements for Dry / Mature Skin:
Moisturiser, Night Cream; *Natural
Elements for Normal Skin:* Moisturiser,
Night Cream; *Natural Elements Serum:*
Day, Face Contouring, Night

FAITH PRODUCTS LTD ❶✔⊘👁✂78

Aloe Vera Day Cream, Jojoba Moisture
Lotion, Rose & Wheatgerm Moisturising
Cream

GREEN PEOPLE CO. ™✔⊘

Body Lotion: Body Comfort, Body
Comfort No Scent; Body Tuning
(Cellulite Lotion), *Day Solution:* Day
Cream, SPF 15 Day Cream; *Fruitful:*
Days (Light Day & Evening Gel), Nights
(Night Cream); *Men's Range:* Cool
Down Moisturiser, Vita Min Boost SPF
15 Cream; *Vita Min Fix:* Day & Night
Cream, No Scent Day & Night Cream

HEALTHQUEST LIMITED ™✔⊘

Body Lotion

HEMP UNION ™✔⊘

Hemp Oil Body Lotion

HERBS HANDS HEALING ✔⊘

Balm of Gilead Cream

HONESTY COSMETICS LTD
☺❶✓🚫⊘✈♿76

Geranium & Ylang Ylang Moisturising Lotion, Lavender & Geranium Moisturising Cream, Peach & Vanilla Moisturising Lotion, *Unscented Moisturiser:* Cream w Vitamin E, Lotion w Cocoa Butter, Rich Cream w Carrot & Jojoba

JOPHIEL ☺❶✓🚫

Body Lotions & Creams: All

JURLIQUE ✓🚫

Aromatic Hydrating Concentrate: Chamomile & Rose, Lavender & Lavendin, Lemon & Lime, Pine Needles, Rosemary & Sage; Calendula Lotion, Day Moisturising Lotion, Neck Serum, Night Treatment Gel, *Oil:* Body Care, Carrier, Day Care, Lavender Body, Pure Rose Body; Viola Cream

KENT COSMETICS ☺✓⊘🚫

Australian Organics Body Lotion

KISS MY FACE ✓

Ester C: Body Lotion, Facial Creme, Serum; *Obsessively Natural Moisture Creme:* All Day, All Night; *Obsessively Natural Moisturizer:* Alpha Aloe Oil Free Fragrance Free, Alpha Aloe Oil Free w Vanilla, Chinese Botanical, Everday SPF 15, Lavender & Shea Butter, Oil Free w NaPCA, Olive & Aloe Fragrance Free, Olive & Aloe Moisturizer, Peaceful Patchouli, Peaches & Creme w/4%

Alpha Hydroxy Acids, Vitamin A&E; *Obsessively Organic Moisturizer:* Anti-Ox Facial Serum, Aromatherapeutic Alpha Hydroxy Creme, C the Change - Ester C Serum, Cell Block SPF15 Facial Creme, Organic Botanical Lifting Serum, Ultra Light Facial Creme, Under Age Ultra Moisturizer, Vitamin C&A Ultra Rich Moisturizer

KOBASHI ☺™✓⊘🚫

Aloe Vera: Gel, Liquid; *Luxury Lotions:* Baby Lotion, Fragrance Free Moisturiser, Rose Facial

LUSH ✓🚫

Hand & Body Creams: Dream Cream, Potion, Sympathy for the Skin; *Moisturisers:* Celestial, Cosmetic Lad, Enzymion, Imperialis, Skin Drink; *Skin Conditioners:* Buffy the Backside Slayer, King of Skin

MARTHA HILL ❶✓🚫

Body Oil: Evening Primrose & Lavender, Orange; Camomile Moisture Milk, *David Hill:* Extra Rich Treatment Cream, Skin Soothing Daytime Moisturiser; Evening Primrose Body Lotion, Herbal Skin Care No 3 Day Cream, *Moisturiser:* Enriched Body, Evening Primrose; *Seaweed:* Body Toning Gel, Enriched Body Treatment Cream

MEADOWSWEET ☺™✓⊘🚫

Aloe Vera: Day Cream, Moisturising Lotion, Night Cream, Skin Repair Gel; *Creams:* Carrot Oil, Comfrey & Carrot

Night, Comfrey & Jojoba Complex Repair, Comfrey & Vitamin E Moisturising, Comfrey & Vitamin E Ointment, Evening Primrose, Herbal Skin Soothing, Melon & Carrot Day, Melon & Jojoba Night, Vitamin E; *Fragrance Free:* Day Cream, Moisturising Lotion, Night Cream; *Lotions:* Avocado & Cucumber Moisturising, Comfrey & Cocoa Butter, Evening Primrose Body, Herbal Aromatic Soothing Body, Rosemary Herbal Face

MODERN ORGANIC PRODUCTS ✔ ⊘

Lotion: Oatmeal Coconut, Pear

MOLTON BROWN COSMETICS ✔ ⊘

Body: Heavenly Gingerlily Cream, Rejuvenating Artic Shajio Moisturiser, Relaxing Yuan Zhi Moisturiser, Sensual Satiniser, Ultra Smooth Lotion; Instant Matte Moisturiser, Intensive Daily Replenisher

MOTHER HEMP LTD. ™ ✔ ⊘

Moisturiser

NAPIERS DISPENSARY ✔

Cream: Arnica, Bilberry, Chamomile, Chamomile & Peppermint, Comfrey, Eyebright, Frankincense Night, Infant Starflower, Neroli Day, Pilewort, Seven Herb, Starflower, Vegan Base, Venatone, Wild Yam; *Lotion:* Base, Chamomile & Peppermint, Neroli, Starflower; *Moisturisers:* Chamomile, Marigold, Rose

NATIONAL TRUST ENTERPRISES ✔ ⊘ ⚘ 98

English Lavender Hand & Body Lotion

NATURAL COLLECTION ✔ ⊘

Body Lotion: Aloe Vera, Children's, Naked Hemp, Orange & Lavender; *Cream:* Rejuvenation, Solace Soothing Moisturiser, SOS Skin Rescue

NATURE KNOWS BEST ✔ ⊘

Apricot: Body Lotion, Moisture Cream; Pure Vegetable Glycerine, Vitamin A Cream

NATUREWATCH ☺ ✔ ⊘ ⚫ ⚘ 76

Camomile & Lavender Facial Moisturising Fluid, *Clearly Compassionate Body Lotion:* Lavender & Geranium, Mandarin & Lemongrass; Sandalwood & Vitamin E Facial Replenishing Cream

NEAL'S YARD REMEDIES ✔ ⊘

Cocoa Butter

NEW SEASONS ✔ ⊘

Neutral Base Moisturising: Cream, Face & Body Gel, Lotion

ORD RIVER TEA TREE OIL ™

Hand & Body Lotion

ORGANIC BOTANICS ☺ ❶ ✔ ⊘

Moisturising Nutritive: Extra Rich, Medium Light; Simple Daily Moisturiser

TOILETRIES & COSMETICS

POTIONS AND POSSIBILITIES ✔ ⊘

Essential Night Repair Formula, Evening Primrose Moisture Relief for the Complexion, Frankincense Neroli & Evening Primrose Hand & Body Lotion, St John's Ointment

PURPLE FLAME AROMATHERAPY ✔ ⊘

Aloe Vera Gel, *Moisturising Base:* Cream, Lotion, Vitamin E

QUINESSENCE AROMATHERAPY ☺❶✔⊘👁

Aloe Vera & Seaweed Gel, *Cream:* Age Defying, Anti-Wrinkle Base, Hydrating Day, Hydrating Night, Moisture Deluxe, Neroli Night, Vitamin E Base; *Lotion:* Base Carrier, Hand & Body, Moisture

RHEMA UK LTD ❶✔⊘

Cento Per Cento: Hand & Body Lotion, Moisturisers (1, 2 & 4)

ROMANY ✔⊘

Creams: Anti-Wrinkle, Lavender Essential Oil

SCENT BY NATURE ☺✔⊘

Tea Tree Antiseptic Face Cream

SHANTI HEALTH & BEAUTY PRODUCTS ☺❶✔⊘

Skin & Body Oil / Cream, Skin Nourishment Oils

THURSDAY PLANTATION ✔⊘⚡-95

Macadamia Face & Body Oil, Tea Tree

Hand & Body Lotion

TREE-HARVEST ✔⊘

Frankincense & Geranium Moisturising Lotion

URTEKRAM ⊘✔

Body Lotion: Aloe Vera, Camomile, Children, Lavender, Rose, Tea Tree

VEGANSTORE.CO.UK ☺™❶✔⊘

Cariad: Chamomille Cream, Rose Facial Gel, Vitamin E Gel; Escential Botanicals Day Moisturiser, *Kiss My Face Moisturiser:* Chinese Botanical, Oil Free, Peaches & Cream

VITA YOUTH ✔⊘

Aloe Vera: Moisturiser, Skin Gel; Tea Tree Oil Moisturiser, *Vitamin E:* Moisturiser w Rose Water, Moisturising Oil, Skin Conditioner

WELEDA ✔⊘👁⚡-85

Almond Facial Oil, *Men's Range:* Akneodoron Lotion, Specialist Skin Care, Wild Rose Body Oil

XYNERGY HEALTH PRODUCTS ✔⊘

Aloe 99 Moisture Balancing: Cream, Lotion

YIN YANG BEAUTY CARE ☺✔⊘

Body Cream: CHL, MSM, SBG, ZSB6; Botanical Protein, *Cream:* Organic Aloe, Wild Yam; *Four Herb:* Cream, Lotion; Natural Moisturiser, pH-Amino - Gold

Body Moisturiser, Provit-En, Yin Yang Skin Conditioner

YOAH

Moisturiser

YOUR BODY ™ ✔ ◉ ⊘

Aromatic Hand & Body Lotion, *Body Lotions:* Aloe Vera, Cellulite Control Firming, Cocoa Butter, Musk, Orchid & Jasmine, Ti-Tree, Vitamin E; Cellulite Control Body Refining Gel For All Skin Types, *Creams:* Aloe Vera, Medicated, Orchid Day, Vitamin E; Jojoba Lotion, Linden Flower Moisturiser, Men's Jojoba & Soya Face Protector, *Moisture Cream:* Aloe Vera, Avocado, Ginseng; *Night Cream:* Aloe Vera, Evening Primrose, Vitamin E; Pure Jojoba Oil

SKINCARE – CLEANSERS & TONERS

ANIMAL AID ☺ ❶ ✔ ⊘ ⚕ 76

Aloe & Papaya Cleansing Lotion, Aloe & Papaya Toner, Fruit & Nut Face & Body Scrub, Kiwi & Grapefruit Facial Wash

ANNE-MARIE BORLIND ❶ ✔ ⊘

Combination Series: Cleansing Gel, Day Essence, Facial Toner; *LL Regeneration Series:* Blossom Dew Gel, Cleansing Milk; *Rosedew Series:* Cleansing Milk, Facial Toner; *System Absolute Series:*

Beauty Fluid, Cleanser; Young Beauty – Peach Series Cleanser, *Young Beauty – U-Series:* Cleansing Milk, Facial Toner, Ultra Stick; *ZZ Sensitive Series:* Cleansing, Facial Toner

ARBONNE ❶ ✔ ⊘

Bio-Hydria Gentle Exfoliant, *Bio-Matte Oil-Free:* Cleanser, Personalizer, Toner; *Cleansing:* Cream, Gel, Lotion; *Clear Advantage:* Acne Lotion, Acne Wash, Refining Toner, System; Facial Scrub, Freshener, *Skin Fitness for Men:* Balancer, Cleansing Scrub; Toner

BAREFOOT BOTANICALS ™ ✔ ⊘

Rosa Fina Cleansing Milk

BAY HOUSE AROMATICS ✔ ⊘ ⚕ 78

Floral Waters: All; *Unfragranced Lotions & Cleansers:* Chamomile Cleanser, Cocoa Butter Lotion, Exfoliating Face & Body Scrub, White Base Lotion

BEAUCAIRE ☺ ✔ ⊘

Cleansing Milk, Face Cleanser, Pimple Cream

BEAUTY THROUGH HERBS ☺ ✔ ⊘ ◉

Galeno Gold Face Scrub, *Phyto Care:* Clearskin Herbal Gel, Coolskin Herbal Gel, Facial Wash; *Phyto Marine:* Facial Cleansing Cream, Mild Exfoliant Wash, Sun & Sea Gel Wash

BLACKMORES ✔ ⊘

Anti Bacterial: Face Wash, Pimple Gel;

Blackhead Remover, Cinnamon Refiner, *Cleanser:* Almond, Cucumber, Foaming Papaya; *Toner:* Aloe, Oil Controlling, Witch Hazel

BODY REFORM (UK) LTD ❶ ✔ ⊘ ☞

Cleanser: Rosemary, Skin Friendly; *Facial Scrub:* Apricot, Men's Reform Walnut; *Facial Wash:* Aloe Vera, Tea Tree; Tea Tree Facial Freshener, *Toning Lotion:* Chamomile, Orange Blossom, Peppermint, Skin Friendly

CAMILLA HEPPER LTD ✔ ⊘✈87

Cleanser: Azufre, Men's Face Wash, T-Zone Foaming; *Cleansing Milk:* Lemon Balm, Meadowsweet; Elderflower Skin Toner; *Flower Water:* Orange, Rose; Marsa-Med Cleansing Bar, Mint & Olive Stone Scrub, T-Zone Balancing Freshener

CAPITELLI OILS ™✔ ⊘

Cleansing Lotion & Make-Up Remover

CELESTIAL DESIGNS AROMATHERAPY ™

Cleanser, Toner

CHIKPE ✔ ⊘

Cleansing Lotion w: Chamomile, Lavender & Geranium; *Face Scrubs:* Almond & Oatmeal, Coconut; *Facial Toners w:* Chamomile, Lavender & Geranium

CHRISTY ✔ ☞

Facial Scrub Sachet: Cranberry & Lemongrass, Pineapple & Almond Crush

DOLMA ☺™✔ ☜⊘

Almond & Orange Facial Scrub, Aromatic Face Shampoo, Camomile & Mint Facial Wash, Carrot Oil Cleansing Wash, *Cleansing Lotions:* Fragrance Free, Lavender & Camomile; *Oil Free Cleanser/Toners:* Astringent, Freshening, Gentle, Purifying

DR HADWEN TRUST ☺✔ ⊘

Cleansing Gel: Cucumber & Fennel, Lime Blossom & Orange Flower; *Cleansing Milk:* Apricot, Orchid; Comfrey plus Yarrow Cleansing Lotion, *Face Scrubs:* Comfrey plus oatmeal, Oatmeal Scrub Cream, Passion Fruit; *Facial Wash:* Comfrey plus Clivers, Elderflower Cream, Pineapple & Peach Cream; *Toners:* Avocado & Cucumber, Elderflower, Orange Flower

ESCENTIAL BOTANICALS LTD.™✔ ⊘☜

Classic Facial Toner: Dry, Normal / Oily; Classic Sensitive Skin Cleanser, *Exotic Deep Cleansing Lotion:* Dry, Normal / Oily; Fruit Range Foaming Facial Cleanser

ESSENTIALLY YOURS ™✔ ⊘

Natural Elements for Combination / Oily Skin: Antimicrobial Face Wash, Cleanser, Exfoliating Lotion, Toner; *Natural Elements for Dry / Mature Skin:* Cleanser, Face Wash, Toner; *Natural Elements for Normal Skin:* Cleanser,

Face Wash, Toner

FAITH PRODUCTS LTD ❶✔◐◑◉⚹–78

Essential Facial Wash, Rosewater Toning Lotion, Seaweed Cleanser, Seaweed Cleansing Lotion (Whole Body)

GREEN PEOPLE CO. ™✔◐

Fruit Scrub, Gentle Cleanse, Gentle Tone

HEMP UNION ™✔◐

Hemp Oil Cleanser

HERBS HANDS HEALING ✔◐

Herbs & Flowers Cleansing Cream, Herbs & Flowers Skin Toner, Lavender Water, Rose Water Facial Tonic, Skin Guard Water

HONESTY COSMETICS LTD ☺❶✔◐◉⚹–76

Cleansers: Lavender & Geranium, Unscented w Chamomile; *Facial Toners:* Lavender & Geranium, Unscented w Chamomile; Papaya Facial Wash, Spicy Orange Scrub

JOPHIEL ☺❶✔◐

Skin Toners & Floral Water: All

JURLIQUE ✔◐

Face Wash, *Floral Waters:* Chamomile, Lavender; Hydrating Toner Gel

KISS MY FACE ✔

Acne Gel: Botanical, Break Out Acne

Gel, Citrus Essence Astringent; Aloe & Chamomile Toner, Aloe & Tea Tree Astringent, *Face Wash:* Exfoliating, Jump Start Exfoliating; *Facial Cleanser:* Citrus, Foaming, Gentle; *Facial Scrub:* Organic Jojoba & Mint, So Refined Jojoba & Mint

KOBASHI ☺™✔◐◉

Neroli Water, Rose Water

LITTLE MIRACLES / APHRODITE'S ROSE ✔◐

Aphrodite's Rosewater Rejuvenating Spray, Rosewater

LUSH ✔◐

Cleansers: Angels on Bareskin, Baby Face, Coalface, Fresh Enzynamite, Fresh Farmacy, Fresh Strawberry Boat, Herbalism, Sweet Japanese Girl; *Toners:* Breeze on a Sea Air, Eau-Roma Water, Tea Tree Water

MARTHA HILL ❶✔◐

Camomile Cleansing Gel, David Hill Deep Cleansing Lotion for Men, *Evening Primrose:* Cleansing Lotion, Toning Gel; *Herbal Skin Care:* No 1 Cleansing & Conditioning Milk, No 2 Toning Gel; *Skin Tonic:* Cucumber, Rosewater

MEADOWSWEET ☺™✔◐◉

Cleansing Gel: Cucumber & Fennel, Lime Blossom & Orange Flower; *Cleansing Milk:* Apricot, Orchid; Comfrey & Clivers Facial Wash,

Complexion: Dry Skin - Jojoba & Unrefined Avocado, Mature Skin - Carrot w Vitamin E Enriched Wheatgerm, Normal Skin - Orchid Oil & Cocoa Butter, Oily Skin - Fullers Earth & Lemon Juice, Rejuvenaid Scrub Bar - Oatmeal & Evening Primrose; *Creams:* Cucumber Astringent, Facial Blemish; *Lotions:* Comfrey & Yarrow Cleansing, Fragrance Free Cleansing, Herbal Aromatic Problem Skin; *Scrubs:* Comfrey & Oatmeal Facial, Oatmeal, Passion Fruit Facial; *Toners:* Avocado & Cucumber, Elderflower, Lavender / Geranium / Ylang-Ylang, Orange Flower; *Wash Cream:* Elderflower, Pineapple & Peach

MOLTON BROWN COSMETICS ✔ ⊘

Face Zone Overnight, Gentle Exfoliating Toner, Refreshing Facial Wash, Total Makeup Cleanser

MOTHER HEMP LTD. ™✔ ⊘

Hemp Oil Cleanser

NAPIERS DISPENSARY ✔

Cleanser: Chamomile, Marigold, Rose; *Freshener:* Chamomile, Marigold, Rose

NATURE KNOWS BEST ✔ ⊘

Apricot: Skin Cleanser, Toner; Rosewater, *Vitamin A:* Cleanser, Foaming Facial Wash; Witch Hazel

NATUREWATCH ☺✔ ⊘👁⚗–76

Clearly Compassionate Camomile & Lavender: Facial Cleanser, Facial Toner,

Foaming Facial Wash

NEAL'S YARD REMEDIES ✔ ⊘

Calendula Cleanser

NEW SEASONS ✔ ⊘

Flower Water: Chamomile, Lavender, Orange Flower, Rosewater; *Neutral Base:* Cleanser, Facial & Body Scrub; Solubiliser, Vegetable Glycerine, Witch Hazel

ORGANIC BOTANICS ☺❶✔ ⊘

Floral Toning Lotion - Alcohol Free, Gentle Deep Cleansing Milk

ORIGINAL SOURCE ™

Foaming Face Wash: Tea Tree & Lemon, Tea Tree & Mint; Tea Tree, Mint & Herbs Facial Sauna

POTIONS AND POSSIBILITIES ✔ ⊘

Tea Tree & Lavender Facial Cleanser

PURPLE FLAME AROMATHERAPY ✔ ⊘

Base Cleansing Lotion, Tea Tree Moist Wipes

QUINESSENCE AROMATHERAPY ☺❶✔ ⊘👁

Facial Exfoliator, *Lotion:* Antiseptic, Cleansing; Problem Skin, Rose Facial, Rose Toner

RHEMA UK LTD ❶✔ ⊘

Cento Per Cento: Skin Tonic, Toner

ROMANY ✔ ⊘

Rosewater Cooler Spray

SCENT BY NATURE ☺ ✔ ⊘

Aloe Vera & Ylang Ylang Facial Cream

THURSDAY PLANTATION ✔ ⊘ ⚕ 95

Tea Tree: Blemish Gel, Blemish Stick, Cleansing Face Wash

VEGANSTORE.CO.UK ☺ ™ ❶ ✔ ⊘

Cariad Flower Waters, Conscience Cosmetics Passion Fruit Scrub, *Essential Botanicals:* Foaming Facial Cleanser, Gentle Facial Toner, Sensitive Skin Cleanser; *Jason:* 3 in 1 Scrubble, Quick Clean Make Up Remover Pads; Tisserand Moist Lavender Tissues, *Tisserand Tea Tree:* & Grapefruit Skin Wash, Blemish Stick

VITA YOUTH ✔ ⊘

Aloe Vera: Cleanser, Toner; *Tea Tree Oil:* Antiseptic Spot Oil, Antiseptic Wipes, Foaming Skin Cleanser; Vitamin E Cleanser

WELEDA ✔ ⊘ 👁 ⚕ 85

Almond Cleansing Lotion, Iris Facial Toner

XYNERGY HEALTH PRODUCTS ✔ ⊘

Aloe 99 Pure Facial Cleanser

YIN YANG BEAUTY CARE ☺ ✔ ⊘

Cleansing Wash, Orange Water Skin Tonic, Yin Yang Skin Cleanser

YOUR BODY ™ ✔ 👁 ⊘

Anti-Spot Lotion, *Cleansing Lotions:* Marshmallow, Seaweed; *Cleansing Milk:* Aloe Vera, Cucumber, Orchid Oil, Vitamin E; *Facial Scrubs:* Aloe Vera, Lemon, Orange & Almond, Vitamin E; *Facial Wash:* Aloe Vera, Aromatherapy, Vitamin E; Lime Blossom Cleansing Cream, *Men's Range:* For Men Aromatic Facial Wash Gel, Olive Face Scrub; Rosewater Skin Freshener, *Skin Tonic:* Aloe Vera, Cucumber, Sage & Yarrow, White Grape; Ti-Tree Skin Wash, *Toners:* Aloe Vera, Elderflower, Vitamin E, Witch Hazel

SKIN MAKE-UP

ANNE-MARIE BORLIND ❶ ✔ ⊘

Compact Powder, Fluid Make-Up, Powder Make-Up, Powder Rouge

ARBONNE ❶ ✔ ⊘

Cream Concealer, *Global Color Blusher:* All; *Match Perfect Oil Free Foundation SPF8:* All; Peach Concealer Pencil, Translucent Finishing Powder, Transluscent Pressed Powder, *True Color Soft Finish Make-up SPF8:* All

BARRY M COSMETICS ✔ 👁 ⚕ 85

Body Glitter Shaker Pots, Fine Glitter Dust, Natural Dazzle Powder Loose (Not Compact), Translucent Powder Loose (Not Compact)

BEAUCAIRE ☺ ✔ ⊘

Make up: Beige, Bronze, Dark, Light

BIOCOSMETICS

Soothing Concealer

BLACKMORES ✔ ⊘

Treatment Cover Stick

HONESTY COSMETICS LTD
☺❶✔⊘👁⚓76

Beauty Without Cruelty: Natural Look
Tinted Moisturisers, Super Fine Powder
Blushers, Super Fine Pressed Powders,
Ultra Fine Loose Powders

KISS MY FACE ✔

Obsessively Natural Tinted Moisturiser:
Beach, Branch, Clay, Manilla, Rattan,
Sisal

MOLTON BROWN COSMETICS ✔ ⊘

Bareface Tinted Bronzing Gel, Cheek To
Cheek Compact Powder Blush, Easy
Cover Compact Powder Foundation,
Take Cover Face, Under Control
Compact Loose Powder, Under Cover
Liquid Light Foundation

STARGAZER ✔ ⊘

Face & Body Jewellery

VEGANSTORE.CO.UK ☺™❶✔⊘

Anne Marie Borlind: Compact Powder,
Fluid Make up, Powder Rouge

SOAPS

AMPHORA AROMATICS LTD ✔ ⊘

Aromatherapy Soap: Bergamot,
Chamomile, Lavender, Neroli,
Sandalwood, Tea Tree; *Clear Glycerine
Soap:* Citrus Woods, Lavender, Lemon,
Red Rose, Tea Tree, Vit E; Clear Melt &
Pour Soap, Tea Tree Liquid Soap

ANIMAL AID ☺❶✔⊘⚓76

Calder Valley Soap, Calendula & Vanilla
Liquid Soap

ASCENT ☺✔⊘

*Vegetable & Glycerine w Natural
Perfume:* All

BAY HOUSE AROMATICS ✔⊘⚓78

Almond Oil, Aloe Vera & Ylang Ylang,
Bitter Orange & Cinnamon, Chocolate,
Cinnamon & Vanilla, Geranium &
Rosewood, Hemp w Green Tea &
Lemongrass, Lavender, Lavender Olive
Oil, Liquid, Patchouli & Rosewood, Pine
& Fennel, Rose, Rosemary Lemongrass
& Tea Tree, Tea Tree & Lavender, Tea
Tree Liquid Soap, Ylang Ylang &
Lemongrass

BIO-D CO. LTD ☺™✔⊘⚓83👁

Aromatherapy Soaps, Fragranced Hemp
Oil Soaps, Hemp Bran, Hemp Oil

BLACKMORES 🗸 ⊘

Marshmallow, Purifying

CALDER VALLEY SOAP ™🗸 ⊘ ◉

Almond Blossom, Aloe Vera, Anise, Avocado and Cucumber, Camomile & Lime, Coconut Palm, Customised shaped soaps, Dewberry, Grapefruit, Lavender, Lemongrass, Lime, Oatmeal Scrub, Orchard Apple, Peppermint & Poppyseed, Rose, Sandalwood, Sea Kelp, Tea Tree, Vanilla, Violet, Wild Raspberry

CAMILLA HEPPER LTD 🗸 ⊘ ⚗-87

Pure Vegetable Oil Soap: Avocado, Grapefruit, Orange Blossom

CAPITELLI OILS ™🗸 ⊘

Liquid Soap: Bene, Invigorante

CELLANDE MIDLANDS ☺🗸 ⊘

Lavender & Citronella Liquid Soap

CHIKPE 🗸 ⊘

Aromatherapy Soap: Alternative Remedy, Coconut Slice, Flower Power, Sea Breeze, Tea Tree Teaser; *Designer Soap:* Boy, Cherish, Fantasy Flowers, Ginger Fish, Girl, Happy Face, Little Bit O' Luck, Midnight Blue, Paradise Sunset, Peace, Pikaki, Raspberry Mocha, Smooches, Symphony, Teed Off!; Double Decker, *Foam Soap:* Berry Beauty, Pink Horses, Stress Surfer; *Loofah Soap:* Lemon & Eucalyptus, Strawberry, Ylang Ylang; *Natural Soap:*

Calendula, Chocolate, Fly Away Home, Lavender, Patchouli

DOLMA ☺™🗸 ◉ ⊘

Glycerine Soaps: 'Niamh' De-Luxe, Carrot, Ho-Leaf & Orange, Hemp Seed Fragrance Freed, Lavender & Jojoba, Tea Tree & Calendula

DR HADWEN TRUST ☺🗸 ⊘

Aromatherapy Soap: Bergamot & Orange, English Lavender, Grapefruit & Juniper, Neroli & Lemongrass, Orange Blossom w Orange Oil & Poppy Seeds, Tea Tree w Eucalyptus, Ylang & Ylang

DROYT PRODUCTS LTD ☺🗸 ⊘ ⚗-84

Clear Glycerine Soap

ECOLINO ™

Handsoap

FAITH PRODUCTS LTD ❶🗸 ⊘◉⚗-78

Aloe Vera & Ylang Ylang, Gingko Biloba, Hemp & Lemongrass, Lavender, Orange, Organic Chocolate, Pine, Rosemary, Tea Tree, Unfragranced Seaweed

FREERANGERS ☺™🗸

Soap Set

GREEN PEOPLE CO. ™🗸 ⊘

Liquid Soap: Aloe Vera, No Scent, Rosemary

HEMP SHOP LTD ❶ ✔ ⊘

Dr Bronner Magic Soap: Almond, Aloe-Vera, Eucalyptus, Lavender, Peppermint, Tea Tree; *Natural Soap:* All

HEMP UNION ™ ✔ ⊘

Hemp Soap: Exfoliating, Natural

HONESTY COSMETICS LTD ☺❶ ✔ ⊘ ☜ ⚥ 76

Apple & Sandalwood, Carrot & Jojoba, Geranium & Lavender, Orange, Strawberry & Papaya

HUMANE RESEARCH TRUST ☺❶ ✔ ⊘

Norfolk Lavender: Lavender Hand Soap, Men's Soap, Soap Leaves

KENT COSMETICS ☺ ✔ ⊘ ☜

Australian Organics Pure Plant Soap

KISS MY FACE ✔

Obsessively Natural Bar Soap: Olive & Aloe, Olive & Chamomile, Olive & Herbal, Pure Olive Oil; *Obsessively Natural Liquid Soaps:* Almond Creme, Fragrance Free, Melon, Orange Blossom, Original, Peaceful Patchouli, Peaches & Creme, Pear, Pear Liquid, Tea Tree germs aside

KOBASHI ☺™ ✔ ☜ ⊘

Liquid Soap: Fragrance Free Soap Base, Tea Tree & Lemon

LITTLE MIRACLES / APHRODITE'S ROSE ✔ ⊘

Aphrodite's Rosebud

LUSH ✔ ⊘

Alkmaar, Bamboo, Banana Moon, Bohemian, Demon in the Dark, Figs & Leaves, I Should Coco, Red Rooster, Sea Vegetable, Sunny Citrus

MARTHA HILL ❶ ✔ ⊘

Apple, Avocado, Camomile, *Handmade Soap:* Evening Primrose, Lavender, Orange & Lemon, Palmarosa & Grapefruit, Rose Geranium; Peach, *Rope of Soaps:* Marine, Spice; Vitamin E

MAXIM MARKETING COMPANY ™

Amber Sandalwood Beauty

MEADOWSWEET ☺™ ✔ ☜ ⊘

Fragrance Free Liquid Soap

MODERN ORGANIC PRODUCTS ✔ ⊘

Body Bar: Basil-Lime, Cranberry-Kiwi, Oatmeal-Coconut

MOLTON BROWN COSMETICS ✔ ⊘

Calming Zhan Zhi, Purifying Seamoss

NATIONAL TRUST ENTERPRISES ✔ ⊘ ⚥ 98

English Lavender: Bath Soap, Glycerine Soap

NATURAL COLLECTION, THE ✔ ⊘

Aloe Vera, Baby Purity Bar Soap, Chamomile, Exfoliating Hemp, Hemp, Lavender, Lavender & Olive Oil, Lavender Swirl, Lemon & Almond, Neem, Olive Oil, Pack of 6 egg-shaped Soaps, Rosehip & Patchouli, Sandlewood, Seaweed, Tantra, Wild Collection, Zen

NEAL'S YARD REMEDIES ✔ ⊘

Calendula & Evening Primrose, Citrus Glycerine, French Almond, French Lavender, Geranium & Orange, Geranium & Sweet Almond Oil, Lavender, Lavender Glycerine, Lavender & Olive Oil, Lavender & Tea Tree, Lemon & Coriander, Marseille Block, Neem, Rose, Rosemary, Seaweed

PERFUMERS GUILD LTD ☺ ❶ ✔ 👁 ⊘

Glycerine Soap: Lavender, Rose

POTIONS AND POSSIBILITIES ✔ ⊘

Double Luxury Soap: Bergamot & Neroli, Frankincense, French Lavender & Evening Primrose, Myrrh & Orange Sweet, Rose & Cinnamon Blend, Serenity Perfume Blend; *Hand-made Soap:* Bergamot & Neroli, Chamomile & Wild Dock, Frankincense, Green Mandarin, Lavender & Evening Primrose, Orange & Calendula, Orange Sweet, Rose & Cinnamon, Rosemary & Wild Mint, Serenity, Vanilla & Poppy Seed, Violet & Calendula; *Hand-Made Soaps w Essential Oil:* All; *Luxury Soap*

Stack Collection: Contemporary, Traditional

PURPLE FLAME AROMATHERAPY ✔ ⊘

French Lavender, Organic Tea Tree

RHEMA UK LTD ❶ ✔ ⊘

Vegan Soap: All

SCENT BY NATURE ☺ ✔ ⊘

100% Plant-Based Essential Oil Soap: Grapefruit & Juniper, Neroli & Lemongrass, Tea tree & Eucalyptus

SEVEN WIVES OF ST IVES SOAP CO ☺ ✔ ⊘

Care Range: Avocado & Cedarwood, Avocado & Lavender, Lavender & Cocoa, Lavender & Rosewood – Exfoliating Bar; *Castille Range:* Hazelnut & Lavender, Shea Butter & Cedarwood, Shea Butter & Hazelnut, Shea Butter & Lavender

SIMPLY SOAPS ™ ✔ ⊘

Banana & Citron, Calendula & Lavender, Cedarwood, Geranium & Rose, Hemp, Orange, Rosemary & Lavender, T—Tree

SOLANO TRADING ™ ✔ ⊘

Almond, Lavender, Scented

SUMA WHOLEFOODS ™ ⊘ ✔

County Garden: Camomile, Mixed Pack, Rosemary, Violet; *Exotic:* Cinnamon & Sandalwood, Mixed Pack, Nutmeg &

Vanilla, Tea Tree; *Extra Gentle:* Avocado & Cucumber, Desert Aloe Vera, Fragrant Coco Palm, Mixed Pack; *Glycerine Soaps:* Almond, Cucumber, Lavender, Mandarin, Rose, Vitamin E; *Handmade Gifts:* Box of Soaps, Trio of Treasures; *Old English:* Elderflower & Apple, English Lavender Blossom, Mixed Pack, Rose of York

TANJERO ☺™ ◢ ⊘

Apple & Orchid, Carrot & Hempseed, Chamomile, Cucumber & Mint, Gardenia, Grapefruit & Orange, Jasmine, Just Carrot, Kitchen Coffee Bar, Lavender, Lavender & Aloe Vera, Lavender & Chamomile, Lavender & Oatmeal, Lavender w Flowers, Litsea Cubeba, Musk, Patchouli, Pure Aloe Vera, Tanjero No. 1, Tanjero No. 2, Tea Tree & Aloe Vera, Tea Tree & Lavender, Tea Tree & Lavender w Oatmeal, Tea Tree & Mint, Tea Tree & Oatmeal, Violet, Ylang Ylang

TARA TOILETRIES ☺❶ ◢ ⊘

Liquid Soap

THURSDAY PLANTATION ◢ ⊘ ⚥–95

Tea Tree Deep Cleansing Vegetable Soap

TLC COLLECTION ◢ ☜ ⊘

Nougat Caring Liquid Soap

TOM'S OF MAINE ◢ ⊘

Natural Deodorant Soap: Calendula, Unscented; *Natural Glycerin Bar Soap:* Herbal Lemon Verbena, Jasmine Rose,

Refreshmint, Unscented; *Natural Glycerin Liquid Soap:* Herbal Lemon Verbena, Jasmine Rose, Refreshmint, Unscented; *Natural Moisturising Soap:* Calendula, Lavandin, Unscented

TREE-HARVEST ◢ ⊘

Artisan Natural Soap: Calendula, Cedar & Lemon, Forest Spice, Gardener's, Geranium & Chamomile, Hemp, Lavender, St Clement's Frankincense & Myrrh, Tea Tree

URTEKRAM ⊘ ◢

Almond, Aloe Vera, *Bath Soap:* Almond, Lavender, Lime, Orange, Sandelwood; Camomile, Flower, Herbal, Lavender, Rhassoul, Rose, Rose Liquid Handsoap, Sandalwood, Tea Tree

VEGANSTORE.CO.UK ☺™❶ ◢ ⊘

Faith In Nature, *Gourmet Soap:* Almond Flip, Artica, Zanzibar; Kiss My Face Liquid Moisture, Ord River Natural Tea Tree, Woods Spirits

VIVA! ☺❶ ◢ ⊘

Banana & Citron, Cinnamon & Cedarwood, Geranium & Rose Petal, Lavender & Calendula, Ti-tree & Calendula

WELEDA ◢ ⊘ ☜ ⚥–85

Iris, Rosemary

WORLDS END TRADING ☺❶ ◢ ⊘

Chandrika Ayurvedic, Mysore Sandalwood

YOUR BODY ™✔👁⊘

Aloe Vera, Chamomile, Cinnamon, Mint, *Soaps For All Skin Types Except Sensitive:* Lemon & Tea Tree w Macadamia Scrub, Watermelon, White Jasmine; Vitamin E

SUN CARE

ANIMAL AID ☺❶✔⊘⅄76

Honesty Sun Tan Lotion

ANNE-MARIE BORLIND ❶✔⊘

After-Sun Gel, Sun Block Balm Factor 30, Sun Lotion Factor 12 & 24, Sun Milk Factors 10 & 12, Sun Spray Factor 15, Sunless Bronze

ARBONNE ☺❶✔⊘

After Sun Lotion, Lip Protector SPF 15, Self Tanner for Face & Body, *Take Cover for:* Face & Body, Face SPF 15, Hand & Body SPF 15

BEAUCAIRE ☺✔⊘

Self Tanning Cream, Sun Gel Factor 8, Sun Lotion Factor 12

CAMILLA HEPPER LTD ✔⊘⅄87

Tropical: After-Sun Soother, Coconut Suntan Oil (no sunscreen), Suntan Lotion (SPF10), Suntan Oil (SPF8), Tanning Butter (SPF6)

DESERT ESSENCE ✔⊘⅄85

Desert Sun Tanning Lotion (SPF15)

GREEN PEOPLE CO. ™✔⊘

Edelweiss Sun Lotion - SPF 8, SPF 15, Water Lily After Sun

HONESTY COSMETICS LTD ☺☺✔⊘👁⅄76

Aftersun Lotion, High Protection Sun Lotion (SPF15), Medium Protection Sun Lotion (SPF8), Moisturising lotion w UVB filter, Sun & Sport Shower Gel

KISS MY FACE ✔

After Sun Aloe Soother w Jewelweed & Yucca, Natural Instant Sunless Tanner w Walnut Extract, Repair & Prevent SPF 15, Spray On Sun Screen SPF 30, *Sun Screen w Oat Protein Complex:* SPF 18, SPF 30; Sunswat Sun Screen & Natural Insect Repellent SPF 15

MALIBU HEALTH PRODUCTS LTD ✔⊘

After Sun: Glitter Gel, Moisturising Spray, Soothing, Soothing w Insect Repellent; *High Protection Lotion:* SPF15, SPF20, Spray SPF15; Moisturising Self-Tanning Lotion, *Protective Sun Lotion:* SPF12, Spray SPF8

MARTHA HILL ❶✔⊘

After Sun Skin: Calming Gel, Repair Lotion; Hair Protection Mist, *Sun Protection Lotion:* SPF 15, SPF 25; Sun Protection Oil SPF 10

MOLTON BROWN COSMETICS ✓ ⊘

Aftersun Skin Sense

NEAL'S YARD REMEDIES ✓ ⊘

Chamomile & Aloe Vera After Sun Lotion, Lavender Sun Block, Lemongrass Sun Lotion

NEW SEASONS

Neutral After Sun Gel Base

ROMANY ✓ ⊘

Coconut Suntan Oil, Romany After-Sun Lotion

URTEKRAM ⊘ ✓

Solar Creme: Blocker, Factor 12-14, Factor 6-9

VEGANSTORE.CO.UK ☺™❶ ✓ ⊘

Jason SPF 26: Goodbye Bugs Sun Spray, Sun Block; *Kiss My Face:* Aftersun Aloe Soother, Instant Sunless Tanner, Sun-swat SPF 15; Reform SPF 15 Sun Cream

YOUR BODY ™✓ ☻⊘

Aloe Vera Aftersun w Vitamin E, Self-Tan Lotion w Vitamin E UVA & UVB 2 - 4, *Suntan Lotion w Vitamin E:* UVA + UVB 2 - 4, UVA + UVB 6 - 8, UVA+ UVB 15+

TALCUM POWDERS

CAMILLA HEPPER LTD ✓ ⊘ ⚒ 87

Avocado, Orange Blossom, White Musk

DOLMA ☺™✓ ☻⊘

Orange Blossom Talc

HUMANE RESEARCH TRUST ☺❶✓ ⊘

Norfolk Lavender Talcum Dusting Powder

JURLIQUE ✓ ⊘

Silk Dust: Lavender, Rose

LUSH ✓ ⊘

Dusting Powder: Bare Naked Lady, Karma, Silky Underwear, T for Toes

MARTHA HILL ❶✓ ⊘

Body Talc, Lavender

NATIONAL TRUST ENTERPRISES ✓ ⊘ ⚒ 98

English Lavender Talcum Powder

VEGANSTORE.CO.UK ☺™❶✓ ⊘

Jason Aloe Vera 84% Body Powder

YOUR BODY ™✓ ☻⊘

Talcum Powder: Lavender & Bergamot, Musk, Orange & Lemon Shower, Rosemary & Cedarwood Shower

TOOTHPASTES & ORAL HYGIENE

ABSOLUTE AROMAS LTD ✔ ⊘

Ord River Toothpaste

CAMILLA HEPPER LTD ✔ ⊘ ⚹–87

Natural Spearmint Mouthwash

CLEARSPRING ☺™❶ ⊘

Dentie: Toothpaste, Toothpowder

DENTAL HERB CO. ✔ ⊘

Tooth & Gum: Paste, Spritz, Tonic

GREEN PEOPLE CO. ™ ✔ ⊘

Herbal Fresh Toothpaste: Citrus, Mint; Mint Mouthwash

HERBS HANDS HEALING ✔ ⊘

Mouthwash Water

HERBS OF GRACE ™

Mouth Wash

HOLLYTREES ✔ ⊘

Mouthwash: Fennel, Sage & Calendula; *Toothpaste:* Fennel, Lemon, Orange

KINGFISHER NATURAL TOOTHPASTE ☺ ✔ ⊘ ⚹–81

Aloe Vera Tea Tree Fennel, Aloe Vera Tea Tree Mint, Baking Soda Mint, Fennel, Fennel Fluoride Free, Mint w Lemon, Mint w Lemon Fluoride Free

KISS MY FACE ✔

Organic Aloe Vera Mouthwash, *Toothpaste:* AloeDyne Triple Action, Whitening

MAXIM MARKETING COMPANY

Amber Toothpaste (sugar free)

NATURAL COLLECTION, THE ✔ ⊘

Mouthwash, *Toothpaste:* Kids, Lemon, Mint

NEAL'S YARD REMEDIES ✔ ⊘

Lemon & Mint Mouth Freshener, Toothpastes

THURSDAY PLANTATION ✔ ⊘ ⚹–95

Tea Tree: Mouthwash, Toothpaste

TOM'S OF MAINE ✔ ⊘

Natural Alcohol-Free Mouthwash: Cinnamint, Gingermint Baking Soda, Peppermint Baking Soda, Spearmint; *Natural Toothpaste for Sensitive Teeth:* Fennel, Wintermint; *Natural Toothpaste w Fluoride:* Cinnamint, Fennel, Gingermint Baking Soda, Peppermint Baking Soda, Spearmint, Wintermint

VEGANSTORE.CO.UK ☺™❶ ✔ ⊘

Logona Herbal Dental Gel, *Tom's of Maine:* Peppermint Baking Soda, Spearmint Mouthwash; *Toothpaste:* Kingfisher Lemon & Mint, Ord River Tea Tree

WELEDA ✔ ⊘ ◉ ⚕ 85

Toothpaste: Calendula, Plant Gel, Ratanhia, Salt

WORLDS END TRADING ☺ ❶ ✔ ⊘

Vicco Pure Herbal Ayurvedic Toothpaste

NOTES

■ **Body Shop** Cannot state that any of their products are free from animal derived ingredients.

■ **contact lenses** Classed as a medicine under the Medicines Act, all contact lens solutions and associated products have been safety-tested (which invariably entails animal testing at some point). Such products are listed in the *Animal Free Shopper only* if the company under whose name they are sold meets the Shopper's 'animal testing' criterion *(see **ANIMAL-FREE CRITERIA**, page 270)*.

■ **dental products** Little research has been conducted in this area, however, it is known that glycerin *(possibly* animal-derived) is used extensively — especially in the manufacture of mouthwashes and toothpastes. Floss may contain beeswax or propolis.

■ **Superdrug** are currently compiling a vegan list – phone 0870 333 5666 for details.

HEALTHCARE

CONTRACEPTIVES

CONDOMI HEALTH UK LTD ☺™✔⊘

Condoms: Condomi, Condomis, Mondos

NATURAL COLLECTION ✔⊘™

Latex Condoms, *Condoms:* SuperSafe, Strong, Noppy, Nature, Fruit, Light, XXL, Mix

VEGAN SOCIETY

Condoms: SuperSafe, Strong, Nature, Fruit, Light, XXL, Mix

FOOD SUPPLEMENTS

AQUASOURCE ☺™✔⊘

Bifidus Complex & Klamath Lake Algae 90 V - Caps, Cell Power – instant nutrition, CoQ10 Complex w Chromium Polynicotinate and Algae 30 V - Caps, Digestive Enzymes & Klamath Lake Algae 60 V - Caps, Green Energy — Algae, Hawaiian Spirulina and Alfalfa 75 & 300 V - Caps, Klamath Lake Algae 60 & 120 V - Caps, Klamath Lake Algae Powder 50g & 150g, Klamath Lake Algae Suspended in Organic Apple Juice 60ml, Lactobacillus Acidophilus & Klamath Lake Algae 90 Capsules, Lighten-Up! Advanced Meal Replacement with Algae, Vanilla Flavour, Protein Shake w Klamath Lake Algae, Vanilla 300g & 600g, Spirulina Pacifica — Hawaiian Spirulina Kona Coast 250g, *Start Easy Pack:* Bifidus Complex & Klamath Lake Algae 50 V - Caps, Digestive Enzymes & Klamath Lake Algae 60 V - Caps, Klamath Lake Algae 50 V -Caps, Lactobacillus Acidophilus & Klamath Lake Algae 50 V - Caps; Sun Power – instant nutrition, Super Antioxidant w Pycnogenol 60 V - Caps

ARKOPHARMA (UK) LTD ☺✔⊘

Arkocaps: Alfalfa, Artichoke, Bamboo Gum, Bilberry Leaves, Californian Poppy, Common Plantain, Damiana, Devil's Claw High Potency, Feverfew, Ginger, Ginkgo Biloba, Ginkgo Biloba One A Day, Great Burdock, Green Tea, Guarana, Ispaghula, Milk Thistle, Phyto Slim, Phytocalm, Phytocold, Phytomenapause, Phytomenapause Value, Phytorelax, Pineapple, Siberian Ginseng, St John's Wort, Stinging Nettle, Vegetable Charcoal, Witch Hazel; Basikol, Ginseng Forte, *Hair & Nails:* Cheveux Plus / Hair Plus, Forcapil; *Health From The Sun:* Borage Oil – Vegetarian, Evening Primrose Oil, Organic Fibroflax, Organic Flax Lignan Gold, Organic Flax Liquid Gold, Organic Flax Oil – Vegetarian; *Oils in Gelatin Free Capsules:* Evening Primrose, Natural Vitamin E, Organic Flax, Pumpkin Seed Oil & Saw Palmetto, Starflower; *Organic Plant Liquid Extracts:* Dandelion, Devil's Claw, Ginkgo, Great Burdock, Green Tea,

Hawthorn, Panax Ginseng; *Phyto Soya,
Phyto Soya Double Potency, Slimming:*
Exolise, Mincifit Hodeol Unidose

BEAUCAIRE ☺ ⚕ ⊘

Dietary Supplement

BIO-HEALTH LTD ☺ ⚕ ⊘

Raspberry Leaf tablets, *V-caps:* Super
Kelp & Vitamins, Super Rutin &
Buckwheat

BIOCARE ⚕ ⊘

Femforte: 1 (uncoated tablet), 2 (V-
cap); Kombucha Drink, Maleforte,
Osteoplex, *Sweet Wheat:* Powder, V-
caps; Synergy Spirulina

BLACKMORES ⚕ ⊘

Alfalfa, Bilberry 2500, Cascara & Cape
Aloes, Cranberry Forte, Dong Quai,
Echinacea: Complex, Forte 3000,
Lozenges; Garlix, Ginkgo Forte 2000,
Ginkgo Plus, Hawaiian Pacifica Spirulina
- tablets & powder, Herbal Fluid
Balance, Horseradish & Garlic,
Hyperiforte, Kelp, Milk Thistle,
Raspberry Leaf, Slippery Elm tablets,
Super Horseradish & Garlic, Valerian
Forte

BRUNEL HEALTHCARE ⚕ ⊘

Vertese Capsules: Evening Primrose Oil,
High Strength Evening Primrose Oil
(1000mg), High Strength Garlic
(350mg)

CAMBRIDGE BIOCEUTICALS ☺™⚕ ⊘

Bio-Kult

CLEARSPRING ☺™❶⊘

Organic Omega Oil, *Seagreens Food
Capsules:* Organic, Wild Seaweed One-
a-day

DAVINA SPORTS NUTRITION ⚕ ⊘

Soya Protein Powder (Natural)

FLORA ⊘ ⚕

Flor-Essence: Dry Herbs, Liquid Herbal
Tea; *Flora-Vision Spring Horsetail:*
Powder, V-Caps; St John's Wort oil (not
capsules), Swedish Bitters, *V-Caps:*
Beyond Grape Seed, Milk Thistle

FSC ⚕ ⊘

V-caps: Acidophilus, Bifidus, FOS non-
dairy, Prune & Senna, Whole Bulb Garlic

GNC ⚕ ⊘

Aloe Vera Liquid: C/Berry, ConcX4
C/Berry, ConcX4 Orange, ConcX4
Unflav, Orange, Unflav; *Tablets:*
Bromelain 100gdu, Dong Quai, Red
Rasberry 500mg, Whole Rice B-50
Complex; *V-Caps:* American Ginseng,
Bilberry 500mg, Black Cohosh,
Cranberry 500mg, Dandelion 500mg,
Devils Claw, Echinacea 500mg,
Feverew, Ginger 500mg, Ginkgo Biloba,
Hawthorne 500mg, Horse Chestnut,
Horsechestnut 150mg, Kava Kava,
Korean Ginseng, Milk Thistle, Nb
Acidophilus Bifidus Fos, Nettle 500mg,

Red Clover, Saw Palmetto, Saw Palmetto 500mg, Scullcap, Siberian Ginseng 500mg, St Johns Wort 500mg 6x90, Triple Ginseng, Valerian, Wild Yam Root 500mg

GR LANE ✔ ⊘

Brewers Yeast Tablets, Intune, Lecigran, Spirulina, Thompson's Slippery Elm Food Unmalted

GREEN PEOPLE CO. ™✔ ⊘

Capsules: Echinacea, Ginger, Milk Thistle, Saw Palmetto, Seaweed, Siberian Ginseng, St John's Wort, Valerian; *Liquids:* Hawthorne & Artichoke Formula, Herbal X-tra, Herbal X-tra concentrate, Omega 3 & 6 Fuel 1:1, Omega 3 & 6 Fuel 3:1; Omega 3 & 6 Sprinkle

HEALTH PLUS ™✔ ⊘

Acidophilus, Aloe Vera Juice, Ascorbic Acid Powder 250g, Black Cohosh, Bright-Eyed Bilberry, Cats Claw, Citri-Trim Plus, Digest Plus , Dong Quai, EPO Liquid, Folic Acid, Ginger Root, Konjac Fibre, Korean Ginseng, Liquid Essential Lecithin 550mg, Liquid Essential Lycopene Plus, Megadophilus, Milk Thistle, MSM, Multi Probiotic, Premier Garlic, Psyllium Seed Husk Fibre, Sodium Ascorbate Powder, Spirulina, Tribula Plus, Whole Grape

HEALTHQUEST LIMITED ™✔ ⊘

Body Shield, Chill Out, Lift, Man, Nutri-Aid, Woman

HEMP SHOP LTD ❶✔ ⊘

Hempseed Oil

HERBS HANDS HEALING ✔ ⊘

Superfood

HIGHER NATURE ✔ ⊘

Aloe Gold Liquids: Cherry & Cranberry, Natural; Get up & go! Powder, *Liquids:* Aloe Gold Digestive Formula, Herbal Aloe Gold Detox; *Patrick Holford's Tablets:* Advanced brain foods, Advanced Optimum Nutrition Formula, Immune C; *Tablets:* Chlorella, Soyagen, Superpotency soyagen; *V-caps:* Cat's Claw, Guarana

KUDOS VITAMINS AND HERBALS LTD ✔ ⊘

Acidophillus plus Bifidus, Allerplex, Amino Acid Complex, Butchers Broom Complex, Coenzyme Q10 40mg, Cranberry Complex, D.L.P.A. plus Vitamin B6, Digestive Enzymes, Evening Primrose Oil Powder, Eye Bright Formula, Garlic & Parsley 1000mg, Hair Nutrient Formula, L -Carnitine & Vitamin B6, L-Arginine & L-Ornithine & Vitamin B6, L-Cysteine & Vitamin B6, L-Glutamine & B6, L-Methionine & B6, Livoplex L-Lysine & B6, Maca 900mg, Menoplex, Nails & Skin Nutrient Formula, Pineoxenol, Rhodiola 900mg, Soya Isoflavones

LIFEPLAN PRODUCTS LTD ™✔ ⊘

Calcium Pantothenate - 250mg,

Caprylic Acid, Cranberry Extract - 200mg, Culture Care - 28g, Echinacea - 360mg, Fibre - 440mg, High Strength Odour Controlled Garlic - 300mg, Lutein, Nettle Leaf, Eyebright ansd Echinacea, Pycnogenol - Maritime pine bark extract - 300mg, Red Clover, Saw Palmetto, Siberian Ginseng High Strength - 600mg, Soyplus - soya isoflavones with Folic Acid, St. John's Wort Extract - 333mg, Standardised Extract of Ginger - 50mg, Standardised Extract of Kava Kava - 150mg, Standardised Extract of Milk Thistle - 175mg, Triple Source Magnesium

NATURE'S AID LTD ✔ ⊘

Acetyl-L-Carnitine, Alpha Lipoic Acid, Brewers Yeast, Conc. Garlic 400mg, Cranberry, Devil's Claw, Kelp, Pycnogenol, Soya Isoflavones

NATURE'S DREAM ✔ ⊘

E'lifexir - Flat Tummy 500mg Tablets

NATURE'S PLUS ⊘

Chewable Leci-Thin, CoQ10 Lipoceutical Spray, Lecithin Granules, Nutri-Zyme Chewable, Oxy-Nectar, Papaya Enzyme Chewable, SAMe Rx-Mood, *V-Caps:* Acidophilus, Beta-Pro, Garlite, Ginkgo-Combo, Liv-R-Actin, Say Yes To Beans

NATURE'S REMEDIES ✔ ⊘

Zotrim

NUTRITIONAL HEALTHCARE ✔ ⊘

Agnus Castus, Barley Grass, Black Cohosh, Cyan Artichoke, Dong Quai, *Eros:* for Men, for Women; Garlic w Vitamin E, Ginger V-caps, Ginkgo Biloba, *Maxisulph:* Echinacea & Vit C, Gel, Powder, Tablets; Milk Thistle, Red Ginseng, Saw Palmetto

PHARMA NORD (UK) LTD ⊘

Bio-tablets: Biloba 100mg, Carnitine 250mg, Garlic, Lipoic Acid 50mg, MSM & Silica

PITROK LTD ✔ ⊘

Tofupill, Tofupill 30+

POWER HEALTH PRODUCTS ✔ ⊘

Alfalfa, Alfalfa 500mg, *Aloe Vera Supplements:* Double Strength, Juice Drink 99.7%, Standard Strength, Ultra Strength; Bromelain & Papain 100mg, Chromium Picolinate 200µg, Citrin 500mg (250mg HCA), *Cranberry Juice:* & Aloe Vera 6000mg, & Vitamin C Concentrate Drink Mix, Concentrate Drink Mix, Double Strength 4500mg; Dolomite 400mg, *GLA cold pressed oils:* Borage (starflower), Evening Primrose; *Herbal Supplements:* Bilberry 2500mg, Cat's Claw 500mg, Echinacea 400 (Standardised 4% extract), Kava Kava Root Powder 100mg, Kelp 500mg, Olive Leaf 450mg, Power ACE Super Antioxidant, Pro-Amino Yeast 500mg, Spirulina 500mg, Superlec Liquid (Soya Lecithin), Valerian 112mg & Hop 120mg; Kelp & Yeast

PRINCIPLE HEALTHCARE ™

Bilberry tablets, Co enzyme Q10 30mg VegaGels TM, Cranberry tablets 200mg, Evening Primrose Oil 1000mg VegaGels TM, Folic Acid 400 mcg tablets, Ginger tablets, Odourless Garlic 2mg VegaGels TM, Sea Kelp tablets

PROBIOTICS INTERNATIONAL LTD. ™ ✔ ⊘

Protexin Natural Care

PROSTA KIT ✔ ⊘

Saw Palmetto

QUEST VITAMINS ™ ✔ ⊘

Agnus Castus, Bilberry, Black Cohosh 40mg extract tablets, Cal-Mag Plus, Cats Claw 250mg extract tablets, Coenzyme Q10 30mg, Cranberry 200ml extract tablets, Devil's Claw, DL-Phenylalanine, Don Quai 250mg extract, Echinacea, Energy Nutrient Complex, Enzyme Digest, Ginger, Ginkgo Biloba, Hawthorn 250mg extract tablets, Heart Nutrient Complex, Kava Kava, Kyolic garlic 100, 350, 600 & Liquid, L-Arginine, L-Glutamine 500mg, L-Lysine, L-Ornithine 500mg, L-Phenylalanine 500mg, L-Tyrosine 500mg, Lactase, Milk Thistle, Non-Dairy Acidophilus Plus, Pre-Natal Folic Acid, Rhodiola 250mg extract tablets, Saw Palmetto, Senna, Siberian Ginseng, Synergistic Boron, Synergistic Iron, Synergistic Magnesium, Synergistic Selenium, Synergistic Zinc, Uva Ursi

REEVECREST HEALTHCARE ✔ ⊘

Ginseng-Red Roots, Nutrimental Plus, Super Nutrimental Plus

RELIV UK ™ ✔ ⊘

Reliv Classic, 504g

RHEMA UK LTD ❶ ✔ ⊘

Bio-Kult Probiotic, *Klamah Blue Green Algae:* Powder, Tablets, V-Cap

SAGE NUTRITIONALS ™ ✔ ⊘

Echinacea Formula, Healthy Joints, Healthy Woman, Menopause, Pregnancy, Time Out, Vitality

SALUS ✔ ⊘

Gallexier Artichoke Food Supplement, Pagosid (Devil's Claw Tablet), Siberian Ginseng Elixir

SAVANT ❶ ✔ ⊘

L-Glutamine Powder, Silver Colloid Liquid

SEAGREENS CO LTD ☺™ ✿ ⊘

Wild Seaweed Food Capsules

SKANE DAIRY UK LTD ⊘

ProViva Drink: Blackcurrant, Strawberry

SOLGAR VITAMINS LTD ✔ ⊘

ABC Dophilus, *Advanced Acidophilus products:* All; Alfalfa, Antioxidant Free Radical Modulators, Beta 1,3 Glucans, Brewers Yeast, Broccoli, Bromelain,

Cardiovascular Support, Cell Support, Certified Organic Garlic, Cholesterol Factors, *Co Q10:* 120mg, 200mg, 60mg; Energy Modulators, *Full Potency (FP) Herbs:* All; Glucose Factors, GSH Modulators, *Herbal Complexes:* All; Homocysteine Modulators, Hydroxy Citrate, Ipriflavone, Iso Soy, Lactase, Lipotropic Factors, Lutein Lycopene Carotene Complex, Lycopene Carotenoid Complex, Maximised Caprylic Acid, Microbial Modulators, MSM 1000mg, Multi-acidophilus Powder, Natural Cranberry Extract w Vitamin C, Octacosanol, Phosphatidyl Serine, Prostate Support, Quercetin, Reishi Shiitake Maitake Mushroom Extract, Soya Lecithin '95' Granules, Spirulina, *Standardised Full Potency (SFP) Herbs:* All; Super Concentrated Isoflavones, Upper Klamath Lake Blue Green Algae, Vegan Digestive Enzymes, Vegan Digestive Modulators

SOLO NUTRITION LTD ✔ ⊘

Chromium Polynicontinate Complex, D-Tox Formula, Echinacea Complex, Ester C-750mg, Evening Primrose Oil plus Borage Oil, Ginkgo Biloba, Kava Kava Root, Korean Ginseng, Milk Thistle Herb & Seed, Rhodiola Root, Saw Palmetto Berry Complex, Siberian Ginseng, St John's Wort, Super Acidophilus w F. O. S

THORNCROFT ☺ ⊘

Thorncroft Cordials & Herbal Fusions: Cranberry & Hibiscus, Elderflower,

Nettle, Pink Ginger, Rosehip; *Well Being Cordials:* Detox, Kombucha

UDO'S CHOICE ✔ ⊘

Beyond Greens Tonic, Digestive Enzyme Blend V-Caps, Omega 3 Basic (Master Nutrient Formula), Ultimate Oil Blend

UNICHEM LTD

2814 St John's Wort 333-complex

VEGA NUTRITIONALS ™ ✔ ⊘

Amino Complex Plus B6, Pine Bark Extract 30mg, Beta Carotene 170mg Dunaliella Salina, Pyridoxal '5' phosphate 25mg, Biotin 1000mcg, Choline Plus Inositol 250mg/250mg , Folic Acid 400mcg, P.a.b.a Para Aminobenzoic acid 300mg, Ester-C Complex, Kelp & Greens Formula, EPO + B6 + Mexican Yam 250mg, Soya Lecithin Plus Starflower Oil (Omega 3+6), Non Dairy Acidophilus Plus Bifidus Complex, Digestive Enzymes, Psyllium Fibre 450mg, Gastro-eze Formula, Multi Detox Formula, Hi-Active control Formula, Memory + Formula, Co-Enzyme Q10 30mg Extra High Potency, Garlic (deodorised) 400mg High Potency, Multigluco T Factors w Karella, Cran-Biotic Plus Caprilic Acid, Champignon Plus FOS, Chlorella & Spirulina, Brain Fuel Amino Acids, Vitamins and Ginkgo Biloba, Cellulite Vitamins, Herbs & Amino Acid, Energiser Amino Acids Plus Herbs, Cholestatin Formula, Agnus Castus 300mg High Potency, Aloe Vera 500mg

High Potency, Cat's Claw 1000mg High Potency, Devil's claw 300mg High Potency, Dong Quai 750mg high Potency, Echinacea 750mg High Potency, Ginkgo Biloba 750mg High Potency, Panax Ginseng (Korean) 800 complex, Ginseng (Siberian) Complex, Kava Kava 750mg High Potency, Milk Thistle 200-Complex, Valerian 900-Complex

VIRIDIAN ⚐ ⊘

100% Organic Food Blends: Blue, Green, Red; *100% Organic Oils:* Gold Flax Seed, Hemp, Pumpkin seed; Tri-blend Probiotic Powder, *V-caps:* Grape Seed Extract, Grapefruit Seed Extract, High Potency Digestive Aid, Pycnogenol w Grape Seed Extract, Tri-blend Acidophilus w FOS

XYNERGY HEALTH PRODUCTS ⚐ ⊘

Jagulana, Lifestream Biogenic Aloe Vera Juice, Optimum Source Chlorella, Premium Organic Spirulina, Pure Planet Red Marine Algae & Spirulina, Pure Synergy, *Seagreens:* Culinary Ingredient, Table Condiment, Wild Seaweed Food Capsules; Spirulina, Sweet Wheat, *V-Caps:* Aloe Vera, Spirulina, Sweet Wheat; *Vita Synergy for:* Men, Women

INSECT REPELLENTS

AMPHORA AROMATICS LTD ⚐ ⊘

Bugs Away insect repellent spray

BAREFOOT BOTANICALS ™ ⚐ ⊘

Zap Natural Insect Repellant

BAY HOUSE AROMATICS ⚐ ⊘ ✄ 78

Insect repellent gel

BEAUTY THROUGH HERBS ☺ ⚐ ⊘ 👁

Insect Barrier: Cream, Spray

CAPITELLI OILS ™ ⚐ ⊘

Zanzara Via

KISS MY FACE ⚐

Swy Flotter Natural Tick & Insect Repellent

KOBASHI ☺ ™ ⚐ 👁 ⊘

Insect Repellent

NATURAL COLLECTION, THE ⚐ ⊘

Anti-Mite Spray, Click Insect Bite Soother, Natural Moth Repellent, Zap Insect Repellent

NATURE'S DREAM ⚐ ⊘

Stop Pic - Roll on Applicator

SHANTI HEALTH & BEAUTY PRODUCTS ☺❶ ⚐ ⊘

Help to Repel Insects

THURSDAY PLANTATION ⚐ ⊘ ✄ 95

Tea Tree Walkabout: Lotion, Roll-on

VEGANSTORE.CO.UK ☺™❶ ⚐ ⊘

Kiss My Face Swyflotter Natural Insect Repellant

XYNERGY HEALTH PRODUCTS ✔ ⊘

India Tree Herbal Insect Repellent

REMEDIES

ABSOLUTE AROMAS LTD ✔ ⊘

Ord River Antiseptic Cream

AMPHORA AROMATICS LTD ✔ ⊘

Aromatherapy Sprays: Antiseptic, Body De-Stress, Body Revitalise, Face Freshener, Foot Reviver, Mind De-Stress

ARKOPHARMA (UK) LTD ☺ ✔ ⊘

Essential Oil Roll-Ons: Migrastick, Teenstick

AROMIST SPRAYS ✔ ⊘

Aro: -bronc, -digest, -fem, -gorge, -phen, -stress

BAY HOUSE AROMATICS ✔ ⊘ ⚕ 78

Herbal Candies: Angelica, Aniseed, Chamomile, Cinnamon & Clove, Cough Assortment, Eucalyptus, Fennel, Ginger & Orange, Gingko Biloba, Ginseng, Green tea, Lavender, Lemon balm, Liquorice & Anise, Peppermint

BENNETT NATURAL PRODUCTS ⊘

Obbekjaers Peppermint: Powder, Pure Oil of Peppermint, Tablets

BIO-HEALTH LTD ☺ ✔ ⊘

'Pure-fil' V-caps: Agnus Castus, Anti-Oxidant Herbs, Bachu Leaf, Black Cohosh, Capiscum Fruit, Celery Seed, Chamomile Flowers, Cramp Bark, Cranesbill Root, Damiana Herb, Dandelion Lea, Devil's Claw, Echinacea Root, Fenugreek Seed, Feverfew Leaf, Ginger Root, Gingko Leaf, Golden Seal, Hawthorn Berry, Kava Kava, Korean Ginseng, Liquorice Root, Melilot Herb, Milk Thistle, Misteltoe Herb, Nettle Root, Passiflora Herb, Prickly Ash Bark, Primula Root, Psyllium Husk, Red Clover Flowers, Sage Leaf, Senna Leaf, Skullcap Herb, Slippery Elm, St John's Wort, Valerian Root, Whole Garlic, Wild Yam Root, Willow Bark

BIOCOSMETICS ✔ ⊘

Soothing Witch Hazel Gel

BLACKMORES ✔ ⊘

Acidophilus Bifidus, Acidophilus plus Pectin, Digestive Aid, Lypsine

BODY REFORM (UK) LTD ❶ ✔ ⊘ 👁

Muscle Balm, Muscle Soothing Lotion

CAMILLA HEPPER LTD ✔ ⊘ ⚕ 87

Aromatherapy Oils: Hair Loss treatment, Relaxing Bath, Soothing Bath, Tension; *Herb Ointments:* Comfrey, Leg & Vein, Marigold

COTSWOLD HEALTH PRODUCTS ☺ ⊘

Liquorice Juice Sticks, *Natural Herb V-caps:* Devils Claw, Echinacea, Ginko

Biloba, Kava Kava, Milk Thistle & Dandelion, St John's Wort, Valerian

DOLMA ☺™✔👁️⊘

Avasafab Antiseptic Cream

DR HADWEN TRUST ☺✔⊘

Muscle & Joint Lotion

ESSENTIAL OIL COMPANY ☺✔⊘👁️

Cherrystone Pillow, Hot-Pak Herbal Heat Pillow, Magnotherapy products, Nitebalm Herbal Tincture

FSC ✔⊘

Creams: About Nails, Evening Primrose Oil, Spotoway Antiseptic, Vitamin E Cream & Lotion; *Herbcraft Formulae:* Agnus Castus Premenstrual, Black Cohosh & Wild Yam Menopause, Black Walnut & Calendula, Chamomile for Children, Dandelion, Dandelion & Burdock Cleansing, Echinacea, Echinacea, Eyebright & Bilberry, Garlic & horseradish Winter, Ginseng & Saw Palmetto for men, Liquorice, Mullein, Passiflora & Valerian, Peppermint, Reishi Shiitake Mushrooms; *Tablets:* Agnus Castus Premenstrual Formula, Astragalus & Reishi, Bilberry 500mg, Black Cohosh & Liquorice Formula, Black Cohosh 500mg, Cranberry 2400mg, Dandelion 500mg, Deglycyrrhized Liquorice 200mg (sugar-free, chewable), Devils Claw Plus 400mg, Echinacea, Feverfew 150mg, Ginger 500mg, Ginkgo Biloba 500mg, Ginkgo Biloba Standardised 24%

ginkgoflavones, Goldenseal 250mg, Hawthorn 500mg, Kava Kava 250mg, Milk Thistle 100mg standardised 70mg silymarin, Organic Echinacea 500mg, Red Raspberry 500mg, Slippery Elm 250mg, St John's Wort 500mg Standardised 1500µg hypericin, Valerian 500mg, Wild Yam 500mg; *V-caps:* About Face One-a-Day, Echinacea & Goldenseal, Eyebright 250mg, Head High Hair Vitamins, One-a-Day, Red Clover Standardised 40mg isoflavones, Saw Palmetto Standardised 320mg, Siberian Ginseng 1000mg, Valerian Formula

GR LANE ✔⊘

Charcoal Tablets, Herbalene, Herbelix Specific, *Modern Herbals:* Cold & Catarrh Syrup, Sleep Aid Tablets, Trapped Wind & Indigestion Tablets; Naturest, *Olbas:* Bath, Inhaler, Oil, Original Pastilles

HAMBLEDEN HERBS ⊘

Organic Tinctures: all EXCEPT propolis

HEALTH PLUS ™✔⊘

St. John's Wort

HEALTHPOL ☺✔⊘

Delacet Scalp & Hair Cleanser (lice/nits solution)

HEMP SHOP LTD ❶✔⊘

Merry Hempster Hemp Zap Deep-Heating Rub

HEMP UNION ™ ✔ ⊘

Hemp Oil T-Tree Cream

HERBS HANDS HEALING ✔ ⊘

Fennel & Peppermint Drops, Herbal Snuff, *Herbal Tincture Formulae:* All; *Oral Capsules:* All

HERBS OF GRACE ™

Adrenotone, Age Delay, Aller-G, Anti-Fung, Anti-Spasmodic, B.F.C., B-T-A, B-T-B, B-T-C, Beat Easy, Bentonite Clay, Breathe Easy, Calc Solv, Cascade, Chonic Purify, Chyavanaprash, Colflam, Colloidal Silver Spray, Dermaherb, Digestaid, Emotional Balance, Endobal, Ener-Plus, Espect Relief, Ferroton, Heavy Metal Purify, Hepatobal, Herbolax, Homeguard, Hypertens, I.B.S., Menotone, Mental Clarify, Nite Grace, Nrv-Ton, Nrv-Vitalizer, Paragon Programme, Pilease, Pre-Natal, Pure Flow, *Single Herbs:* All; Stone Solv, Sweet Sleep, Thyobal, Trikatu, Triphala, Uri/ad, Urooton, Vitral Flow, Weight Loss, Winterton, Womans Friend, Wormwood Combination, Yamoa Powder

HIGHER NATURE ✔ ⊘

Chocolate Memory Drink, Citricidal Liquid, Colofibre Powder / V-caps, MSM Tablets/V-caps/powder, *Powders:* Acidobifidus, FOS, Glutamine, HiPC Lecithin Granules, Zinc Citrate; *Tablets:* Brain Food, Citrilean, Ginkgo Biloba 30mg, GTF Chromium, Lactogest, Lysine 500mg, Neversnore, Osteofood, Serotone 5HTP, Tyroplex; The Ultimate

Aloe Vera Skin Gel, *V-caps:* Betaine HCL, Candiclear 350 Herbal-clear, Choice, Coloclear, Easigest, Echinacea & Black Elderberry, Glutamine, Menophase, Mexican Yam, Olive Leaf extract, Paraclens, Periwinkle extract, Pre-mens Prevention, Probiogest, St John's Wort, Super Strength Cranberry, Supergar 400mg, The Sher System Skin Support Formula

HUMANE RESEARCH TRUST ☺ ❶ ✔ ⊘

Assisi & Berwitz Homeopathic Remedy Creams: Acne Itching, Anal Itching, Arnica, Athletes Foot, Cuts & Sores, Dry Skin Cream, Haemorrhoids, Healing, Itching Eczema, Wart

J. L. BRAGG LTD ☺ ⊘

Bragg's Medicinal Charcoal Biscuits & Tablets

JAN DE VRIES ✔ ⊘

Botanical Formulae: Blood, Digestive, Head Clear, Nerve

KUDOS VITAMINS AND HERBALS LTD ✔ ⊘

Aloe Vera 20,000mg, Black Cohosh 900mg, Cat's Claw 900mg, Cleansoplex, Devils Claw 900mg, Dong Quai 900mg, Echinacea 900mg, Feverfew 900mg, Gingko Biloba 900mg, Korean Ginseng 900mg, Milk Thistle 900mg, Phyto-Nutrient Complex, Saw Palmetto 900mg, Siberian Ginseng 900mg, St John's Wort 900mg, Valerian 900mg

LITTLE MIRACLES / APHRODITE'S ROSE ✓ ⊘

Rose Essences: Bouquet, Clarity, Infinite Love, Inner Beauty, Intuition, Joy, Passion

MARIGOLD HEALTH FOODS ❶⊘

Golden Temple Ancient Herbal Formula: Bedtime, Breathe Deep, Calming, Cold Season, De-tox, Ginger Lemon, Men's Stomach-ease, Revitalize, Throat Comfort, Women's

MEADOWSWEET ☺™✓ ☜⊘

Nature Power Muscle & Joint Lotion

MONTAGNE JEUNESSE ✓ ☜⊘

Bath: Dead Sea Mud Aches-Away, Eucalyptus & Camphor Anti-Cold

NAPIERS DISPENSARY ✓

Adaptogenic Reviver, BPT Formula, Bug buster Lotion, Cellulite Gel, Composition Essence, *Compounds:* Birch Herbal, Bladderwrack, Buchu, NC, Skullcap, Thuja (for warts), Withania; *Creams:* Bug Buster, Capsicum & Ginger, Thuja; Duncan Napier's Cough Remover, Gentian Bitters, Joint-Ease, *Liquid Formulas:* Herbal Tonic (stress-relief), Valerian, Willow Bark; Lobelia Cough Syrup, Napiers Detox Plan, Natural Bacterial Balance, Nettle Blend (anti-hayfever), *Oil Blends:* Circulation, Mullein Formula, Muscle Ache, Sleepy Time; *Ointments:* Drawing, Marigold, Pilewort, Pokeroot; *Powders:* Psyllium &

Slippery Elm, Slippery Elm; *Pregnancy oils:* Stretch Mark, Wheat Germ; Sinus Rub, Special Mixture no.7, *Tablets:* 969, Aimcalm, Devil's Claw, Garlic, Gingko, Ginkgo Extract 2:1, Natural Herb, Slippery Elm; *Tinctures:* Arnica & Comfrey, Echinacea, Ginkgo Extract 2:1, Hawthorn, Salvia, Vitex

NATURAL COLLECTION ✓ ⊘

Kiss-it-Better Spray, Manage the Menopause Natural Supplement V-caps, Natural Nit Formula, *Organic Tinctures:* Echinacea, Hawthorn, Lemon Balm, Red Clover, St John's Wort; Snoreeze

NATURALIFE ✓ ⊘

Combinations: Black Cohosh Wild Yam Plus, Osha Plantain Plus (spray), Saw Palmetto Ginseng Plus; *Complex:* Ashwaganda Liquorice, Bone-Set Cleavers, Cats Claw Echinacea, Usnea Echinacea, Valerian Kava; *Single Tinctures:* Black Cohosh, Cats Claw, Echinacea, Kava Kava, Kids Echinacea, Milk Thistle, Red Clover, Valerian

NATURE'S AID LTD ✓ ⊘

Agnus Castus, Aloe Vera 50mg, Bilberry, Black Cohosh, Dong Quai, Echinacea, Feverfew, Ginger, Ginkgo Biloba, Good Health, Kava Kava, Korean Ginseng, Milk Thistle, MSM, Rhodiola, Saw Palmetto, Siberian Ginseng, St Johns Wort, Traditional Herbal Bronchial Balsam, Valerian, Wild Yam

NATURE'S MOTHER ✔ ⊘

Stretch Mark: Cream, Oil

NEAL'S YARD REMEDIES ✔ ⊘

Aloe Vera Juice, *Aromatherapy for:* Balance, Breathing Easy, Clarity, Energy, Passion, Relaxation; *Bach Flower Remedies:* All; *Chinese Herbal Tinctures:* All; *Herbal Tinctures:* All; *Homeopathic Tinctures:* All; *Macerated Oil:* Arnica, Calendula, Carrot, Comfrey, Mullein, St John's Wort; *Oils:* Detox Toning, Evening Primrose, Ginger & Juniper Warming, Inhalation; Ointment Base, *Ointments:* Arnica, Baseline, Calendula, Comfrey, Hypericum & Calendula, Hypericum & Urtica, Rhus Tox & Ruta, Stellaria; *Remedies to roll for:* Energy, Jetlag, Passion, Sleep; Witchazel

NUTRITIONAL HEALTHCARE ✔ ⊘

Maxisulph Echinacea & Vit C, Sleepyhead, St Johns Wort

PHARMA NORD (UK) LTD ⊘

Bio-tablets: Fiber 80, Trim

POTIONS AND POSSIBILITIES ✔ ⊘

Clinical Range of Aromatherapy Bath Oils: Executive Stress Relief, Fatigue Relief, Hormone Relief, Joint Ease, Sleep Easy, Ultra Relaxing; *Cushions:* Aromatherapy Wheat, Car Alert, Sleep & Relax; Heavy Duty Relief Gel, *Relief Balms:* Concentration / Student, Courage, Fatigue, Head-Ease, Mood, Relaxation

POTTER'S HERBAL MEDICINE ✔ ⊘

9 Rubbing Oils, Acidosis Mixture / Indigestion Mixture No 147, Backache Mixture No 84, Kas-Bah Herb Remedy, Life Drops, Medicated Extract of Rosemary, Pegina, Potters Cleansing Herbs, Potters Indian Brandee, Rheumatic Pain Tablets, Skin Clear Ointment, Stomach Mixture No 93, Vegetable Cough Remover

POWER HEALTH PRODUCTS ✔ ⊘

Arthur's: Balm w Boswellian Extract, Oil; *Balms:* Chilli Muscle Rub, Comfrey & Vitamin E, Double Comfrey, Evening Primrose, Garlic w Lemon Oil, Garlic – extra strong, Leg & Vein Balm, Marshmallow & Slippery Elm, Tea tree; Chest Rub, *Comfrey, Arnica & Witch Hazel:* Balm, Foam Bath, Lotion; Pilewort Ointment, Witch Hazel Cream

PURPLE FLAME AROMATHERAPY ✔ ⊘

Tea Tree Pessaries

QUEST VITAMINS ™ ✔ ⊘

Feverfew, Green Tea, St John's Wort, Valerian

QUINESSENCE AROMATHERAPY ☺ ❶ ✔ ⊘ ☻

Essential Oil Synergies: After Flight, Anti-pollen, Anti-Virus, Antiseptic, Breathe Ease, Cellulite, Foot Ease, Head Ease, Immune Booster, Invigorating, Joint Mobility, Menopause, Muscle Ease, Pre-Menstrual, Problem Skin,

Relaxing, Restful Sleep, Sinus, Stress, Uplifting

SALUS ☑ ⊘

Fresh Plant Juices: Birch, Gingko, Hawthorn, Horsetail, Manna Fig w Senna; *Pure Plant Juices:* Artichoke, Black Radish, Celery, Coltsfoot, Dandelion, Echinacea, Fennel, Plantain, St John's Wort, Stinging Nettle, Thyme, Valerian, Yarrow

SCENT BY NATURE ☺ ☑ ⊘

Green Clay: Fine Powdered, Ready-to-use, w Organic Lemon Supplement

SCOTTISH HERBAL SUPPLIES

Clays, Herbal Alcoholic Tinctures, Vegetable Creams, Vegetable/Herbal Ointments

SHANTI HEALTH & BEAUTY PRODUCTS ☺ ❶ ☑ ⊘

Lotions: Antiseptic / Acne, Burn, Hair Lice, Sunburn; *Oils:* Anti-cellulite, Arthritis & Rheumatic, Backache relief, Coldsore, Eczema / Psoriasis, Sciatica Relief, Tinnitus Control, Varicose Vein Pain Relief; Sinus Pain Relief

TAYLOR JACKSON HEALTH PRODUCTS ☺ ❶ ☑ ⊘

M-folia for Psoriasis & Eczema: Herbal Extract, Bath Oil, Conditioner, Cream, Ointment, Scalp Oil, Shampoo

THURSDAY PLANTATION ☑ ⊘ ✂ 95

Tea Tree: & Eucalyptus Chest Rub, & Eucalyptus Inhalant, & Lavender Solution, 15% Oil Lotion, Antiseptic Cream, Antiseptic Ointment

TREE-HARVEST ☑ ⊘

Arboretum Space Spray, Elderflower, Holy Thorn Healing Cream, Horsechestnut & Rowan Gel, Pau d'Arco, *Pulse points:* Elderberry, Lavender, Linden, Mate, Pau d'Arco, Rose, Willow; Tree Companion, *Tree Essences:* All

URTEKRAM ⊘ ☑

Panther Muscle Balm

VEGA NUTRITIONALS ™ ☑ ⊘

Anti-Oxidant Formula, Multi Antioxidant, Pre-Natal Formula, Vitalize-Regenerative Formula, Inflam-eze Formula, Maxijoint Formula, Aller-G Formula, Nico-Quit Herbal Support, Hair-Skin-Nails Formula, Menopause Formula, Prostate Formula, Slimming Hydroxy-Citric Acid and Chromium, Vein Support, Cardiohealth Support, Opti-Care 20:20 Formula, Feverfew 750mg high potency, Vegatonic herbal formula, Paracidal formula *(neem)*

VEGANSTORE.CO.UK ☺™❶ ☑ ⊘

Cariad: Muscle Rub, Tea Tree Gel; Ord River Antiseptics

VIRIDIAN ✓ ⊘

Herbal V-caps: Agnus Castus Berry, Bilberry w Eyebright, Black Cohosh Root, Boswelia Resin, Coleus Forskholii, Cranberry Berry, Dandelion w Burdock, Dong Quai Root, Echinacea Root & Leaf, Gingko Biloba Leaf, Hawthorn Berry, Horse Chestnut Seed, Kava Kava Root, Licorice Root, Milk Thistle Herb & Seed, Oregon Grape Root, Rhodiola Rosea, Saw Palmetto Berry, Schisandra Berry, St John's Wort Herb

WELEDA ✓ ⊘ ◉ ⚘ 85

Chamomilla 3x Drops, *Elixir:* Birch, Blackthorn, Cough, Sandthorn; *Homeopathic / Herbal Remedies:* request vegan version; *Massage Balms:* Arnica, Calendula; *Ointments:* Antimony prp, Copper; Ol Rhinale, Rhinodoron, WCS Dusting Powder

XYNERGY HEALTH PRODUCTS ✓ ⊘

Aloe 99 Gel, *Lifestream Biogenic Aloe Vera:* Gel, Mist

YIN YANG BEAUTY CARE ☺ ✓ ⊘

pH-Amino Protein Treatment Creams (for use during hormonal changes): All; Scalp Cream

YOAH ™☺❶ ✓ ⊘

Hemp Oil Salve

VITAMINS & MINERALS

BIO-HEALTH LTD ☺ ✓ ⊘

Buffered C Crystals, *V-caps:* B Complex (High Potency & Yeast-Free), Bio-Caps Multivitamin & Mineral, Bio-E, Extra Calcium, Extra Iron, Extra Magnesium, Extra Mineral Complex, Extra Selenium, Extra Zinc, Super Kelp & Vitamins, Vitamin C – 500mg (Buffered), Vitamin C – 500mg w Bioflavonoids

BIOCARE ✓ ⊘

Adult Multivitamins, B-Complex (Enzyme Activated), Folguard, Vitamin C

BLACKMORES ✓ ⊘

45 Plus, Active Woman Formula, B Plus C, Balanced B, Bio C 1000mg, Bio Iron, Buffered C, Executive B, Naturetime B Complex, Phytolife Plus, *Vitamins:* B1 100mg, B12 100mcg, B2 50mg, B3 250mg, C 500mg, E 500iu tablets

BRUNEL HEALTHCARE ✓ ⊘

Vertese Capsules: High Strength Natural Vitamin E, Mutivitamins w Evening Primrose Oil

FSC ✓ ⊘

Tablets: B Complex, B Supreme 50 + C, B Supreme Hi-Potency (Sustained Release), Biotin 2.5mg, Cal, Mag & Zinc, Dolomite 1000, Enada NADH 5mg, Folic Acid 400µg, L-Lysine 500mg, Magnesium & B6, Niacinamide

HEALTHCARE

500mg (Vit B3), Pantothenic Acid 500mg, Sea Kelp & Potassium, Super Cal/Mag, Super Multi-Minerals, Vitamin B6 (50mg, 100mg), Vitamin C 500mg (Low Acid), Vitamin C Complex 500mg, Zinc 4mg; *V-caps:* Chromium Picolinate 200µg, Family Daily Multi Vits & Mins, H Manganese 10mg, Healthy Heart Formula, Iron Complex 14mg, Magnesium 500, Quercetin 400mg, Selenomax Selenium 200µg, Vitamin B12 1000µg, Zinc Picolinate 30mg; Vitamin C Powder (Low Acid), Zinc Lozenges

GNC ⚜ ⊘

Tablets: Big 100, Biotin 300mcg, Boron Trivalent 3mg, Cal / Mag / Zinc, Calcium & Magnesium, Calcium Citrate Malate Plus, Chrom Pic 200mcg 90s, Copper & L-Glutamic Acid, Copper 2mg Chelated, Folic Acid 400mcg, GTF Chromium 200mcg, Magnesium 250mg, Manganese 10mg, Niacin 100mg, PABA 500mg, Rutin 500mg, Selenium 100mcg 1/100, Tr B Complex w C, Tr Ester C 500mg/1000m, Vit B1 300mg, Vit B12 500mcg, Vit B2 50mg, Vit C Ester 500mg/1000mg, Vit C One Gram, Zinc 10mg/30mg; *V-Caps:* Chrome PIC 200mcg, GNC Women's Iron Complex; Vit C Powder 225g

GR LANE ⚜ ⊘

Preconceive Folic Acid Tablets, Top C Chewable, Vegevit B12

HEALTH PLUS ™ ⚜ ⊘

Amino L-Arginine, Amino L-Glutamine, Amino L-Lysine, Amino L-Methionine, Amino L-Tyrosine, Calcium Ascorbate + Ascorbic Acid Powder 250g, Calcium Ascorbate Powder 250g, Chelated Iron, Chewable Vit C 500mg, Kelp 300mg, Liquid Essential E400, Magnesium L'Aspartate, Organic Selenium, Potassium 100mg, Saw Palmetto + Zinc, Selenium, Selenium 200µg, Zinc Citrate

HIGHER NATURE ⚜ ⊘

Powders: Calcium Ascorbate, High Potency Vitamin B12 200µg, Vitamin B12 20µg; *Tablets:* B Complex, B-vital, B6, Beta Carotene, Bio Minerals, Calcium & Magnesium, Chromium Polynicotinate, Co-enzyme Q10, Folic acid 400µg, Lysine-C, Magnesium, Ocean Kelp, Rosehips C 1000, Sea Calcium, Selenium, Selenium 200µg, Supernutrition Plus, Truefood C, Ultra C Plus, Vitamin E 200iu, Zinc; *V-caps:* Alpha, Easy Iron, Maxi CO-Q

KOBASHI ☺™ ⚜ ◉ ⊘

Vitamin E

KUDOS VITAMINS AND HERBALS LTD ⚜ ⊘

Antioxidant, Beta Carotene, Calcium & Magnesium & Zinc, Chelated Multimineral Formula, Chromium, Iron Amino Acid Chelate 30mg, Magnesium & Potassium, Prenatal, Vit B Complex, Vit B12 & folic acid, Vit B6 & Zinc, Vit C 500mg Complex, Vit C plus Bioflavonoids, Vit E 200iu/ 400iu, Zinc Citrate 20mg, Zinc gluconate 50mg

LIFEPLAN PRODUCTS LTD ™

Acetyl L Carnitine & Alpha Lipoic Acid, Boron Triple Source Trace Mineral, Buffered vitmin C w Rosehip, Acerola, & Citrus Bioflavonoids - 500mg, Calcium & Magnesium - 500mg Powdered Dolomite, Calcium & Magnesium - 800mg Powdered Dolomite, Chewable Vitamin C - 100mg, Chewable Vitamin C High Strength w Acerola & Bioflavonoids - 500mg, Enzyme Plus, Hair Care Nutrients, High Strength Vitamin B6 - 100mg, Multi Minerals, Sea Kelp w added Calcium - 400mg, Time Release B Complex Vitamins in a Herbal Base, Vitamin B12 - 25ug, Vitamin B6 - 50mg, Vitamin C & Zinc, Zinc - 10mg

NATURE'S AID LTD

200µG Elemental, B & C, Calcium, Chromium Picolinate, Folic Acid, Magnesium & Boron, Vit B Complex, Vit B6 50 + 100mg, *Vit C:* 200mg, 500mg, 500mg Sugar Free, Low Acid, Time Release; Zinc Gluconate, Zinc Picolinate

NATURE'S PLUS

Acerola-C Complex Chewable 250/500mg, Chewable E 400 Iu, Green Lightning Phyto-tein, Love Buffs Chewable C 250 mg, Lovites Chewable C 250/500mg, Milk-Free Chewable Calcium, *OJC Chewable:* 1000mg, 250mg, 500mg; Potent C Packets (Effervescent Powder), Shot-O-B12 5000 mcg V-Cap, Shot-O-B12

Lipoceutical Spray, *V-Caps:* Dry E Caps 400 IU, Super B-50, Vitamin C 500 mg; Vitamin B-12 1000 mcg Lozenges, Vitamin C Micro-Crystals

NDS HEALTHCARE

Essential Fatty Acids, Selenium 125mcg/200mcg, Vitamin C 200mg

NUTRITIONAL HEALTHCARE

Maxisulph Multivits & Mins, Selenium Maxi Plus ACE, Zinc

PHARMA NORD (UK) LTD

Bio-tablets: C-vitamin 750mg, Chromium 100mg, Magnesium 200mg, Pycnogenol 40mg

POWER HEALTH PRODUCTS

Calcium 400mg, Calcium Pantothenate (Vitamin B5) 500mg, *Ester C:* 250mg, 500mg; *Folic Acid:* 400µg, 400µg + B Complex; Hi Zinc (2mg elemental), Iron Amino Acid Chelate (14mg iron), MSM 1000mg, Multimineral & Zinc, Oral Zinc (3.5mg elemental) Lozenges, Potassium 200mg + Vitamin C 50mg, *Selenium:* 100µg & Zinc 2mg, Organic Gold Seal; Super Vitamin B Complex (100% RDA), *Tri:* Calc (100% RDA), Iron 14mg, Mag 300mg, Zinc 15mg; Vitamin B1 100mg, *Vitamin B12:* 500µg, 500µg (yeast-free), 50µg; *Vitamin B6:* 100mg, 200mg, 50mg; *Vitamin C:* 1000mg w Citrus Bioflavonoids, 250mg, Powder (Drink mix); *Vitamin C Fruiti:* Blackcurrant 120mg, Orange (w Sugar / Sugar-Free) 500mg; Xtra Zinc 15mg elemental

PRINCIPLE HEALTHCARE ™

Calcium 400mg/Vitamin D2 2.5 mcg Blackcurrent Tablets, Magnesium 150mg Tablets, Super B Complex Tablets, Synthetic Vitamin E 200iu VegaGels TM, Synthetic Vitamin E 400iu VegaGels TM, Vitamin B12 100 mcg Tablets, Vitamin C 500mg Chewable Tablets, Zinc 15mg tablets

QUEST VITAMINS ™ ◢ ⊘

Bio C Complex (Vitamin C & Bioflavinoids), Buffered C, Chewable Vitamin, Folic Acid with B vitamins, Mega B-100 Timed Release, Mega B-50, Multi B Complex, Multiminerals, Super Mega B + C, Super Once A Day Vegan (multi vitamin & minerals), Vitamin B12 500ug, Vitamin B6 50mg, Vitamin C 1000mg Timed Release, Vitamin C 500mg

REEVECREST HEALTHCARE ◢ ⊘

Ultra Zinc (15mg Elemental Zinc)

RHEMA UK LTD ❶ ◢ ⊘

Alpha Guard V-caps

SALUS ◢ ⊘

Calcium Liquid Mineral Supplement, Floravital Yeast & Gluten-Free Liquid Iron Formula

SEVEN SEAS ™ ◢ ⊘

Seven Seas One-a-day Multivitamins plus Minerals for Vegetarians & Vegans

SOLGAR VITAMINS LTD ◢ ⊘

Amino Acids: All; *Antioxidants:* All EXCEPT Pycnogenol 30mg; B1 500mg, *B12:* 1,000ug, 100ug; B6 50mg, *Calcium:* Chelated, Chewable Wafers, Magnesium; *Calcium Magnesium:* Boron, Chelated 1:1, Citrate, Zinc; *Chelated:* Copper, Manganese, Molybdenum, Solamins; Choline, Choline / Inositol, *Chromium:* Picolinate 100ug, Picolinate 500ug, Polynicotinate; Dry Vitamin A Tablets, *Fibre Products:* All; Folacin (Folic acid), Inositol, *Iron:* Chelated, Gentle; Kelp Tablets, *Magnesium:* Chelated, Chelated w Calcium 2:1, Citrate, w B6; Megasorb B12 Nuggets 5,000ug, Niacin, Niacinamide, No-Flush Niacin, Oceanic Silica, P-5-P, PABA, Pantothenic Acid, *Potassium:* Amino Acid Complex, Gluconate, Magnesium Aspartate; Selenium, *Vitamin B Complexes:* All; *Vitamin C:* All; *Vitamin E:* 165mg (200iu), 330mg (400iu), 495mg (600iu), 83mg (100iu), Liquid, w Selenium; Vitamin K 100ug Tablets, *Zinc:* 50mg, Chelated, Flavo-, Picolinate

SOLO NUTRITION LTD ◢ ⊘

Advanced Vitamin B Complex, ZincFifty

TREFRIW WELLS SPA ☺ ◢ ⊘

Spatone Iron +

VEGA NUTRITIONALS ™ ◢ ⊘

ZM3 Multivitamin & Minerals, Spectrum Adult (Multi Vitamin), Vitamin B1 100mg (Thiamine), Vitamin B2 100mg

(Riboflavin), Vitamin B6 Plus p-5-p 50mg, Vitamin B6 Plus p-5-p 100mg, Vitamin B12 1000mcg, Vitamin B3 No Flush (nicotinamide), Vitamin B5 200mg (Calcium Pantothenate), Vitamin B complex, Vitamin B & C complex, Vitamin C 500mg Plus Bioflavinoids, Gentle Vitamin C 1000mg (calcium ascorbate), Vitamin C 1000mg, Vitamin C 1500mg, 1625 Vitamin C 1000mg SR, Zinc C Formula, 17 Vitamin E 200iu 134mg Dry Plus Selenium Yeast Free, 1710 Natural Vitamin E 400iu 335mg Dry, Chelated calcium 500mg, Calcium Magnesium Zinc Plus Boron, Chromium Polynicotinate 200mcg Yeast Free, Zinc Citrate 50mg, Selenium 200mcg Yeast Free, Calcium Citrate, Magnesium Citrate, Iron Bisglycinate 50 mg Non Constipating, ZMM High Potency Multi Mineral Complex, Colloidal minerals w kelp, PMS b6, Epo, Zinc, Minerals & Herbs

VEGANSTORE.CO.UK ☺™❶ ⚐ ⊘

Calcium Citrate, Multi Vitamin plus Minerals, Vitamin B Complex

VIRIDIAN ⚐ ⊘

Amino Acid Powders: L-Arginine w L-Ornithine 2:1, L-Glutimine; *Calcium Magnesium Powder w:* Boron, Zinc; *V-caps:* Antioxidant formula, Balanced Iron Complex, Balanced Zinc Complex, Betatene, Co-enzyme Q10 w MCT, Complete Fibre Complex, Ester-C, GTF Chromium Complex, Folic acid w DHA, High Five B complex w Magnesium Ascorbate, High Five Multivitamin &

Mineral Formula, L-Carnitine, L-Lysine, Magnesium Citrate w B6, Natural Vitamin E, Potassium / Magnesium Citrate, Quercetin B5 complex, Trace Mineral Complex, Vitamin B5

WASSEN INTERNATIONAL LTD ⚐ ⊘

Coenzyme Q10 w: Magnesium, Vitamin E; Confiance, Estroven, Magnesium B

XYNERGY HEALTH PRODUCTS ⚐ ⊘

Pure Radiance C

NOTES

■ **alternatives** Herbalists, homoeopaths *(but see **homoeopathy**, right)*, acupuncturists etc; self-health books; and remedies available from health/wholefood shops and chemists, may provide an alternative to animal-tested synthetic drugs.

■ **beta-carotene and D2** (See **gelatine carrier** page 95).

■ **capsules** Most are still made of gelatine. Vegicaps are an increasingly popular animal-free alternative.

■ **contraceptives** May have been tested on animals or contain animal-derived ingredients.

■ **condoms** Usually made from latex — in which case casein (a milk protein) will have been used as a processing aid. Condomi (available from The Vegan Society) are an animal-free brand.

■ **oral** Lactose (milk sugar) and magnesium stearate (possibly animal-derived) are found in virtually every contraceptive pill. The only product free of animal ingredients (but not animal testing) is Femulen — a progestrogen-only pill made by PD Searle & Co (a branch of Monsanto).

■ **drugs** May or may not contain animal-derived ingredients but all will have been tested on animals at some stage of production.

■ **homoeopathy** Homoeopathic remedies are derived from plant, mineral or animal substances. Tablets usually contain lactose, and remedies may also include animal-derived minerals. *Common: Apis* — honey bee, *Cantharis* — Spanish fly, *Lachesis* — snake poison; *Uncommon: Ambra grasea* — secretion from the sperm whale, *Astacus fluviatilis* — crawfish, *Asterias rubens* — Red Starfish, *Badiaga* — freshwater sponge, *Blatta americana* — cockroach, *Blatta orientalis* — Indian cockroach, *Bufo* — poison of toad, *Castor equi* — rudimentary thumbnail of horse, *Castoreum* — beaver, *Cenchris-contortrix (Ancistrodon)* — Copperhead snake, *Chenopodi glauci aphis* — plant lice from *Chenopodium*, *Cimex-acanthia* — bed bug, *Coccinella septempunctata* — ladybird, *Crotalus horridus* — rattlesnake, *Doryphor* — Colorado potato bug, *Elaps corallinus* — Coral snake, *Fel tauri* — ox gall, *Formica rufa (Myrmexine)* — crushed live ants, *Hydrophobinum* — saliva of rabid dog, *Latrodectus mactans* — spider, *Medusa* — jelly fish, *Murex* — Purple fish, *Mygale lasiodora* — Black Cuba spider, *Naja tripudians* — cobra venom, *Oleum animale* — Dippel's animal oil, *Oleum jecoris aselli* — cod liver oil, *Oniscus asellus-millipedes* — wood louse, *Pulex irritans* — common flea, *Robinia* — Yellow Locust, *Sepia* — inky juice of cuttlefish, *Tarantula* *cubensis* — Cuban spider, *Tarantula hispania* — Spanish spider, *Theridion* — Orange spider, *Thyroidinum* — live wasp, *Vespa vulgaris* — live wasp, *Vipera* — German viper.

■ **prescriptions** The Department of Health's Medicines Control Agency (MCA) states it is lawful for a doctor to prescribe *any* medicinal product (whether or not it has marketing authorisation from the MCA) to a named patient. Theoretically this means that providing an animal-free product is available, a GP can prescribe it. If a GP is unwilling to ascertain the animal-free status of a product, the patient may have to undertake his/her own research. Chemists are useful sources of information and libraries may be able to help with manufacturers' addresses.

BABY, INFANT & CHILDCARE

FOOD & DRINK

BABYNAT ⊘

Apple, Apple & Banana, Apple & Blueberry, Apple & Prune, Apple & Quince, Broccoli & Carrot, Carrot & Pumpkin, Carrots, Cherry & Pear, French Beans, Fruit Cereals, Fruit Cocktail, Garden Veg, *Juices*: Apple & Orange, Cocktail Juice; Kiwi & Banana, Pasta Meal, Peach, Pear, Potato & Leek, Provencale Veg, Vanilla Cereal (4m+)

BICKIEPEGS LTD ☺⊘

Teething Biscuits for Babies

H J HEINZ ™⊘

Farley's Soya Infant Formula 450g, 900g, *From 1 Year:* Farley's Breadsticks, Vegetables & Rice In A Mild Sweet & Sour Sauce; *From 4 Months:* Banana Delight, Country Vegetables & Rice, Farmhouse Vegetable Special; *From 7 Months:* **Organic Vegetables & Lentils**; Farley's Pastini Hoops, Farley's Pastini Stars; *Organic From 4 Months:* **Apple, Apple & Apricot, Apple & Apricot Muesli, Apple & Blueberry, Apricot & Strawberry Breakfast, Banana Breakfast, Carrots & Sweetcorn, Carrots Parsnips & Peas, Country Cereals, Mixed Fruit, Pea & Parsnip, Peach & Pear, Pear &**

Banana, Pure Baby Rice, Simple Oaty Porridge; *Pure Fruit From 4 Months:* Apple & Apricot, Apple & Banana, Apple & Mango, Just Apple, Mixed Fruit, Summer Fruit; Purified Water w A Hint Of Strawberry, *Ready To Serve Juice From 4 Months:* Apple, Apple & Blackcurrant, Apple & Carrot, Apple & Cherry, Pear

ORGANIX BRANDS PLC ✿⊘

Desserts: **Apple & Apricot, Apple & Blackberry Pudding, Apple & Peach Pudding, Apple & Strawberry Pudding, Apple Strawberry & Blueberry Compote, Apples, Berries & Cherries, Banana & Blueberry, Banana & Mango Coulis, Banana & Passionfruit, Banana & Strawberry Rice Pudding, Banana, Apricot & Rice, Fruit Compote, Orchard Fruit Compote**; *Organic Fruit & Cereal Bars:* **Apple & Orange, Raspberry & Apple**; *Organic Mini Breadsticks:* **Olive Oil, Tomato & Basil**; *Savouries:* **Baby Rice First Food, Baby's First Vegetables, Quick Cook Pasta ABCs, Rice Cakes, Sweetcorn & Potato, Tender Sweetcorn Carrot & Pea, Vegetable & Coconut Korma**; *Stage 1 (From 4 Months) Cereals:* **Apple & Banana Muesli, Apple & Blackberry, Apple & Oatmeal, Apple & Pear, Apple & Raspberry, Apricot, Banana & Fig Muesli, Banana Porridge, Oat, Apple & Pear, Pear & Banana, Prune & Oatmeal, Prune & Oatmeal**

Porridge, Sunshine Fruits; *Stage 2 (From 7 Months) Cereals:* Apple & Banana Breakfast, Apple & Prune, Banana & Fig, Pear Apple & Oats; *Toddler Jars (From 12 Months):* Fruity Vegetable Korma, Sweetcorn & Potato

FOOTWEAR & CLOTHING

GREEN SHOES ✍ ⊘

The Childrens Collection: Bar Sandal, Bridge Sandal, Buckle Boot, Dart Shoe, Ivy Boot, Lace Up Boot, T-Bar Sandal

HEALTH CARE

AROMAKIDS ✍ ⊘

Mike Mozzie: Rub-Away Gel, Spray-Away; Toby Tumble Balm

BIO-HEALTH LTD ☺ ✍ ⊘

Junior Bio-Caps Multivitamin & Mineral

BIOCARE ✍ ⊘

Children's Multivitamins & Minerals

HIGHER NATURE ✍ ⊘

Dinochews Vitamins & Minerals

LITTLE MIRACLES / APHRODITE'S ROSE ✍ ⊘

Flower Essences: Braveheart, Chill Out, Exam Buster, Fair Play, Focus Pocus, Short Fuse, Soft Touch Gel, SOS, Spray

NATURE'S PLUS ⊘

Children's Chewable: Love Bites, Orange, Pineapple; OJC Chewable Jr. 100 mg, *Source of Life Animal Parade:* Assorted, Calcium, Cherry, Grape, Orange, Shake, Vit. C

NUTRITIONAL HEALTHCARE ✍ ⊘

Mighty Vita Kids Vitamins

POWER HEALTH PRODUCTS ✍ ⊘

Children's 60mg Chewable Vit C

RHEMA UK LTD ❶ ✍ ⊘

Hopi Ear Candles

TOM'S OF MAINE ✍ ⊘

Natural Children's Nasal Decongestant: Daytime Formula, Night-time Formula

VEGANSTORE.CO.UK ☺™❶ ✍ ⊘

Baby Bliss Nursery Vapour Oil

NAPPIES

BIO-D CO. LTD. ☺™✔️⊘👁✂-83

Nappy Fresh

NATURAL COLLECTION ✔️⊘

Nappy Fresh Nappy Sanitiser, Wide Range of Eco Disposable Nappies

READING

PLAMIL ☺™❶⊘

Vegan Infant Case Histories

TOILETRIES ETC

AMPHORA AROMATICS LTD ✔️⊘

Bubble Bath: Happy Hopper, Honey Bear's Treat, Goodnight Sleeptight; Goodnight Sleeptight Massage Oil

ARBONNE ☺❶✔️⊘

Baby Care: Body Lotion, Body Oil, Hair & Body Wash, Herbal Diaper Rash Ointment

AROMAKIDS ✔️⊘

Bunged Up Bertie's: Aromatic Gel, Humidifier Oil; *Ellie Smelie:* Baby Wipes, Barrier Cream; *Freddy Frog:*

Bubble Bath, Soap; *Joob-Joob's:* Body Lotion, Body Wash; *Massage Oils:* Betta-Bee, Crabby Chris, Freddy Frog, Noo-Noo's Newborn, Sleepytime Sam; Sleepytime Sam Bubble Bath

BABY NATURALS ✔️⊘

Cream, Bubble Bath, Lotion, Oil, Powder (Talc-free), Scalp Oil, Shampoo, Wipes

BEAUCAIRE ☺✔️⊘

Baby Cream, Baby Cleanser

BODY REFORM (UK) LTD ❶✔️⊘👁

Moisturising Baby Barrier Cream, *Baby:* Bath, Lotion, Powder, Shampoo

CAPITELLI OILS ™✔️⊘

Dolci Bambini Baby Moisturising Oil: 1-6 Months, 6+ Months

DR HADWEN TRUST ☺✔️⊘

Baby Soft Bubble Bath, Gentle Baby Lotion, Baby Cream

EARTH FRIENDLY BABY ✔️⊘

Lavender Cleansing Bar, Chamomile Shampoo & Bodywash

GREEN PEOPLE CO. ™✔️⊘

Organic Children: Conditioner, Mandarin Toothpaste, Bath & Shower Gel, Shampoo, Top to Toe Lotion, Shampoo, Spearmint & Aloe Vera Toothpaste; Baby Wash, Baby Lotion

JURLIQUE ✔ ⊘

Baby's Oils: Calming Bath, Calming Massage, Colic Relief Massage; Baby's Gentle Cleansing Balm

KISS MY FACE ✔

Kiss Kids: Grape Jelly Bubble Wash, Grape Jelly Moisture Soap, Natural Hold Up! Styling Gel, Grapefruit, Natural Knot! Detangler

MARTHA HILL ❶ ✔ ⊘

New Parent Revitaliser, New Mother Bath Soak, Baby Soap, *Pre-natal:* Anti Stretch Oil, Bath Soak; *Perfect Pregnancy Kit:* Bath Soak, Revitaliser, Unwinder; *New Parent Survival Kit:* New Mother Bath Soak, New Parent Revitaliser, Baby Bath & Baby Massage Oil

MEADOWSWEET ☺™✔ ⊚⊘

Baby Soft Bubble Bath, Baby Lotion, Baby Cream

MOLTON BROWN COSMETICS ✔ ⊘

Go Baby Go Traveller, Wash Baby Wash, Soft Baby Soft, Sleep Baby Sleep, Go Baby Go Gift Box – Mini

NAPIERS DISPENSARY ✔

Children's Oil Blend, *Skin Creams:* Calendula, Infant Starflower

NATRACARE ✔ ⊘

Baby: Shampoo, Bath, Lotion, Nappy /

Barrier Cream

NATURAL COLLECTION ✔ ⊘

Lavender Cleansing Bar, Baby Wipes

SHANTI HEALTH & BEAUTY PRODUCTS ☺❶✔ ⊘

Baby Massage Oil

TOM'S OF MAINE ✔ ⊘

Natural Honeysuckle Baby Shampoo, *Natural Fluoride Toothpaste for Children:* Outrageous Orange, Silly Strawberry; Natural Soap for Children

URTEKRAM ⊘✔

Children's Shampoo, Children's Soap

VEGANSTORE.CO.UK ☺™❶✔ ⊘

For Kids Only Extra Mild shampoo, *Baby Bliss:* Gentle Cleansing Bar, Gentle Foaming Bath Wash, Soft Touch Massage Oil, Soothing Lotion

WELEDA ✔ ⊘⊚⚕85

Children's Tooth Gel, *Calendula Baby Range:* Oil, Soap

NOTES

■ **infant formula** Farley's Soya Infant
Formula is the only known animal-free
complete infant formula

■ **vegan babies** The Vegan Society
produces a range of information on
raising vegan children – visit our
website or contact us for details. See
'Suggested Reading' (page 293) for
further resources.

FOOTWEAR & CLOTHING

BELTS, WALLETS, BAGS ETC

ANIMAL AID ☺❶✔⊘✄76

Black Belts: 'Silver' Buckle, Gold-Plated Buckle, Solid Brass Buckle; *'Old Gold' Buckle Belt:* Black, Brown

DR HADWEN TRUST ☺✔⊘

Belts: Black Gold-Plated Buckle, Black Silver Half Buckle, Black Solid Brass Buckle, Black Square Buckle, Brown Gold Buckle

FREERANGERS ☺™✔

Briefcase, Conker Rucksack, *Fleece:* Cushion Cover, Throw; Glasses Case, Key Rings, Petal Bag, Purse, Rowan Bag

HEMP SHOP LTD ❶✔⊘

Hemp: Holdall, Travel Wallets, Wall-Stores, Wallets, Watchbands

VEGAN SOCIETY

Black Wallet / Purse w Vegan Logo

veganline ☺❶

30mm macho belt & chrome buckle, Cleat belt, Hemp canvas wallets

VEGANSTORE.CO.UK ☺™❶✔⊘

Business Belts, Ladies Gloves, Men's Wallets, Wallet, Watch Strap

VEGETARIAN SHOES ☺❶

Belts: Jeans, Select, Solo, Suit, X belt; Record Bag, Shoe Laces, Wallet

VIVA! ☺❶✔⊘

Fabric Briefcase, Wallet

CLOTHING

ANIMAL AID ☺❶✔⊘✄76

2 in 1 t-shirt, *Baseball Shirt:* Long-Sleeve, Short-Sleeve; Choose Life T-shirt, Hooded Sweatshirt, Outdoor Fleece, Polar Fleece Beanie Hat, Round-Neck sleeveless T-shirt, Skinny-fit Strap Camisole, Skinny-fit v-neck T-shirt, Zip Neck Sweater, Zip-up Hooded Sweatshirt

DR HADWEN TRUST ☺✔⊘

Cat Nap Sleepshirt, Fleece Jacket w Poppy Design, Fleece Jacket w Sheep Design, Fleece Jumper w Sheep Design, Sleeveless Fleece w Cat Design, *T-shirts:* 4 Smiling Cats T-shirts, Cat Motif Black Top T-shirt, Dogs T-shirt

FREERANGERS ☺™✔

Fleece: Gilet, Hooded Gilet, Tees thermactiv, Trent Galebreak; *Fleece Hat & Scarf Set:* Roll Brim, Tassel

HEMP SHOP LTD ❶✔⊘

Classics Men's Shirts, Cotton & Hemp

Socks, Drawstring Trousers, Jeans, Jumpers, Ladies' Top & Skirts, Men's & Women's Organic Vests (100% hemp), Men's & Women's T-shirts, Slippers, Yoga Trousers

PEOPLE TREE ⊘

Organic Cotton: Hats, Skirts, T-shirts, Trousers, Underwear

ROGUE DEVELOPMENT ☺™✔⊘

T-Shirts

VEGAN SOCIETY

T-Shirts

veganline ☺❶

Hemp t-shirts, Leather-like jackets, Waterproof breathable socks

VEGANSTORE.CO.UK ☺™❶✔⊘

Chelsea Coat, *Jackets:* Camden, Harley, London, Soho; *No Bull Jackets:* Camden, Harley, London, Soho; Surf Vegan Shirt, *T-Shirts:* Bit of a Vegetable, Compassion to All Beings, Love Animals, Tofu Totty, Vegan Definition, Wear Your Own Skin

VEGETARIAN SHOES ☺❶

Black gloves: Gents, Ladies; Cow T-shirt, *Jackets:* Angel, Biker-style, Box, Cutie, Dean, Ladies Reefer, Phoenix, Skipper, Tina; *Jeans:* Black, Fake leather

VIVA! ☺❶✔⊘

T-shirts & Sweatshirts: All

FOOTWEAR — GENERAL

ANIMAL AID ☺❶✔⊘⚡76

Ethical Wares Boots: Chandler, Hartland, Holly, Laced Ankle, Ranger, Scandinavian, Tibet, Trekking, Tyneham; *Ethical Wares Shoes:* Court, Ebony Sandal, Shaka Sandal, Skate, Tie, Trainer

DR HADWEN TRUST ☺✔⊘

Sandals: Amethyst, Ebony; *Shoes:* 'Suede' Gibson, Megan, Monk, Oxford

ETHICAL WARES ☺™✔

Amethyst Wedge, *Boots:* Buckle, Chukka, Dealer, Desert, Holly, Jupiter, Laced Ankle, Safety, Susie, Traeth, Zip Suedette; Chandler, Creeper, Derby, Gibson, Hartland, Monk, *Mules:* Onyx, Sapphire, Spider; Oxford, Ranger, *Sandals:* Amethyst, Arizona, Closed-Toe, Ebony, Explorer, Hiker, Milano, White Water; Scandinavian, Semi-Brogue, *Shoes:* Bobby, Court, Jasper, Jungle, Katie, Megan, Sam, Slate, Sling Back, T-Bar, Tie; *Slippers:* Dolphin, Dragon, Womble, Yeti; Studland, 'Suede' court, 'Suede' Gibson, 'Suede' Monk, Tibet, Trekking, Tyneham, Weald

FREERANGERS ☺™✔

Ladies' Footware: Alder Shoe, Beech Shoe, Birch Shoe, Chicory Mule, Coral

Shoe, Daisy Shoe, Fennel Mule, Fern Shoe, Heather Clog, Jess Boot, Laurel Shoe, Sage Sandal, Spruce Sandal, Willow Mule; *Men's Footware:* Cedar Shoe, Drifter Shoe, Dune Shoe, Elm Sandal, Heather Clog, Maple Shoe, Oak Sandal, Pine Shoe, Ross Boot

GREEN SHOES ✔ ⊘

The Boot Collection: Belstone, Buckle, Dartmoor, Field, Pie Crust, Polly; *The Sandal Collection:* 2 Piece Toggle, Bridge, Clasp, Denbury, Eclipse Mule, Hope, Mule; *The Shoe Collection:* Bar Sandal, Dartmoor Shoe, Eclipse Lace, Eclipse Strap

IMPACT RTR ✔

All PVC Safety Boot

MADE TO LAST WORKERS CO-OPERATIVE ❶ ✔ ⊘

All made-to-measure styles can be made vegan

NATURAL SHOE STORE

Birkenstock Vegan Sandals: Arizona, Boston Clog, Milano; City Collection Woven Fabric Espadrille, *Comfort:* Slipper Style Shoe, Supportive; *Komodo:* Hemp Boot , Thong Sandals w Grass Footbed & Tyre Sole; *Vegetarian Shoes:* 502, Hemp Skate Shoe, Ladies Loather, Mary Jane, Office Style 4 hole laceup

PEOPLE TREE ⊘

Sandals

ROGUE DEVELOPMENT ☺™✔⊘

Double Six, Gimp Boots, Rogue Six

veganline ☺❶

Equity Sandal, Garmont Hikers w Waterproof Breathable Socks, Hiking Boots w Waterproof Breathable Socks, *Safety:* Boots, Shoes, Trainer Look-alikes; T-bar Women's Sandals, Traditional Uni-Sex Shoes & Boots, Trainers w Skate-Style Soles, *Women's Loafers:* 'Snakeskin', Plain; Women's Mules

VEGANSTORE.CO.UK ☺™❶✔⊘

Bella Loafer, *Boot:* Diva, Savage, Starlet, Wanderlust, Zip Up; Comfort Sandal, *No Bull Footware:* 9 to 5 Loafer, BFB Shoe, Comfort Sandal, Diva Boot, Double Soul Shoe, Executive Shoe, Heeled Loafer, Men's Brogue, Metro Shoe, Oxford Shoe, Urban Legend Shoe, Zip Up Boot; Ola Clog, *Shoes:* Brogue, Deck, Executive, Holden, Metro, Oxford, T Strap, Wanderlust; *Steel Toe Caps:* BFB, Urban Legend

VEGETARIAN SHOES ☺❶

Airseal Boots: 14-eye w Steel Toe, 20-eye w Steel Toe, Boulder, Chelsea, Engineers w Steel Toe, Para w steel toe, Range, Redstone; *Airseal Shoes:* 3-eyelet, Bump w steel toe, Padded Collar, T-Bar Sandal; *Birkenstock Sandals:* Arizona, Boston clog-style, Milano; *Boots:* Combat, Cyber Biker, Derby, Desert, Jodhpur, Logga, Site Boot w steel toe; *Dr Martens:* Boots, Coppa Shoe, Hiker Boot, Shoe;

Everyday Shoes: Canyon Sandal, Chunky Gibson, Chunky Monk, Creeper, Hemp Skate, Kalahari, Mariner, Street Sneaker, Wombat; *Men's Boots:* Alex, Mikey; *Men's Shoes:* Brogu, Broker, Casino, City, Dylan Slip-on, Johnny Loafer, Montana, Office, Oxford, Square-toe Loafer; *Women's Boots:* Emma, Hi, Jenny, Jo, Metro; *Women's Sandals:* Comfort, Daisy, Lucy; *Women's Shoes:* Black Pump, Judy, Kelly, Marrakesh Mule, Simple Loafer, Stephanie, Tab

WATERPROOFERS, POLISHES & CLEANERS

VEGETARIAN SHOES ☺❶

Black Animal-Friendly Polish, Clear Animal-Friendly Dubbin, Insoles

FOOTWEAR — SPORTS

DR HADWEN TRUST ☺✔️⊘

Boots: Dealer, Desert, Ranger, Trekking, Tyneham

ETHICAL WARES ☺™✔️

New Balance: Style 587, Style 587 – Mens Tregaron, Style 763 - Ladies

NATURAL SHOE STORE

Komodo: Hempies, Shell Toed Trainers

VEGETARIAN SHOES ☺❶

Cheetah Trainers: Navy / Reflective, Red / Reflective, White / Green, White / Navy; *Walking Boots:* Approach Shoe, Nevis Boot, Trail Boot, Veggie Trekker

NOTES

■ **footwear** Quality animal-free footwear is generally available only by mail order from specialist companies. Cheap non-leather styles are stocked by many high street retailers. It has become common practice to use synthetic adhesives, but it is difficult to obtain guarantees.

■ **motorcyclist clothing** For details of gloves, boots and suits contact the Vegan Bikers Association (see **USEFUL ADDRESSES,** page 288).

■ **running and training shoes** Models change frequently and are invariably manufactured in the Far East. Many sports footwear companies stock models made entirely of non-animal materials but commonly are unable to guarantee, or are unwilling to ascertain, that the adhesives used are non-animal. Be wary of the term 'synthetic leather'; it may well describe a non-leather material but it *may* also indicate leather that has been treated differently to 'normal' leather! 'Nubuck' is leather; 'Durabuck' is non-leather, animal-free and tends to be more expensive.

■ **textiles** Under The Textile Products (Indications of Fibre Content) Regulations 1986, the term 'textile fibres' may include wool from sheep or lamb; wool or hair from alpaca, llama, camel, cashmere goat, angora goat, angora rabbit, vicuna, yak, guaco, beaver or otter; horse, goat or other animal hair — with or without an indication of the kind of animal; silk from the silkworm; protein obtained from natural protein substances regenerated and stabilised through the action of chemical agents.

visit

WWW.VEGANSOCIETY.COM/SHOP

Or phone 0845 45 88244 now for your free copy of The Vegan Society catalogue.

Browse through pages of great vegan products including a comprehensive range of animal-free cookbooks, nutrition guides and the complete selection of Vegan Society publications and leaflets

Includes:

Travel ■ Music ■ Chocolate ■ Footwear ■ Clothing Soaps, candles, socks, and many, many more

All a vegan could wish for…

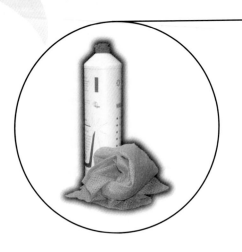

HOME
& OFFICE

AIR FRESHENERS

AMPHORA AROMATICS LTD ✔ ⊘

Incense Sticks: Cedarwood, Frankincense, Gardenia, Honeysuckle, Jasmin, Lavender, Lemon, Neroli, Patchouli, Rose, Sandalwood, Ylang Ylang

ASCENT ☺ ✔ ⊘

Lingerie Sachets of Herbs & Flowers w Natural Perfume

BODY REFORM (UK) LTD ❶ ✔ ⊘ ☞

Room Fragrance Mood Sprays: Relaxation, Romance, Vitality

EARTH FRIENDLY PRODUCTS ☺ ✔ ⊘

Aromatherapy Air Fresheners: Cinnamon, Citrus, Lavender; Food Freshener for the Fridge

KISS MY FACE ✔

Airea Room Sprays: Anti-Stress, Lavender, Meadow, Sanctuary

MOLTON BROWN COSMETICS ✔ ⊘

Air Of: Calm, Joy, Sleep

NATURAL COLLECTION, THE ✔ ⊘

Orange & Lime Air Therapy

PERFUMERS GUILD LTD, THE ☺ ❶ ✔ ☞ ⊘

Incense Cones

PURPLE FLAME AROMATHERAPY ✔ ⊘

Pure Resin Pearls: Benzoin, Frankincense, Myrrh

QUINESSENCE AROMATHERAPY ☺ ❶ ✔ ⊘ ☞

Mood enhancers: Arabian Nights, Autumn Meadows, Celestial Dream, Elemental Forest, Fantasia, Forbidden Fruit, Illuminessence, Moonflower, Purple Valley, Secret Garden, Tranquilla, Wild Passion

ROBERT MCBRIDE LTD ✔

English Garden Aerosol Air Freshener: Jasmin, Lavender, Lemon, Peach, Rose, Wild Fruits; Q Wet Aerosol Airfreshener, *Springfresh Aerosol Spray Air Freshener:* Anti Tobacco, Azure Breeze, Blue Lagoon, Cool Lagoon, Forest Fruits, Lemon Zest, Peach Orchard, Tropical Burst, Wild Orient; Springfresh Bin Fresh

SHANTI HEALTH & BEAUTY PRODUCTS ☺ ❶ ✔ ⊘

Incense Oil, Incense Sticks, Natural Perfumed Spray

TREE-HARVEST ✔ ⊘

Hand-blended Incense: Moon, Sun, The Planets; *Rare Gums & Resins:* All

BLEACHES

ECOVER ™✔⊘

Bleach

NATURAL COLLECTION, THE ✔⊘

Laundry Bleach

CANDLES

AMPHORA AROMATICS LTD ✔⊘

Essential Oil Candles

HEMP UNION ™✔⊘

Hemp Oil Candles

KISS MY FACE ✔

Airea Soy Wax Candle: Anti-Stress, Lavender, Meadow, Sanctuary

MOLTON BROWN COSMETICS ✔⊘

Air Candles: Relaxing, Sensual; *Air Lights:* Heavenly Gingerlily, Perfume River, White Mulberry

NEAL'S YARD REMEDIES ✔⊘

Citronella Candle in a Jar, Night Lights, Orange Spice Candle, White China Burners

PERFUMERS GUILD LTD ☺❶✔👁⊘

Scented Candles: Christmas, Frankincense & Myrrh, Gardenia & Tuberose, Hyacinth & Bluebell, Lavender & Amber, Rose & Geranium, Scent of India, Winter Amber

PURPLE FLAME AROMATHERAPY ✔⊘

Aromatherapy Candles: All

SHEARER CANDLES ✔⊘

Candles: All

TREE-HARVEST ✔⊘

Pure Plant Wax Candles: Aromatherapy, Dinner Candles, Floating

VEGANSTORE.CO.UK ☺™❶✔⊘

Candles in Presentation Tins, Dinner Candles in Presentation Boxes, Nature's Candles, Pillar Candles

CARPET PRODUCTS

BETTERWARE ✔✂2000

Carpet & Upholstery Shampoo

ELCO ☺❶✔⊘

Carpet Shampoo

CLEANERS — GENERAL

AURO ORGANIC PAINTS ⊘

Plant Soap Concentrate (411)

BETTERWARE ✔ ⚡ 2000

Computer & Telephone Wipes, Demist Wipes, Descaler Bags, Foaming Car Interior Cleaner, Fridge & Freezer Defroster, Fungus & Mildew Control, Kitchen Surface Wipes, Marvel Household Cleaning Paste, Miracle Metal Cream, Multi-Use Descaler, Net & Lace Curtain Whitener, Oil Patch Remover, Pet Accident Sanitary Cleaner, PVC Frame & Furniture Cleaner, Sink Outlet Slime Remover, Smear-Free Window Foam, Stain Wipes, Sticky Stuff Remover, Super Stain Remover, Surface Limescale Remover, Tile Grout Whitener

BIO-D CO. LTD. ☺™✔ ⊘ ⚡ 1983👁

Glass & Mirror Cleaner, Multi-Surface Cleaner

CELLANDE MIDLANDS ☺✔ ⊘

Glass & Plastic cleaner for computers, spectacles, etc

DRI-PAK LTD ☺❶✔ ⊘

Aqua Softna: Washing Machine Descaler, Water Softener Powder & tablets, Water Treatment; Liquid Soda Multipurpose Cleaner

EARTH FRIENDLY PRODUCTS ☺✔ ⊘

Complete Home Detox Kit, Cream Cleaner, Earth Enzymes Drain Cleaner, Fruit & Vegetable Wash, *Orange Plus:* Complete, Concentrate, Ready to Use; Parsley Kleener, Shower Kleener, Stain & Odour Remover, Window Kleener

ECOLINO™

All-purpose Cleaner

ECOVER ™✔ ⊘

Cream Cleaner, Heavy Duty Cleaner, Multi-Surface Cleaner, Natural Citrus Cleaner & Degreaser, Water Softener

FOOD SAFE LTD ☺❶✔ ⊘

Salad Safe, Veggi Wash, Veggi Wipe

GREEN PEOPLE Co.™✔ ⊘

Micro-fibre Cleaning Cloth, Multi-purpose Cleaner (Concentrated), Organic Aroma Clean

HERBS HANDS HEALING ✔ ⊘

Home & Kitchen Cleaner

HOMECARE PRODUCTS ☺✔ ⊘

Bar Keepers' Friend - Powerful Powder, Bath Brite - Bath & Sink Descaler, Copper Glo - Powder Copper Cleaner, Four Hob Hotplate Polish, Hob Brite - Ceramic Hob, Homecare Stainless Steel, Shiny Sinks - Cream

JURLIQUE ✔ ⊘

Sparkle All Purpose Cleaner

LIBERON WAXES LTD ✔

Brass & Copper Cleaner, Cold Patination Pre-Treatment, Fullers Earth Cleaning Powder, Ring Remover

NATURAL COLLECTION 🦊 ⊘

Brass, General Glass / Mirror, Hemp, Household Paste, Multi-surface, Orange Degreaser, Powerful Bathroom, Silver

OSMO ❶ 🦊 ⊘

Gard Clean Green Growth Remover, Liquid Wax Cleaner

ROBERT McBRIDE LTD 🦊

Brio All-Purpose Cleaner: Lemon, Pine; *Brio Antibacterial Trigger Spray, Brio Cream Cleaner:* Lemon, w Bleach; *Brio Kitchen plus Bleach:* Gel, Trigger Cleaner

URTEKRAM ⊘ 🦊

Uniclean Multi Cleaner

VEGANSTORE.CO.UK ☺™❶🦊 ⊘

Fruit & Vegetable Wash, Orange Plus, Shower Cleaner, Window Cleaner

VINDOTCO UK LTD ☺🦊 ⊘

Dirt & Stain Remover

DISHWASHER PRODUCTS

EARTH FRIENDLY PRODUCTS ☺🦊 ⊘

Rinse Aid, *Wave Dishwasher:* Liquid, Powder

ECOLINO ™

Dishwashing Powder, Rinse Aid

ECOVER ™ 🦊 ⊘

Dishwasher Tablets, Rinse Aid

NATURAL COLLECTION, THE 🦊 ⊘

Liquid, Rinse-aid, Tablets

OPAL ☺❶🦊 ⊘

Automatic Dishwasher Detergents: Liquid, Powder, Tablet; Dishwasher Cleaner, Granular Salt, Rinse Aid

URTEKRAM ⊘ 🦊

Shine Dishwasher: Lemon Tablets, Original Tablets, Powder, Rinse Aid, Green Clean Dishwashing

VEGANSTORE.CO.UK ☺™❶🦊 ⊘

Wave Dishwasher Gel

FLOOR PRODUCTS

AURO ORGANIC PAINTS ⊘

Floor Cleaner (427), Floorcare (427)

BETTERWARE 🦊 ⋏2000

Laminate & Wood Floor Cleaner

ECOVER ™ 🦊 ⊘

Floor Soap

LIBERON WAXES LTD ⚡

Floor: Cleaner, Protector, Sealer, Wax;
Floor oil: Maintenance, Natural; *Floor
Varnish:* Natural Finish, Traditional;
Laminate Floor: Cleaner, Sealer; *Stone
Floor:* Cleaner, Sealer, Shine

OSMO ❶⚡⊘

Wash & Care Floor Cleaner

ROBERT MCBRIDE LTD ⚡

Springfresh Summer Blossom Carpet
Freshener Powder

FURNITURE & OTHER POLISHES

BETTERWARE ⚡⚘2000

Wood Furniture & Decking Cleaner

BIO-D CO. LTD.☺™⚡⊘⚘1983◉

General Purpose Polish

EARTH FRIENDLY PRODUCTS ☺⚡⊘

Furniture Polish

LIBERON WAXES LTD ⚡

Polish: Brass & Copper, Silver; *Polishing
Mitts & Cloth:* Brass, Silver

NATURAL COLLECTION, THE ⚡⊘

Furniture Polish, General-Purpose Polish

GLUES, STICKY TAPE, ETC

LIBERON WAXES LTD ⚡

Super Wood Glue

UHU (UK) LTD ☺⚡

All-Purpose: Glue, Solvent-Free;
Contact: Gel, Liquid; *Cover-Up:* Fluid,
Pen, Tape; *Fix & Glaze:* Gloss, Matt; Fix
Pads, *Glue Gun:* Cool Melt, Hot, Stics;
Glue Spray: All Purpose, Power; *Glues:*
Glitter, Kid, Pen, Plastic, Powder, Super,
Super Gel, Twist & Glue, Twist & Glue
Solvent-Free, White, Wood; *Super Glue
Odour-Free:* Gel, Liquid; Tape, *UHU Stic:*
Magic, Power, White; White Tack

PAINT BRUSHES — DIY

LG HARRIS ⚡⊘

Diamond, Fine Finish, Mastercoat, No
Loss, Platignum, Sure Glide, White
Diamond

LIBERON WAXES LTD ⚡

Foam Applicators

OSMO ❶⚡⊘

Quality Brushes & Polishing Pad

PAINT, VARNISHES, WOODSTAINS, ETC

AURO ORGANIC PAINTS ⊘

Borax Wood Preservative - Clear & Odourless (111), Chalk Paint – White – Internal Use Only (325), Colour Concentrates – Deep Shades (330), *Coloured Emulsions – Price Code A, B, C & E:* (321), (322); Matt Emulsion – White – Internal Use Only (321), Multi-Filler – Internal Use Only (329), *Primers:* Clear, Hard (127), Metal Primer & Undercoat – Solvent Based (234), Solvent-Free Oil (122), Special (117), Wood (124); Semi Matt Emulsion – White – Internal Use Only (322), Stain Topcoat (160), Thinner & Brush Cleaner (191), Wallpaper Adhesive (389), *Water Miscible Clear Lacquer:* Gloss (251), Matt (261); White Radiator Paint – Matt Finish – Water Miscible (257), White Topcoat – Eggshell - Water Miscible – Matt Silk Finish (260), White Topcoat – Gloss - Water Miscible (250), White Undercoat – Water Miscible (253), Wood Filler – Internal & External Use (231)

ECOS PAINTS ✔ ⊘

Ecos Garden Spectrum Shed & Fence Treatment: All; *Exterior Woodstains:* All; *Interior Woodstain Varnishes:* All; *Odourless Solvent-Free Organic Paints:* All

ECOTEC ✔

Natural: Pigments, Tinters; *Paint:* Black/Red External Timber, Eggshell, Emulsions, External & Internal Gloss, Silicate Masonry; Primers, Textured Wall Finish, Undercoat, *Wax:* Antique, Preserving, WBC

GREEN PAINTS ☺✔

Gloss & Semi-Gloss Enamels: All; *Matt & Satin Emulsion:* All; *Primers & Undercoats:* All

HOMESTRIP ✔

Paint & Varnish Remover

LA TIENDA ✔

Earth & Mineral Pigments: All

LIBERON WAXES LTD ✔

3-Part Touch up pens: all; *Antique Varnish:* All; Burnishing Cream, *Concentrate Spirit Dyes:* All; *Concentrated Water Based Dyes:* All; *Designer Metallic Varnish:* All; *Earth Pigments:* All; *Exterior Oils:* Decking, Garden Furniture; *Fine Paste Wax (Black Bison):* All; Fine Wood Stripper, Finishing, French Polish Reviver, *Grain Filler:* All; Haematite, *Hardwearing Varnish:* All; Honing Oil, *Interior Oils:* Boiled Linseed, Pure Tung, Raw Linseed, Teak; Iron Paste, Jade Oil, Knotting, Liquid Paraffin, *Liquid Wax (Black Bison):* All; Lubricating Wax, *Natural Finish Varnish:* All; *Palette Wood Dyes:* All; Pumice Powder, Rottenstone,

Sanding Sealer, *Spirit Wood Dyes:* All; *Tint & Wax:* All; Total Treatment for Wood, *Touch Up Pens:* All; Van Dyck Crystals, Wax & Polish Remover, Wood Bleacher, *Wood Filler:* All; *Wood Stopping:* All

NATURAL COLLECTION, THE ✔ ⊘

All Weather Wood Protector: Dark Brown, Light Teak; Solvent Free Paint Stripper

OSMO ❶ ✔ ⊘

Brush Cleaner & Thinner, *Exterior Country Colour:* All; *Exterior One Coat Only:* All; *For Exterior Woods:* Clear Oil Wood Finish, Fence & Garden Stain, Wood Oils, Wood Stain & Preservation, WR Base Coat; *Interior Hardwax Oil:* Special Floor Finish, White Foundation; *Interior Wood Wax Finish:* Clear Extra Thin, Opaque, Transparent; *Opaque Gloss Exterior Wood Stain:* All; Paint-Remover, Wood Filler, Wood Protector, Wood Reviver

TOILET PRODUCTS

BETTERWARE ✔ ⚹2000

Foaming Bathroom Cleaner, Foaming Toilet Cleaner, Toilet Clens, Toilet Clens Wipes

BIO-D CO. LTD.☺™✔ ⊘⚹1983◉

Toilet Cleaner

EARTH FRIENDLY PRODUCTS ☺✔ ⊘

Toilet Bowl Cleaner

ECOLINO ™

Toilet Cleaner

ECOVER ™ ✔ ⊘

Toilet Cleaner

HERBS HANDS HEALING ✔ ⊘

Bathroom Deep Cleaner

NATURAL COLLECTION, THE ✔ ⊘

Toilet Cleaner

ROBERT MCBRIDE LTD ✔

Brio Bathroom: Gel-Bottle, Trigger Cleaner; *Toilet Mousse:* Aqua, Citrus, Pine

URTEKRAM ⊘✔

Green Clean Toilet Cleaner

VEGANSTORE.CO.UK ☺™ ❶✔ ⊘

Toilet Bowl Cleaner

WASHING POWDERS, STARCH, ETC

BIO-D CO. LTD.☺™✔ ⊘⚹1983◉

Fabric Conditioner, Laundry Liquid, Washing Powder

DRI-PAK LTD ☺❶✉☒

Soap Flakes, Soda Crystals

EARTH FRIENDLY PRODUCTS ☺✉☒

ECOS Laundry: Liquid, Powder

ECOLINO ™

Auto-Laundry Liquid, Fabric Softener, Washing Powder, Wool-Wash

ECOVER ™ ✉☒

Automatic Washing Liquid, Concentrated Washing Powder, Fabric Conditioner, Washing Tablets, Wool Wash

ELCO ☺❶✉☒

Laundry Powder, Soda Crystals - Sodium Carbonate Decahydrate

NATURAL COLLECTION, THE ✉☒

Concentrated Fabric Conditioner, Concentrated Laundry Liquid, Washing Powder

RETONE PRODUCTS ☺✉☒

Wonderwash Laundry Ball

ROBERT MCBRIDE LTD ✉

Brio Laundry Powder: Biological, Colour, Non-Biological; Brio Laundry Sachets (Actipods), Clean n Fresh Biological Laundry Powder, Neon Biological Laundry Powder, *Q-matic Laundry Powder:* Biological, Non-Biological; *Starch Aerosol Spray:* Nichol,

Proven, Rapid; *Surcare Non-Biological:* Laundry Powder, Laundry Tablets, Liquid wash

URTEKRAM ☒

Green Clean Washing Powder

VEGANSTORE.CO.UK ☺™❶✉☒

Ecos Laundry Detergent Liquid w built in Soy Fabric Conditioner

WASHING-UP PRODUCTS

BIO-D CO. LTD. ☺™✉☒♻1983👁

Washing Up Liquid

EARTH FRIENDLY PRODUCTS ☺✉☒

Dishmate Natural almond Washing-Up Liquid

ECOLINO ™

Washing-Up

ECOVER ™ ✉☒

Washing-Up Liquid Lemon Scent w Aloe Vera

NATURAL COLLECTION, THE ✉☒

Concentrated Washing-Up Liquid, Washing-Up Liquid

POLYCO LTD ✔ ⊘

Superglove Skincare Velvet (PVC Household Gloves)

ROBERT MCBRIDE LTD ✔

Brio Washing Up Liquid: Green, Lemon, Peach; Surcare Washing Up Liquid

VEGANSTORE.CO.UK ☺™ ❶ ✔ ⊘

Dishmate

NOTES

■ **adhesives** May be processed from hide, bones, fish or dairy products — eg casein. Non-animal adhesives are based on starch, cellulose, natural rubbers, or inorganic substances based on silicone. The trend is towards using cheaper, synthetic materials.

■ **Artex** Ready-To-Mix is free from animal ingredients. The powder mixes contain gelatine and the main product — Artex Textured Finish — contains an animal-based glue.

■ **bank notes** Are produced without the use of gelatine.

■ **beds, mattresses, pillows** Modern beds and mattresses generally contain synthetic materials — such as acrylic, viscose, polyester, polypropylene, nylon or acetate. However, wool may be used in some mattresses. Feather or down may still be used in pillows and continental quilts.

■ **ceramics, glass, pottery** Bone china goods contain around 50% bone. Porcelain, *plain* sanitary items (toilets, cisterns, sinks, etc) and *plain* urbanware glazed mugs (the glazes used are inorganic pigments made from minerals) appear to be animal-free. However, if a motif is added, it may be fixed with animal-derived glues. Glass consists of silica (in the form of sand), sodium oxide, calcium oxide, magnesium oxide and aluminium oxide, and appears to be animal-free.

■ **envelopes** Members of the Envelope Makers & Manufacturing Stationers' Association agree that the adhesives used in making envelopes, and the adhesives on gummed envelopes are animal-free. However, some of the adhesives used on self-seal envelopes contain casein.

■ **fabric dyes** (home use) Usually synthetic, from chemicals, and tested on animals (under current regulations new chemicals must be animal tested). "Natural" dyes are more likely to contain animal substances.

■ **floor covering** The British Resilient Flooring Manufacturers' Association say that many resilient floor covering manufacturers use stearates (principally animal-derived) as stabilisers for PVC and stearic acid (principally animal-derived) as a lubricant during certain production processes.

■ **furniture** May contain synthetic/plant fibres (eg nylon, acrylic, polyester, cotton) or animal-derived materials, including leather, suede, wool felt, animal hair (especially horse) and feathers. Adhesives are commonly PVA (poly-vinyl acetate).

■ **incense sticks** May contain gelatine or other animal substance as a binder.

■ **matches** The heads contain gelatine, which is used as a binder.

■ **paint** May contain casein and/or shellac.

■ **paper** Most papers are sized (enhances the resistance of paper to liquid penetration and provides surface strength, stiffness and a glaze to the finished sheet) with starch derived from maize, wheat, potatoes or rice, but gelatine is still used for high-grade paper products. Casein is sometimes used as a binder in high quality food board and art papers. Some very specialist grades may contain chitin/chitosan.

■ **postage stamps** The gum on British stamps is animal-free, consisting of polyvinyl alcohol (petroleum based) and dextrin (from starch).

■ **rubber** Natural rubber is made from latex (sap obtained from rubber trees) combined with other materials, including the following which could be animal-derived: carbon black (E153), glycerol (E422), salts of fatty acids (E470), stearic acid (E570), calcium stearate (E572). Synthetic rubbers are made from oil and a combination of chemicals.

■ **rubber gloves** may involve the use of milk casein as a processing aid in the latex.

■ **water filters** The charcoal is normally vegetable-based.

ANIMAL CARE

FOOD & FOOD SUPPLEMENTS

DENE'S NATURAL PET CARE LTD ✔ ⊘

Baked Biscuits: Fresh Breath, Low Calorie, Wholegrain; Wholegrain Mixer

GREEN ARK ANIMAL NUTRITION ☺❶✔ ⊘

Organic Dog Cereal Mix

GROOMERS LTD ✔ ⊘

Evening Primrose Oil, Pure Garlic Oil

HAPPIDOG PETFOOD

Dry Vegetarian Dog Food Mix, Vegan Crunchy Nuggets

MISSING LINK ✔ ⊘

Missing Link: Equine (for horses), Vegetarian Formula (for dogs & cats)

VEGAN SOCIETY ™☺❶✔ ⊘

Vegecat pH, Vegecat, Vegekit

VEGEPET ☺❶✔ ⊘

Vegecat, Vegecat Kibble Mix, Vegedog, Vegekit

VIVA! ☺❶✔ ⊘

Dog Chew Bones

YARRAH ❶✔ ⊘

Chewing Bones, Duo Snacks Vegetarian, *Multi Dog Biscuits:* Natural, Seaweed & Yeast; Vegetarian Dog Biscuits, Vegie Ears

HEALTH & CARE PRODUCTS

BAC TO NATURE ✔ ⊘

Allergen Control, Canine Skin Care, Flea Spray, Litter Fresh, Pet Bed Freshener, Pet Coat Stain Remover, Pet Freshener

CAT COUNTRY (CC UK) ☺✔ ⊘

Cat Country Cat Litter

GREEN ARK ANIMAL NUTRITION ☺❶✔ ⊘

Green Food supplement, Herbal Tonic, Herbie Wellbeing, *Powders:* Pure Garlic, Pure Seaweed, Raspberry Leaf; Rhino, Slippery Elm Gruel

GROOMERS LTD ✔ ⊘

Evening Primrose Oil Coat Spray, Groom & Detangle Spray, Ridx Flea Spray, *Shampoos:* Aloe Jojoba, Banana & Mango, Evening Primrose Oil, Medicated w Tea Tree Oil, Pina Colada w Coconut oils, Puppy, Ridasect Flea, Seaweed & Cucumber, Tangerine & Grapefruit

HUMANE RESEARCH TRUST ☺❶✔ ⊘ ⅄—(see note)

Assisi Homeopathic Remedies for Pets: Five Flower Remedy, Sore Paws Ointment; *Natural Drops:* Ear, Eye; *Natural Grooming Lotions:* Cats, Dogs, Small Animals; *Shampoos:* Aromatic for Dogs, Cats, Tea Tree for Dogs & Cats; Tea Tree Coat Conditioner for Dogs

MASON'S PRODUCTS ☺✔ ⊘ ⅄—76

Dog Oil for Massaging (For Dogs, Horses & Humans)

Bright Eye Wipes (for Cats, Dogs, Horses, Rabbits, Hamsters), *Conditioners:* Relax-a-Cat, Relax-a-Dog; Deodorant, Cat, Dog; *Dog Conditioner:* Fierce, Timid; *For Dogs, Cats, Horses, Rabbits:* Battle Wounds Cream, Battle Wounds Spray, Dry Skin Cream; *Lotion for Elderly:* Cats, Dogs; Pad Balm for Dogs, *Shampoo & Conditioner for Dogs:* Dry Skin, Herbal; Travel Trauma Conditioner

SHANTI HEALTH & BEAUTY PRODUCTS ☺❶✔⊘

Lotions / Oils: Flea control, Insect Control; *Remedy Creams / Oils / Powders:* Arthritis, Eczema, Mange, Skin rash, Sweetitch; *Shampoos:* Chamomile, Herbal, Lavender, Rosemary; Worms Herbal Powder

THURSDAY PLANTATION ✔⊘⚡95

Tea Tree Dog Shampoo

YIN YANG BEAUTY CARE ☺✔⊘

Bascule: Horse Hair Restorer, Horse Wash Concentrate, Mud Fever Cream, Sweet-itch Cream; *Show:* Anti-Itch, Dog Wash

HUMANE TRAPS & DETERRENTS

BETTERWARE ✔⚡2000

Small Space Fly & Moth Repellent

Anti-Flea Shampoo & Conditioner for Dogs, *Anti-Mate Spray:* Cats, Dogs; *Bedding Spray:* Cats, Dogs; Buzz Off Insect Repellent, Cat Stroke for Fleas, Flea-Spray, Night-lights, Smelling Strips

NOTES

■ **Humane Research Trust** Stocks products from several companies, each of which has a different fixed cut off date, ranging from 1976-81.

■ **pets** The inclusion of an 'Animal Care' section should not be construed as indicating support for the pet industry or ownership of pet (companion) animals. Pets exist solely for human gain — in the case of the pet trade: financial; in the case of pet owners: pleasure — and their freedom is necessarily restricted. In the quest for the 'perfect' pet, breeds of dog, cat, bird and fish have, through genetic manipulation, been created with 'aesthetically-pleasing' deformities. Many animal free shoppers find pet ownership incompatible with their animal rights philosophy and those who find themselves caring for animals often do so because tens of thousands of domestic animals are unwanted and would otherwise be destroyed.

GARDEN & LEISURE

ARTS & CRAFTS

4-20 ☺™ ❶

Music CD, w plastic jewel case and 5 page booklet insert

DALER ROWNEY LTD ✔ ⊘

Artist Oil Colours: All EXCEPT Ivory Black & Blue Black; *Artists' Brushes:* Cryla, Dalon, Series 260, 270 & 280; *Cryla & Cryla Flow Colours:* All EXCEPT Ivory Black; *Designer's Gouache:* All EXCEPT Neutral Grey 2, Paynes Grey, Lamp Black, Cool Grey 1,2,3 & Warm Grey 1,2,3; *F.W. Artist Inks:* All; *Georgian Oil Colours:* All EXCEPT Ivory Black, Prussian Green & Ceruleum Hue; *Painting Surfaces & Equipment:* All EXCEPT Saunders Waterford Paper, Canvas Panels & Rabbit Skin Size; *Pearlescent Liquid Acrylic Inks:* All; *Rowney Block Printing Colours (water based & oil based):* All; *System 3 Colours:* All EXCEPT Raw Sienna

HEMP SHOP LTD ❶ ✔ ⊘

Hemp Paper

J.P. TEXTILES (EVERGREEN) ✔ ⊘

Hemp / Cotton Fabric, Knitting & Weaving Yarn & Fabric, Recycled Cotton Fabric, Recycled Denim / Pet (Polyester made from recycled plastic bottles)

LIBERON WAXES LTD ✔

Antiquing Fluid, Belt Cleaners, Carnauba Wax Flakes, *Gilding & Framing Products:* Fontenay Base, Frame Filler, Gilt Varnish, Metal Leaf; Whiting, Woodturning Stick

UHU (UK) LTD ☺ ✔

Creative Range, Dehumidifiers & Refills, Epoxy, Fabric Glue, Glue Varnish, Woodtite

VEGAMP ☺™ ❶

Vegamp CD - Vegan Art, Music & Poetry

WINSOR & NEWTON ✔ ⊘

Arcrylic & Oil Mediums & Varnishes: All; *Artisan Water Mixable Oil Colour:* All EXCEPT Ivory Black; *Artists' Oil Colour:* All EXCEPT Blue Black, Carmine, Ivory Black; *Artists' Oilbar:* All EXCEPT Buff Titanium, Ivory Black, Payne's Gray; *Artists Soft Pastels:* All; Bockingford Water Colour Paper, *Brushes:* All EXCEPT Series 7, Series 16, Series 7 Miniature, Cirrus Kolinsky Sable, Pure Squirrel Pointed Wash Brushes, Sceptre Gold II, Artists' Hog, Winton Hog, Azanta Hog; *Designers' Gouache:* All EXCEPT Ivory Black; *Finity Artists' Acrylic:* All EXCEPT Ivory Black, Payne's Gray; *Galeria Flow Formula Acrylic Colour:* All EXCEPT Ivory Black; *Griffin Alkyd Fast Drying Oil Colour:* All EXCEPT Ivory Black; *Winton Oil Colour:* All EXCEPT Ivory Black, Raw Umber

CLEANERS
— OUTDOOR

BETTERWARE ✔ ✂ 2000

Alloy Wheel Cleaner, Car Interior Trim Cleaner, Car Wash 'n' Wax, Carbon Remover, Path Patio & Drive Cleaner,

LIBERON WAXES LTD ✔

Garden Furniture Cleaner, Rust Remover

VINDOTCO UK LTD ☺ ✔ ⊘

Drain Clear, Patio & Path Clear

GARDENING
& COMPOST PRODUCTS

GROWGANIC ☺⊘

Growganic Seaweed Plant Feed: Extract, Tablets

MAXICROP INTERNATIONAL LTD ✔ ⊘

Organic Seaweed Products: Calcified Seaweed, Complete Garden Feed, Flower Fertiliser, Moss Killer & Lawn Tonic, Plant Growth Stimulant, Seaweed Meal, Sequestered Iron, Tomato Fertiliser

ORGANIC GARDENING CATALOGUE ✔ ⊘

Compost Activators: Biotal Compost Maker, Biotal for Grass, Biotal for Leaves, QR Compost Activator; *Fertilisers:* Organic Garden Potash, Rock Phosphate; *Growing Media & Ingredients:* Canu Composts, Coir Fibre Brick/Discs, Humate AG, Moorland Gold, Organic Moisture Retainer, Perlite, Wood Charcoal; Leafmould Compost Kit, Liquid Comfrey, *Liquid Seaweeds:* Seaweed Plus Iron, Seaweed Root Dip, SM3 Seaweed Extract; *Soil Improvers:* Cocoa Shell Mulch, Danu, Dolomite Limestone, Epsom Salts, Gem Peat-Free Soil Improver, Gypsum, Hop Manure, Orgabiose, Seaweed Meal, Sulphur Chips

TAMAR ORGANICS ⊘

Composts: Coir Bricks, Firtile Fibre Vegan Mix Compost, Nature's Own Seed Compost; *Fertilisers:* Cumulus K (potash fertiliser), Rock phosphate (phosphate fertiliser), Seaweed meal, Tamar magic 5:1:10 general purpose fertiliser; *Plant Feed:* Liquid Comfrey, Seaweed Liquid, Wild Magic

SMOKING PRODUCTS

ARKOPHARMA (UK) LTD ☺ ✔ ⊘

Nicotine Free Herbal Cigarettes: NTB Cigarettes, NTB Cigarettes Menthol

SANTA FE NATURAL TOBACCO CO.
🗸 ⊘

*Natural American Spirit Additive Free
Natural Tobacco Cigarettes:* Light,
Regular

NOTES

■ **musical instruments** All modern
guitar strings are made from metal or
nylon. Guitar picks are now made of
plastic. The heads of most modern
percussion instruments are non-animal
'skin'. 'Ethnic' percussion instruments
are still made with animal skins. All
Remo heads are animal-free.

■ **photographic film** All photographic
film and papers (the resulting
photographs) contain gelatine.
However, an expanding range of
(animal-free) digital systems is available.
The cameras are generally more
expensive than their conventional
counterparts but prices are falling.
They also require access to a computer
and, if hard copies are required, a
printer.

■ **Plasticine** Contains tallow.

■ **tennis balls** Contain wool.

■ **video cassette tapes** It would
appear that these are animal-free.

SUPERMARKETS

FOOD

BREADS, ROLLS, PIZZA BASES ETC

Morning Fresh: Crumpets, Fruit Loaf, Stayfresh White Baps; Romano Ciabatta, *Spinaca Bread:* Medium White, Thick White Sliced; *Village Green:* Gold Malted Wheat Loaf, Gold Soft Wholemeal Rolls, Soft Medium Wholemeal Sliced Bread, Soft Wholemeal Thick Sliced Bread, Stayfresh Med Sliced White Bread, White Muffins

BREAKFAST FOODS

Balanced Lifestyle: Multiflake w Fruit, Peach & Apricot Bites

CAKES & CAKE MIXES

Morning Fresh Jam Doughnuts,

CONFECTIONERY & SWEET SNACKS

Dominion Mint Imperials

COOKING AIDS – SWEET

Vitality Sweetner

DIPS & DRESSINGS

Worldwide Tomato Salsa dip

'ICE CREAMS', SORBETS ETC

Macey's Freezepops, Milfina Freshly Squeezed Orange Juice Lollies, Yippee Ice Lollies

PICKLES, SAUCES, VINEGARS ETC

Bramwells: Apple Chutney w Real Ale, Beetroot Relish, Caramelised Onion, Cranberry Sauce, English Mustard, Flame Roast Tomato Chutney, Mint Sauce, Wholegrain Mustard; Centanni Balsamic Vinegar, Colway Squeezy Tomato Ketchup, New Land Pickled Onions, *Worldwide Cook in Sauce:* Black Bean, Creole, Mexican Style Chilli, Smokey BBQ Sauce, Spanish Style Red Wine, Sweet & Sour

SAVOURIES – CANNED/BOTTLED

Corale Premium Baked Beans, Corvana Savoury Pasta Tomato & Herb

SAVOURIES — DRIED

Jade Instant Noodles: Chicken, Curry; *Romano Antipasti:* Artichokes, Dried Tomatoes, Peppers

SAVOURIES — FROZEN

Champion: Battered Onion Rings, Potato Waffles, Wedges

SEASONAL FOODS

Hot Cross Buns

SNACKS — SAVOURY

Balanced Lifestyle Ready Salted Crisps, Sprinters Snack stack

SPREADS — SAVOURY

Harvest Spread Peanut Butter: Crunchy, Smooth

DRINKS

BEERS

Saracen Pills 4 x 440ml

SOFT

Ameristar: Diet Cola, Premium Lemonade; Citrus Sensation, Hyberry Tropical High Juice, *Macey's Flavourades:* Blackcurrant, Sherbet Lemon; Macey's Milkshake Mix Banana, *Moreton Hills Balanced Sparkling Spring Water:* Apple & Raspberry, Elderflower & Lime; Red Thunder Energy Stimulation Drink, Solesta Blackcurrant 3 pk, *Sunquen:* Apple & Blackcurrant, Orange Drink; *Sunsqueeze Crush:* Diet Orange, Pineapple & Grapefruit, Sparkling Orange; *Topstar:* Flavourades - Cherry, Sugar free Lemonade, Sugar free Orangeade; Westdales Traditional Lemonade

SPIRITS & APÉRITIFS

Highland Earl Whisky, Napoleon Brandy, Old Hopking Dark Rum

WINES – WHITE

Cromwell British Fortified Wine, St Amandus Liebfraumilch

FOOD

BISCUITS

Bourbon Creams, Ginger Nuts, Morning Coffee, Rich Tea, Rich Tea Fingers, *Smartprice:* Bourbon Creams, Ginger Nut Biscuits

BREADS, ROLLS, PIZZA BASES, ETC

10 Flour Tortillas, 6 Flour Tortillas, 6 White Pitta Bread, Baguette, *Bakers Gold Thick Sliced Loaf:* White, Wholemeal; *Brown Bread:* Medium Sliced Loaf, Smartprice Medium Sliced; Chapatis 6 pack, Crumpets, *Fresh For a Week Medium Sliced Bread:* White, Wholemeal; Fruit Malt Loaf, Fruited Teacakes, *Greek Style 6 Pitta Breads:* Garlic, White, Wholemeal; Oven Bottomed Muffins, Pain Rustique Twin Pack, *Potato Cakes:* 4 Bacon Flavoured, 6 Pack; *Potato Scones:* 6 Pack, Round; Roasted Onion & Garlic Focaccia, *Rolls:* 12 Fresh For A Week White, 12 Sliced White, 6 Large Sliced Hot Dog, Dusted White Oval, Ploughman's, Smartprice 12 White, Smartprice White Finger 12 Pack, White Finger; Sandwich Baguette Granary, *Scotch Crumpets:* Fruit, Plain; *Tear & Share Bread:* Spicy Tomato Salsa, Sun-Dried Tomato; Traditional French Baguette, Traditional Pizza Base Mix, *White Bread:* **Organic Sliced**, Big Sliced, Danish Soft & Light Thick Cut, Extra Thick Sliced, Harvest Mill Scottish Batch Sliced, Medium Sliced, Smartprice Medium Sliced, Smartprice Thick Sliced, Split Tin, The Simpsons Mega Chunky Loaf, Thick Sliced; *Wholemeal Bread:* **Organic Sliced**, Good For You Square Cut Medium Sliced Softgrain, Medium Sliced, Thick Sliced

BREAKFAST FOODS

Bran Flakes, Cinnamon Apple Oat Sensations, Hawaiian Crunchy, High Bran, Malted Wheaties, *Muesli:* **Organic Whole Wheat**, Good For You Fruit, Wholewheat; **Organic Corn Flakes,** Ready Oats, *Smartprice:* Bran Flakes, Choco Moon Stars, Corn Flakes, Crunchy Oat Cereal, Frosted Flakes, Fruit & Fibre, Wheat Bisks; Sultana Bran, The Big Wheat 18 pack, Wheat Bisks

'BURGERS', 'SAUSAGES', 'MEAT' SLICES ETC

Vegetarian Mince

CAKES & CAKE MIXES

3 Fruit Slices, Assorted Tarts 6 / 12 Pack, Good For You 6 Bramley Apple Pies, Jam Shortbreads, *Smartprice:* 6 Apple Pies, 6 Raspberry Flavour Tarts; Sticky Buns, Victoria Ring

CONFECTIONARY & SWEET SNACKS

Crystal Clear Mints, Fruit Jellies, Lollipops, Mint Humbugs, Pear Drops, Rhubarb & Custard, Sherbert Fruit Cocktails

COOKING AIDS – SAVOURY

Mexican Seasoning Mix, Sage & Onion Stuffing Mix

COOKING AIDS – SWEET

Dessert Sauce: Orange & Cointreau, Raspberry & Drambuie; Glace Cherries, *Marzipan:* Golden, White; Raspberry Topping, *Sweet Pie Fillings:* 66% Fruit Cherry & Amaretto, 66% Fruit Fruits of the Forest

DIPS & DRESSINGS

Chunky Salsa Dips: Barbecue, Hot, Mild; *Dips:* Barbecue Tomato, Oriental, Tomato & Onion; *Dressings:* Balsamic, Extra Special Garlic & Sherry Vinegar, Extra Special Vietnamese, Good For You Lemon & Cracked Black Pepper, Oil Free (Less Than 1% Fat), Vinaigrette Style; *Good For You Dips:* Fresh Extra Hot Salsa, Fresh Salsa; *Houmous:* Fresh, Good For You Fresh (30% Less Fat); *Vinaigrettes:* French Style, Low fat, Mexican Style

GRAVIES & STOCKS

10 Vegetable Stock Cubes

PASTRY

36 Vol Au Vents, *Pastry:* Filo, Puff, Traditional Shortcrust Mix

PICKLES, SAUCES, VINEGARS, ETC

Baby Gherkins in Sweet & Sour Vinegar, *Beetroot:* Baby in Red Wine Vinegar w Orange, Baby in Sweet Vinegar, Crinkle Cut in Sweet Vinegar, Sliced, Smartprice Sliced; *Bruschetta Toppings:* Caponata, Olive & Garlic, Pizzlola; *Chinese Cooking Sauces:* Black Bean, Good For You Sweet & Sour, Sweet & Sour, Sweet & Sour Spicy, Sweet & Sour w Extra Pineapple; *Chutney:* Aubergine, Mango, Sweet Tomato & Chilli; *Cooking Sauces:* Chilli, Green Thai Curry, Sweet & Sour, Tomato & Herb; *Dipping Sauce:* Satay, Soy & Ginger, Sweet & Sour Sesame; *Good For You Fresh Sauces:* Napoletana, Red Pepper; *Indian Cooking Sauces:* Extra Special Goan Curry, Jalfrezi, Madras, Rogan Josh; *Jelly:* Fresh Mint, Redcurrant; *Marinades:* Citrus & Black Pepper, Extra Special Drunken Chicken, Extra Special Sticky Plum; *Mexican Sauces:* Barbecue, Fajita; *Mustard:* Coarse Grain, Dijon, English, French; *Onions:* Hot & Spicy Chilli, Spiced; *Organic Cooking Sauce:* **Sweet & Sour**, **Tomato & Herb**; *Packet Casserole Sauce Mixes for:* Beef in Ale, Sausage; *Pasta Sauces:* **Organic Tomato & Basil**, Chunky Vegetable, Mediterranean Tomato, Original Tomato, Original Tomato, Smartprice Bolognese, Spicy Tomato, Tomato & Garlic, Tomato & Mushroom; *Piccalilli:* Classic, Mustard, Sweet; *Pickle:* Beetroot & Horseradish, Lime, Mixed, Sweet, Sweet Harvest; Red Cabbage w Mustard Seed Redcurrant & Orange, *Relish:* Barbecue, Hamburger, Onion, Sweetcorn; Salsa Roja; *Sauces:* Apple w Scrumpy, Bramley Apple, Brown, Cranberry, Cumberland, Dark Soy, Hot Chilli, Light Soy, Mint, Pakora,

Plum, Smartprice Mint, Squeezy Brown, Sweet & Sour, Sweet Chilli, Tomato Ketchup, Tomato Ketchup, Squeezy Shallots in Sherry Vinegar w Ginger, *Stir Fry Sauce:* Kung Pao, Black Bean, Chinese Style, Chow Mein, Hoi Sin, Lemon & Ginger, Soy. Ginger & Garlic, Sweet & Sour, Teriyaki, Yellow Bean & Cashew Nut; *Tapenade:* Balti , Roasted Red Pepper & Tomato; *Vinegar:* Malt, Red Wine, White Wine

SAVOURIES – CANNED/BOTTLED

Baked Beans: **Organic**, Chilli, Healthy Choice, Smartprice, Standard; *Healthy Choice:* Bombay Potato, Chick Pea Dahl; Penne w Chilli & Red Peppers, *Spaghetti:* Healthy Choice, In Tomato Sauce, Loops In Tomato Sauce, Standard; Vegetable Balti, Vegetable Curry

SAVOURIES — CHILLED/FRESH

Aloo: Mushroom, Potato; *Bhajis:* 6 Onion, Indian 12 Mini Onion Cookie Bag, Mini Onion, Mini Vegetable, Vegetable; *Good For You:* Beetroot Salad, Minted Potatoes, Pasta & Sundried Tomato Salad, Pasta Ratatouille, Savoury Rice Salad, Spanish Style Potatoes, Spiced Rice Salad, Spicy Bean & Cous Cous Salad; *Pakora:* Achari, Broccoli, Cauliflower, Mixed Vegetable, Mushroom, Onion, Tomato; *Pasta Salad:* Italian Style, Tomato & Herb; Potato Wedges w Olive Oil & Rock Salt, *Rice:* **Organic Golden Vegetable**, Pilau, Vegetable Salad;

Spring Rolls: Mini, Vegetable; Vegetable Samosas

SAVOURIES — DRIED

Instant Mash Potato, *Instant Noodle Snacks:* Beef & Tomato Flavour, Chicken & Mushroom Flavour, Paprika Chicken Flavour, Spicy Curry Flavour, Spicy Curry Flavour; Tomato & Basil Pasta In Sauce

SAVOURIES — FROZEN

Frying Chips: Crinkle Cut, Smartprice Straight Cut, Southern Fried Flavour, Steak Cut, Straight Cut, Straight Cut; *Onion Rings:* Battered, Breaded; *Oven Chips:* American Fries, Crinkle Cut, Good For You Straight Cut, Steak Cut, Straight Cut; Potato Croquettes, Roasting Potatoes, Seasoned Curly Fries, Vegetable Chilli w Rice

SEASONAL FOODS

Hot Cross Buns 6 Pack

SNACKS — SAVOURY

Dry Roasted Peanuts, Potato Chips, Ready Salted Crisps, Ready Salted Pretzels, *Tortilla Chips:* Lightly Salted, Salsa, Smartprice

SOUPS

Spicy Tomato & Lentil, Vegetable

SOYA & OTHER 'MILKS'

Soya Milk: **Unsweetened Organic**, Sweetened w Apple Juice

SPREADS — SAVOURY

Good For You Peanut Butter, Sandwich Pickle Tangy Spread, Yeast Extract

DRINKS

BEERS

Indian Beer, Premium Strength Auzzie Beer, Premium Strength Biere De Luxe French Lager

CHAMPAGNE

Vintage Champagne

CIDERS & PERRIES

Perry

'HOT'

Drinking Chocolate

LOW & NON-ALCOHOLIC

Traditional Style Lager Shandy

SOFT

American Ginger Ale, Bitter Lemon, Blue Charge Energy Drink, *Cranberry Fruit Juice Drink:* No Added Sugar, w Blueberry, w Raspberry; Diet Iron Brew, Diet Lemonade, *Fruit Crush:* Citrus, Summer, Tropical; *High Juice:* Blackcurrant, Cranberry & Apple; Indian Tonic Twist Lemon Flavour, Indian Tonic Water, Iron Brew, Just Cola, Just Diet Cola, Lemonade, *Low Calorie:* American Ginger Ale, Bitter Lemon, Indian Tonic Twist Lemon Flavour, Indian Tonic Twist Lime Flavour, Indian Tonic Water; *No Added Sugar Juice Drink:* Apple, Fruit & Barley, Fruit Salad Flavour, Orange, Orange, Peach & Apricot, Variety Pack; *No Added Sugar Squash:* Apple, Apple & Blackcurrant, Blackcurrant, Lemon, Lemon & Lime, Lemon (10% Fruit), Orange, Orange & Pineapple, Strawberry, Tropical; Peach Flavour Spring Water Drink (No Added Sugar), Soda Water, *Squash:* Apple & Blackcurrant, Lemon & Lime, Lime Cordial, Orange, Orange & Pineapple; *Sugar Free Totally Bubbly:* Cherryade, Cola, Lemonade, Limeade, Orangeade; Tonic Water, *Traditional Style:* Cream Soda, Dandelion & Burdock, Diet Lemonade, Ginger Beer, Lager Shandy, Lemonade

SPIRITS & APERITIFS

Cognac 3 Star, Old Kilkenny Irish Whiskey, Peach Schnapps, Premium Gin, *Sherry:* Cream, Fino, Pale Cream; Whisky 3 Year Old, Windward Caribbean White Rum w Coconut

WINES – RED

African Cape: Cab Saw, Merlot, Pinotage, Red; African Pinotage Reserve, *Argentinian:* Red Select Blend, Red Wine, Shiraz; Bulgarian Cabernet Sauvignon, Chardonnay Jardin De La France, *French:* Beaujolais, Chateauneuf De Pape Red Wine, Cotes Du Rhone, Valpolicella, Vin De Table Redwines – rose, French Rose d'Anjou

WINES - SPARKLING

Cava, Cava Rosado, Spanish Cava
Medium Dry, Vintage Cava

WINES – WHITE

African Cape: Chardonnay, Western
Cape Sauvugnan Blanc, White;
Argentinian: Chardonnay, White Wine;
Chilean: Chardonnay, Sauvignon Blanc,
White; *French:* Chablis, Chenin Blanc
Demi-Sec, Macon Village Blanc,
Muscadet, Vin de Table Medium Dry
White Wine; *German:* Liebfraumilch,
Mainzer Domher, Niersteiner Gutes
Domtal; *Hungarian:* Chardonnay Dry
White Wine, Dry Chardonnay, Medium
Chardonnay, Muscat; *Italian:* Oaked
Soave, Soave

FOOD

BISCUITS

Bourbon Creams, Coconut Rings, Country Crunch, Cream Crackers, Everyday Digestive, Everyday Rich Tea Biscuits, Fruit Country Crunch, Fruit Shortcake, Ginger Nuts, Ginger Thins, Morning Coffee, Nice, Rich Tea, Round Lemon Puffs, Shortcake Biscuits

BREADS, ROLLS, PIZZA BASES, ETC

Baps: Large White, White, Wholemeal; Burger Buns, Finger Crumpets, Fruit Brack, Garlic Slices, *Loaves:* Brown, Danish Medium, Danish Thick, Everyday White, Gold White, Healthy Living Wholemeal, Long Life, Premium White, Soft Grain, Soft Wholemeal, White, Wholemeal; *Pitta Bread:* Garlic, White, Wholemeal; Pizza Base Mix, Potato Breads, Potato Cakes, *Rolls:* Crusty, Finger, Morning; *White Part Baked:* Batons, Petit Pain

BREAKFAST FOODS

Bran Flakes, Crisp Rice, Everyday Cornflakes, Everyday Muesli, Frosted Flakes, High Fibre Bran, Instant Hot Oats Cereal, Luxury Fruit Muesli, Luxury Fruit & Nut Muesli, Malt Crunchies, Perfect Choice, Porridge Oats & Bran, Sultana Bran, Wholewheat Biscuits

CAKES & CAKE MIXES

Rock Cake Mix

CHOCOLATE

After Dinner Mints: Chocolate Mints, Plain Chocolate Peppermint Cremes; Plain Chocolate Crystallised Stem Ginger

CONFECTIONERY & SWEET SNACKS

American Hard Gums, Assorted Fruit Flavour Lollies, Clear Mints, Crystallised Stem Ginger, Flying Saucers

COOKING AIDS – SAVOURY

Golden Breadcrumbs, *Stuffing Mixes:* Parsley & Thyme, Sage & Onion

COOKING AIDS - SWEET

Custard Powder, *Fruit Fillings:* Apple, Apple & Blackberry, Blackcurrant, Red Cherry; Glace Cherries, *Marzipan:* Golden, White; Mincemeat, *Mint:* Jelly, Sauce; Mixed Peel, Ready To Roll Icing

CRACKERS, CRISPBREADS, ETC

Breadsticks: Garlic, Plain, Sesame; *Crackers:* Healthy Living Reduced Fat, Savoury Wheat, Traditional; Plain Melba Toast

DESSERTS

Rhubarb Crumble, *Strudels:* Apple, Summer Fruit

DIPS, DRESSINGS, ETC

Dressings: French Salad, Virtually Fat Free Vinaigrette

GRAVIES & STOCKS

Vegetable Gravy: Browning, Mix

'ICE-CREAMS', SORBET, ETC

Sugar Free Mini-Pops: Blackcurrant, Cherryade, Cola, Limeade, Orangeade

PICKLES, SAUCES, VINEGARS, ETC

Apple Sauce, *Brown Sauce: Everyday, Squeezy Bottle, Standard; Cook-In Sauces:* Balti, Jalfrezi, Spanish Style, Sweet & Sour; English Mustard, *Fresh Pasta Sauces:* **Organic Tomato & Basil**, Napoletana; Fruity Sauce, *Malt Vinegar:* Brown, Distilled; Mango Chutney, *Pasta Sauces:* Classico, Healthy Living Light, w Mushrooms; *Relish: Barbeque, Hamburger, Onion, Sweetcorn; Sichuan Cooking Sauce, Sweet Pickle, Tomato Ketchup:* **Organic**, Everyday, Healthy Living, Squeezy, Standard

SAVOURIES – CANNED/BOTTLED

Baked Beans: Everyday, In Tomato Sauce; *Pickled Onions:* In Brown / Clear / White Vinegar, Silverskin, Standard, Strong, Sweet; Red Cabbage, *Spaghetti:* Everyday, In Tomato Sauce, Rings In Tomato Sauce; Spicy Mixed Beans In Tomato Sauce

SAVOURIES – CHILLED/FRESH

Healthy Living Baked Bean Dinner Jacket, Indian Selection Pack, Mini Onion Bhajis, Onion Bhajis, Pilau Rice, Vegetable Samosas, Vegetable Spring Rolls

SAVOURIES – DRIED

Instant Mashed Potato, Tomato & Herb Pasta & Sauce

SAVOURIES – FROZEN

Breaded Vegetable Rings, *Frying Chips:* Crinkle Cut, Steak Cut; Golden Vegetable Rice, *Onion Rings:* Battered, Breaded; Oriental Stir Fry Mixed Vegetables, *Oven Chips:* American, Crinkle Cut, Everyday, Steak Cut, Straight Cut; Oven Crunches, *Potatoes:* Crispy, Roast

SEASONAL FOODS

Hot Cross Buns: Low Fat, Mini, Standard

SNACKS - SAVOURY

Chilli Tortilla Chips, Dry Roast Peanuts, Potato Rings, *Ready Salted:* Crisps, Crunchy Sticks

SOUPS

Potato & Leek, Thick Farmhouse Vegetable, Vegetable

SOYA & OTHER 'MILKS'

Soya Drink: Sweetened, Unsweetened

SPREADS - SAVOURY

Peanut Butter: Crunchy, Smooth; Yeast Extract

SPREADS - SWEET

Bramble Jelly, Ginger Conserve

DRINK

ALCOPOPS

Glitz Ice: Blue, Lemon, Orange, Pina Colada, Watermelon

BEERS

Biere d`Alsace, *Lagers:* **Organic**, Czech, Dutch, Premium French, Premium German; **Organic Ale**

CIDERS & PERRIES

Organic Cider

'HOT'

Drinking Chocolate, Instant Coffee & Chicory Powder

LOW & NON-ALCOHOLIC

Lemonade Shandy

SOFT

American Dry Ginger Ale: Low Calorie, Standard; *Bitter Lemon:* Low Calorie, Standard; *Cola:* Diet, Everyday, Standard; *Cordials:* Elderflower & Lemon, Lime; Cream Soda, *Crush:* Apple, Lemon & Lime, Orange, Pineapple & Grapefruit, Pink Grapefruit; Dandelion & Burdock, Ginger Beer, *Indian Tonic Water:* Low Calorie, Standard, w Lemon; *Iron Brew:* Diet, Standard; *Juice Drinks:* Apple & Blackcurrant, Apple & Mixed Berry, Cranberry, Orange, Tropical, Whole Lemon; *Lemonade:* Everyday, Sparkling, Sparkling Diet, Standard; *No Added Sugar:* Apple, Apple & Blackcurrant, Cola, Lemon, Lemon & Lime, Peach Fruit & Barley Water, Strawberry, Strawberryade, Tropical; *No Added Sugar Squash:* Pink Grapefruit & Barley, Summer Fruits & Barley; Raspberryade, Soda Water, Sparkling Apple Juice, *Sparkling Spring Water:* Apple & Blackberry, Cranberry, Lemon & Lime, Peach, Raspberry; Tonic Water - Low Calorie

SPIRITS & APERITIFS

Gin: London, Premium

WINES - RED

Argentine Carbenet Franc Reserve, Argentine Malbec, Argentine Old Vines Sangiovese 2000, Australian Merlot, Beaujolais 2000, Big Baga 1999, Californian Red Wine, Cape Pinotage, Chestnut Gully, Claret, Co-op Rioja Tinto Vioa Gala, Cotes du Rhone Villages, Explorers Vineyard Cabernet Sauvignon 2000, Hungarian Red Wine, Montepulciano d` Abruzzo, Mountain Vines Cab-Mara Res, **Organic Red Wine, Vin de pays d`oc Organic Merlot Syrah 2000,** Vin de pays d`oc Vegetarian Syrah Malbec

WINES – ROSÈ

Lambrusco, Portugese

WINES - SPARKLING

Australian Sparking Brut, Cava, Cava Rose Brut, English Sparkling Wine Brut,

Saumur Brut Sparkling, Sparkling Chardonnay

WINES – WHITE

Bordeaux Blanc White, **Cape Soleil Chardonnay Organic 1999,** Hungarian Chardonnay 1999, Kabinett, Lambrusco Bianco, Liebfraumilch, Long Slim Chilean Chardonnay Semillon 2000, Niersteiner Gutes Domtul, Piesporter, Sancerre Raimbault, South African French Quarter Semillon, Spatlese 1999, Vin de pays d`oc Cotes des Gascogne 1999, Vin de pays d`oc Veggie Chenin Blanc Chardonnay, Vin de pays Pyrenees Orientales, Vina Galea, Vinho Verde

TOILETRIES & COSMETICS

BATH & SHOWER

Bath Soak: Calming, Soothing, Uplifting; *Creme Bath:* Evening Primrose & Camomile, Fennel & Lily, Lotus Flower & Almond, Peach Blossom & Jasmine, White Lilac & Magnolia; Evening Primrose & Camomile Shower Cream, *Foam Bath:* Everyday, Marine Elements, Meadowsweet; *Mankind Shower Gel:* Invigorate, Refresh; *Shower Gel:* Marine Elements, Meadowsweet

CONDITIONERS & HAIR CARE

Conditioner: Apple & Pear, Lemon & Grapefruit, Peach & Apricot; *Family Conditioner:* Apple & Watermint, White Almond & Jasmine; *Vitamin-Plus Conditioner:* Dry / Damaged, Normal

DEODORANTS & ANTIPERSPIRANTS

AntiPerspirant Deodorant: Active, Atlantic Breeze, Cool Blue, Cool Ice, Cool Peach, For Men, Pacific Blue, Soft Pink; *Body Spray:* Air, Earth, Fire, Water; *Mankind Body Spray:* Invigorate, Refresh; *Roll On Deodorant:* Cool Blue, Sensitive, Soft Apricot, Soft Pink

EYE PRODUCTS

Eye Makeup Remover

HAIR SPRAYS, GELS, ETC

Styling Gel: Extra Firm, Firm Hold; *Styling Mousse:* Extra Firm, Firm Hold

HAND & NAIL PRODUCTS

Hand Wash: Anti-Bacterial, Moisturising, Odour Neutralising

SHAMPOO

2 in 1 Shampoo & Conditioner: Dry / Damaged, Frequent Use, Multivitamin Normal, Normal; *Anti Dandruff:* Dry / Damaged, Frequent / Menthol, Frequent / Normal; *Shampoo:* Apple & Pear, Apple & Watermint, Herbal Frequent Wash, Lemon & Grapefruit, Multivitamin Normal, Peach & Apricot, White Almond & Jasmine

SKIN CARE – MOISTURISERS & BODY LOTIONS

Skin Excellence: Moisturising Cream, Moisturising Fluid

SKIN CARE – CLEANSERS & TONERS

Skin Excellence: Cleansing Lotion, Facial Wash, Toner

SOAPS

Pure

TALCUM POWDERS

Wild Herb

TOOTHPASTES & ORAL HYGEINE

Denture: Cleansing Powder, Extra Strength Tablets, Pearl Powder, Tablets; *Mouthwash:* Coolmint, Ex Strength Coolmint, Ex Strength Original, Freshmint, Mildmint; *Toothpaste:* Children's, Coolmint, Fluoride-Free, Freshmint, Freshmint Flouride Pump, Mildmint, Mildmint Fluoride Pump, Sensitive Teeth, Totalcare, Ultra Care, Whitening

BABY, INFANT & CHILDCARE

TOILETRIES, ETC

Baby: Bath, Bath w Menthol, Oil, Powder, Shampoo, Soap; *Extra Thick*

Baby Wipes: Fragranced, Fragrance-free; *Ultra Soft Lotion Baby Wipes:* Fragranced, Fragrance-free

HOME & OFFICE

AIR FRESHENERS

Gels: Alpine Breeze, Anti-Tobacco, Citrus Zest, Woodland Fruits; *Refresher Oils:* Tranquil Waters, Vital Essence; *Room Sprays:* Tranquil Waters, Vital Essence; *Stick On Pads:* Alpine Breeze, Citrus Zest

BLEACHES

Thick Bleach: Alpine Fresh, Citrus, Marine Cascade, Original

CLEANERS - GENERAL

Cream Cleaners: Aqua, Pine

DISHWASHER PRODUCTS

Lemon: Cleaner, Freshener, Powder, Rinse Aid, Ultra Liquid; *Tablets:* Lemon, Original

DISINFECTANTS

Disinfectants: Antiseptic, Everyday Pine; *Thick Disinfectants:* Fresh Pine, Lemon

FURNITURE & OTHER POLISHES

Multisuface Polish: Citrus, Original

TOILET PRODUCTS

Bathroom Mousse: Citrus, Pine; *Rim Block Freshener*: Citrus, Pine; *Thick Toilet Gel*: Aqua, Citrus; *Toilet Flush*: Blue, Green

WASHING POWDERS, STARCHES, ETC

Starch: 2 in 1 Spray & Easy Iron, Spray

WASHING-UP PRODUCTS

Anti Bacterial Washing Up Liquids: Apple, Lime w Eucalyptus; *Washing Up Liquids*: Concentrated Lemon, Everyday; *Washing Up Powders*: Lemon, Original

FOOD

BISCUITS

Bourbon Creams

BREADS, ROLLS, PIZZA BASES, ETC

Burger Buns, Crumpets, Danish Toaster Soft & Light Loaf, Fruited Teacakes, Garlic Slices, *Homebake:* Baguettes, Petit Pain, White Dinner Rolls; Large Brown Baps, Large White Baps, **Organic White Loaf,** *Pitta Bread:* Garlic, Standard, White; *Premium Sliced White Bread:* Medium, Thick; *Rolls:* **Organic Crisp,** Brown, Burger, White; *Sliced White Bread:* Medium, Thick; *Sliced Wholemeal Bread:* Medium, Thick; Softbake French Sticks, White Muffins

BREAKFAST FOODS

Chocolate Strawberry Crisp Cereal, Cornflakes, Dennis The Menace Frosted Flakes, Muesli, **Organic Wholewheat Bisks,** Whole Wheat Bisks

CAKES & CAKE MIXES

Treacle Tarts

DESSERTS

Strudel: Apple, Woodland Fruit

DIPS & DRESSINGS

Houmous Dip

PICKLES, SAUCES, VINEGARS, ETC

Cooking Sauces: Balti Curry, Black Bean, Chili, Curry, Rogan Josh Curry, Sausage Hot Pot; *Pasta Sauces:* Garlic & Onion, Mushroom, Tomato & Herb; *Sauces:* BBQ Smokin' Joes, Curry, Red Wine Casserole, Sweet & Sour

SAVOURIES – CANNED/BOTTLED

Spaghetti In Tomato Sauce

SAVOURIES – CHILLED/FRESH

Mediterranean Pasta Salad

SAVOURIES - FROZEN

Breaded Onion Rings, Button Mushrooms In Garlic Breadcrumbs, *Chips:* **Organic Oven,** American Style Slim Fries, Chinese Takeaway Oven, Crinkle Cut, Crinkle Cut Oven, Good Choice Oven, Low Fat Oven, Probably The Best&Oven, Southern Fried, Steak Cut, Steak Cut Oven, Straight Cut, Straight Cut Oven, Straight Cut Value; Chow Mein Mix, Hash Browns, Indian Takeaway Pilau Rice, Mini Waffles, Oriental Mix, *Potato:* Crinkle Cut Slices, Croquettes, Noisettes, Traditional Roast, Waffles; Roast Vegetable Mix, Southern Fried Potato Wedges, Vegetables & Savoury Rice

SEASONAL FOODS

Hot Cross Buns

FOOD

BISCUITS

Butter Puff Biscuits, *Digestive:* Biscuits, High Fibre, Reduced-Fat; Ginger Snap Biscuits, Oat Crunchies, Plain Chocolate Ginger Biscuits, *Rich Tea:* Biscuits, Finger Biscuits, Reduced-fat

BREADS, ROLLS, PIZZA BASES, ETC

4 Muffins, 8 Wraps, *Bagels:* 5 Plain, Cinnamon & Raisin, Onion & Poppy Seed; *Baguette:* Half, Large (Eire), Standard (Eire); *Batch:* Brown, Seeded, White Irish; *Black Pepper:* Bruschettine, Focaccia; *Bloomers:* Count on us Sage & Onion, Poppy Seed; *Breads:* Caramel Garlic, Downtown 3 Onion, French Rye, Fruited Soda, Levain, Light Rye, Multiseed, North Italian Style, Red Pepper, Roast Onion, San Francisco, Sunflower Seed, Tomato To Share, Walnut; Campaillou, Ciabatta, *Count On Us:* Country Grain, Crusty Batard, Granary, White, Wholemeal; *Farmhouse:* Bakers Multigrain, Bakers White, Crusty Granary, Crusty Poppyseed, Crusty White, Golden, Oatmeal, Sliced Brown, Sliced White, Sliced Wholemeal, Soft Golden, Soft Grain, Soft White, White, Wholemeal; Golden White, *Granary:* Sliced, Unsliced; *Green Olive:* Bruschettine, Country Bread; Harvest Brown, High Bran, Hovis, Lightly Salted Bruschettine, *Loaves:* Apricot & Sunflower, Cob, Plain, Raisin & Hazelnut, Square, Veda; *Long Life:* White Medium / Thick, Wholemeal Sliced; New York Baily, **Organic: Ciabatta Sticks, Mixed Seed Loaf, White, Wholemeal Sliced**; Pain De Campagne, *Pittas:* 12 Mini, 8 pack; Premium White, Raisin / Hazelnut Nb, *Rolls:* **Organic White**, 12 Split, 2 Ciabatta, 4 Breakfast Morning, 4 Ciabatta, 4 Crusty White, 4 Granary, 4 Soft, 4 White Morning, 6 Rtb White, 6 Soft Wholemeal, 8 White Homebake, B/C White, Brown, Count on Us White, Crusty (Eire); *Sandwich:* Medium, Thick, Unsliced Brown; *Wholemeal:* Crusty, Medium Sliced, Sandwich Medium / Thick

BREAKFAST FOODS

Apple & Cinnamon Flakes, Count On Us Fruit & Flake, *Muesli:* **Organic**, Count On Us, Luxury, Unsweetened; Toffee / Pecan Crunch

CAKES & CAKE MIXES

6 Jam Doughnuts, Large Jam Doughnut

CHOCOLATE

After Dinner Mints, Chocolate Crisp Pieces, Swiss Dark Chocolate Discs Net

CONFECTIONERY & SWEET SNACKS

Fruit Drops, Liquorice Twists, Lollipops, Lolly Rocket, Mint Crumbles, Mint Imperials, Pear Drops, Sherbet Lemons, Strawberry Sherbets, Turkish Delight

COOKING AIDS - SWEET

Cherries In Kirsch, Luxury Mincemeat, Raspberry Sauce Pouch

CRACKERS, CRISPBREADS, ETC

Cream Crackers, Mini Poppadums, Oatcakes, Poppadums, Rice Cakes, Scottish Oat Cakes

DESSERTS

Jelly: Fruit Cocktail, Raspberry; Peach Halves In Brandy, Raspberry In Cassis, Summer Berry Terrine, Summerfruit Compote

DIPS & DRESSINGS

Dressings: Balsamic, Caesar, Creamy Italian, Straw & Balsamic, Tomato & Chilli; *French Dressings:* **Organic**, Count On Us, New Class, Reduced Fat; *Houmous:* **Organic**, Red Pepper, Reduced Fat, Standard; Luxury Aubergine Dip, Salsa, Satay Dipping Sauce, Spicy Salsa

GRAVIES & STOCKS

Vegetable Stock

'ICE-CREAMS', SORBETS, ETC

Fruity Tubes, *Full-Fat Sorbets:* Passion, Raspberry & Black Sorbet; Lemon & Lime Mini Bar, Orange Juice Bars, ***Organic Sorbet:* Lemon**, **Mango**, **Raspberry**

PICKLES, SAUCES, VINEGARS, ETC

Chutneys: Autumn Plum, Boxing Day, Red Pepper/Onion, Rhubarb/Ginger, Sweet Mango, Tomato & Cardamom, Tomato & Olive, Traditional Fruit; *Marinades:* Lime / Ginger / Coriander, Salsa, Soy & Sesame, Sticky BBQ; *Mustards:* Dijon, English, Selection, Wholegrain, Wholegrain Ale; *Pickled:* Cucumbers, Onions; Redcurrant Jelly, *Sauces:* **Organic Tomato & Herb Pasta**, Apple, Arrabiata, Balti, BBQ, Black Bean & Garlic, Black Bean S/Fry, Brown, Chilli Con Carne, Chilli Garlic, Cranberry, Dark Soy, Fajita, Fresh Tomato, Jalfrezi, Madras, Mint, Mustard, Olive Pasta, Passionfruit / Mango, Roasted Italian Veg, Romana, Spicy Pepper, Sundried Tom & Garlic, Sweet & Sour, Sweet & Sour S/Fry, Tomato & Basil, Tomato & Chilli, Tomato & Herb, Tomato Ketchup; Sundried Tomato Paste, *Vinegars:* Balsamic, White Wine

SAVOURIES – CANNED/BOTTLED

Baked Beans

SAVOURIES – CHILLED/FRESH

12 Mini Falafels, Bombay Aloo, Bombay Potatoes, Chunky Chips, *Count on Us:* Chips, Garlic & Herb Wedges, Moroccan Vegetables, Vegetable Casserole, Vegetable Noodles; Couscous & Vegetables (2% Fat), Frites, Onion Bhajias, Penne Pasta & More, *Potato Wedges:* Crispy, Seasoned; Ratatouille, Re-Fried Beans, Roast Courgette & Tomato Tart, Roast Potatoes, Roasted Mixed Peppers, Tenuta Arcamone, Tortilla

SAVOURIES - FROZEN

Chips: Crinkle Cut, Low Fat Just Bake, Microwave; *Fries:* American Style, Crispy Coated; Mediterranean Style Potatoes

SEASONAL FOODS

Xmas Conserve Collection, Xmas Marmalade w Malt Whiskey

SNACKS - SAVOURY

Bombay Mix, *Count On Us:* Balti Bites, Black Pepper & Sea Salt, Pepperoni Bites; *Crisps:* Carrot / Parsnip / Celeriac, Pepper, Ready Salted, Red Duke Of York, Rosemary & Olive Oil, Salt, Thyme & Garlic, Vinegar & Sea Salt; *Hand-Cooked Crisps:* BBQ Chilli, Ready Salted, Salt & Balsamic Vinegar, Salt & Black; Lightly Salted Curvers, Potato Rings, Potato Squares, *Reduced-Fat Crinkle-Cut Crisps:* Ready Salted, Spring Onion; Salt & Pepper Pretzel, Sticks, *Tortilla:* Salsa, Salted; Waffles

SOUPS

Gazpacho, Mediterranean Vegetable, ***Organic:* Carrot & Parsnip, Minestrone, Mixed Bean & Pepper**; Tomato & Basil, Tomato & Lentil

DRINKS

SOFT

Cola, Diet Cola, Diet Lemon & Mandarin, *Dilute:* Blackcurrant, Florida Orange; *Flavoured Water*: Elderflower, Grapefruit & Raspberry, Peach & Lemon; *Hyperpouch*: Apple & Black, Grapefruit; *Juice Drinks:* Cranberry, Mandarine & Cranberry, Orange Pouch, Tropical Pouch; Peach Water Sparkle, *Quest:* Blackcurrant & Blackberry, Grapefruit & Lime, Orange; Revitalise Cranberry & Passionfruit, *Sparkle / Diet Sparkle:* Lemon & Lime, New Orange, Pineapple & Grapefruit; *Still:* Grapefruit & Raspberry, Lemon & Lime, Mandarin & Cherry, Peach & Lemon; *Symphony:* Elderflower, Peach & Ginger

SPIRITS & APERITIFS

Almuran, *Highball:* Grapefruit Vodka Mandarin, Peach Schnapps Redcurrant, Pineapple Rum Lime

WINES - RED

Domaine De Montpertuis

NOTE

Safeway have stated that they no longer keep their vegan list up to date because it was 'too much effort.' We have included details from their November 1999 list as they continue to send this to customers. This information is included for the convenience of those with limited access to other shops, but it is advised that you **check all products carefully** before purchase.

Please encourage Safeway to improve the service they offer to vegans by calling them on their customer care line: 01622 712987.

FOOD

BISCUITS

Bourbon Creams, Chocolate Mint Crisp Cookies, Digestive Fingers, Fig Rolls, Fruit Shortcake, Gingernuts, Morning Coffee, Orange Finger Creams, Pecan Cookies, Rich Tea Fingers, *Savers:* Rich Tea, Shortcake; Shortcake

BREADS, ROLLS, PIZZA BASES, ETC

Delicatessen: Deep Pan Pizza Base, Thin & Crispy Pizza Base, Wheat Flour Tortillas; *Instore Bakery:* Crosscut Batard, Granary Stick, Grand Rustique, Guernsey Planche, Mexican Style Chilli, Parisienne, Petit Parisienne, Pumpkin Seed, Spiced Fruit Feast; *Instore Bakery Bagel:* Onion, Plain, Sesame; *Instore Bakery Baguette:* French, Petite, Sandwich; *Instore Bakery Baps:* White, Wholemeal; *Instore Bakery Bloomer:* Brown, Brown Poppy Seeded, Brown Sesame Seeded, White, White Poppy Seeded, White Sesame Seeded; *Instore Bakery Cob:* Small Granary, Small Pot Wholemeal, Wheatgerm, White Twin; *Instore Bakery Farmhouse:* Granary, Large White, Large Wholemeal, White; *Instore Bakery French:* Baton, Boule, Roll, Stick; *Instore Bakery Hovis:* Large White, Large Wholemeal Country Grain, Small Brown; *Instore Bakery Loaf:* Coarse Brown Country, Wholemeal; **Instore Bakery Organic: Brown**, **White**; *Instore Bakery Pain:* Rustique, Siegle; *Instore Bakery Rolls:* Crusty Round, Soft Brown Cottage, Soft White, Soft White Cottage, White Bouchon; *Instore Bakery Sandwich:* Large White, White; *Instore Bakery Soft White Roll Knotted Seeded:* Poppy, Sesame; *Instore Bakery White Loaf:* Extra, Large Family, Small Tinned, Split Tin; *Pre-packed:* Bacon Flavour Potato Scones, Breakfast Pack, Crumpets, Finger Crumpets, Football Baps, French Stick, Fruit Teacakes, Herb Rustique, Keeps Fresh Crumpets, Mediterranean Style Vegetable Folded Flatbread, Muffins, Potato Scones, Rosemary Ciabattini, Teacakes, Traditional Potato Farls, Traditional Style Potato Scones, Veda Malt Loaf, White Baps,

Wholemeal Baps; *Pre-packed Bread:* Brown, Danish White, Farmhouse Premium Wholemeal, Fibrewhite, Gold Premium White, Granary Malted Brown, Granary Thick Sliced, Keeps Fresh Family White, Keeps Fresh Family Wholemeal, Medium Sliced Brown, Multigrain, Premium Pan, Savers White, Savers Wholemeal, Scottish Plain, Softgrain, Standard White, Traditional Style Plain White, White Batch, White Medium Sliced, White Pan, Wholemeal; *Pre-packed Buns:* Burger, Chocolate & Orange Mini, Currant, Seeded, Topped Wholemeal, White Sliced Burger; *Pre-packed Delicatessen:* 2 Deep Pan Pizza Bases, 2 Thin & Crispy Pizza Bases; *Pre-packed Focaccia:* Garlic & Mushroom, Mediterranean, Rosemary, Tomato; *Pre-packed Hovis:* Premium Brown, Premium White, Premium Wholemeal, Wheatgerm; *Pre-packed Italian Style:* Ciabatta, Ciabatta Flute, Ciabatta Rolls, Ciabattini, Mediterranean Bread, Olive Ciabatta, Sun-dried Tomato Ciabatta; *Pre-packed Muffins:* Cinnamon & Raisin, Fruit & Spice, Plain; *Pre-packed Pitta Bread:* Mini White, Mini Wholemeal, White, Wholemeal; *Pre-packed Rolls:* Farmhouse White, Farmhouse Wholemeal, Finger, Premium White, Premium White Split, Savers Brown, Savers White, Scottish White Morning, Scottish Wholemeal Morning, Soft Brown, Soft White, Split White, Traditional Style Brown Morning, Traditional Style Malted Brown, Traditional Style White, Traditional Style White Morning, White Finger, Wholemeal, Wholemeal Snack

BREAKFAST FOODS

Choc Teddies, Cornflakes, Farmyard Crunch, Fibre Bran, *Flakes:* Bran, Frosted, Tropical Fruit; Instant Hot Oat Cereal, *Luxury Muesli:* Fruit, Fruit & Nut, Tropical; Mixed Berry Wheat Bites, Rice Crunchies, Sultana Bran, Tropical Wheat Bites, Unsweetened Wholewheat Muesli, Wheat Bisks, Wheat Bites

CAKES & CAKE MIXES

Assorted Jam Tarts, Instore Bakery Apple Turnover, *Instore Bakery Gingerbread:* Man, Snowman & Scarf Kit, World Cup Striker England Kit, World Cup Striker Scotland Kit; *Instore Bakery Individual Pie:* Apple, Rhubarb; Savers Apple Pies, Summer Fruit Pie Selection

CHOCOLATE

Thin Chocolate Mint Creams

CONFECTIONERY & SWEET SNACKS

Connoisseur Stuffed Dried Fruit Selection, Crystallised Ginger, Extra Strong Mint Humbugs, Flying Saucers, Fruit Flavoured Slices, Fruit Lollies, Sparkling Mints

COOKING AIDS - SAVOURY

Broth Mix, Bruscetta Topping, Instant Mashed Potato, Sage & Onion Stuffing Mix

COOKING AIDS - SWEET

Crumble Mix, *Sweeteners:* All

CRACKERS, CRISPBREADS, ETC

Breadsticks: Assortment, Garlic, Mini Assortment, Pesto Flavour, Pizza Flavour, Plain; *Crackers:* Cream, Half Fat Cream, Selection; *Crispbread:* Brown Rye, Sesame; High Baked Water Biscuits, Melba Toast, Rough Scottish Oatcakes, *Thins:* Onion & Sesame, Poppy & Sesame

DESSERTS

2 Summer Puddings, Summer Fruit Medley, Summerfruit Compote, Winter Pudding

DIPS & DRESSINGS

Amigo's Salsa Dip: Hot, Mild; *Dressing:* Fresh French, Oil Free Salad, Provençale Vinaigrette, Roast Garlic & Onion, Sun-dried Tomato, Sun-dried Tomato & Basil, Sweet Red Pepper; *Houmous:* Delicatessen, Pre-packed, Reduced Fat Pre-packed; *Pre-packed Salsa:* Fresh, Fresh Green

GRAVIES & STOCKS

10 Vegetable Stock Cubes, Vegetable Gravy Granules

'ICE-CREAMS', SORBETS, ETC

Lollies: 10 Fruit Assorted, 10 Orange Juice, Savers Assorted; *Sorbet:* Blackcurrant, Lemon, Orange

MARGARINES, FATS, OILS, ETC

Dairy Free Margarine, **Organic Spread**

PICKLES, SAUCES, VINEGARS, ETC

Chutney: Curried Fruit, Delicatessen Mango, Drayman's, Farmhouse, Fig & Date, Mango, Peach, Spiced Plum, Tomato; Healthy Choice Salad Cream, *Jelly:* Mint, Redcurrant; *Ketchup:* Savers Tomato, Tomato; *Marinade:* Hickory Smoke Flavour, Hot Sun-Dried Tomato; *Mustard:* Dijon, English, French, German, Wholegrain; *Olives:* Black Pitted, Black Sliced, Green Pitted, Green Pitted & Stuffed w Almonds, Green Pitted & Stuffed w Pimento, Spicy Garlic Green, Whole Green, Whole Queen Green; *Pickle:* Sandwich, Sweet; *Pickled:* Crinkle Cut Beetroot, Dark Onions, Dill Cucumbers, Mexican Style Chilli Onions, Red Cabbage in Sweet Vinegar, Shallots, Silverskin Onions w Turmeric & Mustard Oil, Sliced Beetroot, Strong Onions, Sweet Sliced Beetroot, Sweetened Baby Beetroot, Sweetened Silverskin Onions, Unsweetened Baby Beetroot, Unsweetened Silverskin Onions, Unsweetened Sliced Beetroot; *Sauce:* Apple, Black Bean, Black Bean Stir Fry, Bramley Apple, Cranberry, Cranberry & Port, Dhansak, Fresh Garden Mint, Fruity Brown, Healthy Choice Napolitana, Healthy Choice Sweet & Sour, Jalfrezi, Lemon Stir Fry, Mint, Piri Piri, Red Wine & Mushroom, Redcurrant, Savers Brown, Spiced Wild Cranberry, Spicy Brown, Spicy Creole, Sweet & Sour, Tomato Onion & Herb,

Wild Cranberry w Port & Orange; *Sauce For Pasta:* Basilio, Healthy Choice Italian, Italian Mushroom, Italian Onion & Garlic, Italian Peppers, Primavera, Puttanesca, Traditional Italian; *Sauce Mix:* Casserole Chilli Con Carne, Casserole Spaghetti Bolognese, Simmer White; Traditional Mixed Pickles

SAVOURIES – CANNED/BOTTLED

Beans In Tomato Sauce: Baked, Healthy Choice Baked, Savers Baked; Salad Bean Mix, *Spaghetti In Tomato Sauce:* Rings, Short Cut

SAVOURIES – CHILLED/FRESH

Carrot Dipper w Barbecue Flavour Dip, *Coffee Shop:* Maharajah Vegetable Curry, Vegetarian Chilli; Couscous & Grilled Vegetable Duo, *Delicatessen:* Bombay Potato, Chana Dal, Grilled Onions w Roasted Garlic, Marinated Sun-dried Tomatoes, Mixed Antipasto, Mushroom La Grecque, Onion Bhaji, Onion Pakora, Palum Pakora, Pea & Mushroom Bhajee, Roasted Vegetables, Seasoned Artichokes; *Delicatessen Olives:* Green, Kalamata, Mexican Style, Mixed w Roasted Vegetables, Pitted Black, Pitted Green & Black; *Delicatessen Rice:* Basmati, Mexican, Mild Curry, Pilau; *Delicatessen Salad:* Braised Rice & Wild Rice, Carrot Nut & Sultana, Crispy Vegetable, Economy Tomato Pasta, Indian Rice, Italienne Pasta, Spanish Style Potato, Spicy Bean; *Delicatessen Vegetable:* Bhaji, Curry, Mini Samosa, Rogan Josh, Samosa, Spring Roll; Mediterranean Style

Vegetables, Mexican Style Pan Fry, Potato Wedges For Roasting w Herb Flavoured Oil, *Pre-packed Delicatessen:* Gobi Aloo Saag, Indian Snack Selection, Mustard Bombay Potato, Onion Bhaji, Onion Pakoras w Sweet Chilli Sauce, Pilau Rice, Roasted Vegetables w Couscous, Thai Style Fragrant Rice, Vegetable Chilli, Vegetable Curry, Vegetable Samosas, Vegetable Spring Rolls; *Pre-packed Healthy Choice Salad:* Beetroot, Carrot & Sultana, Couscous, Fruity Rice, Mixed Bean, Tomato & Pasta; *Pre-packed Salad:* Beetroot, Couscous & Pan Fried Vegetables Snack, Italian Style Pasta, Mexican Style Corn, Premium Pasta & Roasted Vegetable; *Stir Fry:* Aromatic, Beansprout, Italian Style Pasta, Japanese Style, Mix, Mushroom, Oriental Style, Sweet & Sour, Thai Style, Vegetable

SAVOURIES - DRIED

Bubble & Squeak, Curry Flavour Super Quick Noodles, Instant Mashed Potato, *Savoury Rice:* Curry Style, Pilau, Spanish Style; Tomato Onion & Herb Pasta Pronto

SAVOURIES - FROZEN

6 Mini: Spring Rolls, Vegetable Samosas; *Breaded:* Garlic Mushrooms, Red Pepper Strips; Microwavable White Rice, Mini Waffles, Savoury Wedges, Stuffing Balls

SEASONAL FOODS

Christmas Pretzels, Instore Mini Hot

Cross Buns, *Mince Pies:* Deep Filled,
Puff Pastry; Mincemeat, *Pre-packed Hot
Cross Buns:* Cluster, White, Wholemeal

SNACKS - SAVOURY

Amigo's: 6 Pack, Sizzling Bacon;
Bombay Mix, Cardamom & Black
Pepper Poppadoms, Dry Roast Peanuts,
Hot & Spicy Snack Selection, *Luxury:*
Fruit & Nut Mix w Belgian Chocolate,
Tropical Fruit & Nut Mix; *Mini:* Garlic
Bread, Poppadoms; Mixed Nuts &
Raisins, Natural Nut Mix, Nut Selection,
Peanuts & Raisins, Potato Sticks, Pretzel
Assortment, Pretzels, *Ready Salted:*
Crisps, Handcooked Chips, Savers
Crisps; *Rings:* Onion, Potato; *Roasted &
Salted:* American Peanuts, Large
American Peanuts, Peanuts; *Roasted &
Salted Nuts:* Cashew, Jumbo Cashew,
Jumbo Pistachio, Mixed, Pistachio;
Snack Mix: American Style, Oriental
Style; Spicy Mix, Tortilla Chips Chilli
Flavour, Vegetable Crackers

SOUPS

Slim Choice Minestrone, Vegetable

SOYA & OTHER 'MILKS'

Soya Alternative to Dairy Milk

SPICES

Curry Powders: All; *Spices:* All

SPREADS - SAVOURY

Peanut Butter: Crunchy, Smooth;
Spread: Mexican Chilli Bean, Savoury,
Spicy Vegetable, Tomato & Onion; Yeast
Extract

DRINKS

CIDERS & PERRIES

Sweet Cider

'HOT'

Drinking Chocolate

SOFT

Soft Drinks & Carbonates: All

SPIRITS & APERITIFS

Fonseca Guimaraens Vintage Port,
Spirits: All

WINES - RED

Australian: Dawn Ridge Red, Hardys
Bankside Shiraz, Hardys Barossa Valley
Shiraz, Hardys Nottage Hill Cabernet
Sauvignon Shiraz, Hardys Stamp Shiraz
Cabernet Sauvignon, Penfolds Bin 389
Cabernet Sauvignon/Shiraz, Penfolds
Koonunga Hill Shiraz/Cabernet 1995,
Penfolds Rawsons Retreat Bin 35 1997,
S/W Australian Red, S/W Oaked
Cabernet Sauvignon, S/W Oaked
Shiraz, S/W Shiraz, S/W Shiraz/Ruby
Cabernet, Wolf Blass Yellow Label Cab
Sauvignon 1994; Bordeaux & Atlantic
Oak Aged Claret S/W Margaux,
Burgundy: Gevrey Chambertin 1995,
Labore-Roi Nuits St Georges 1995, S/W
Beaune 1997; *Côtes du Rhône:* Raison
d' tre, S/W Dom Manoir de Maransan;
Eastern European Dunavar Cabernet
Sauvignon, *Italian:* D'Istinito Nero

d'Avola Nerello Mascalese, S/W Chianti, S/W Chianti Classico, S/W Lambrusco Rosso, S/W Oak Aged Valpolicella; *Midi:* **S/W Organic Vin de Table**, S/W Fitou; North American S/W Californian Oak Aged Cabernet Sauvignon, Portuguese S/W Stanlake

WINES - ROSE

Australian Rosé Hardys Stamp Grenache / Shiraz, Côtes du Rhône Côtes du Luberon Rosé, Italian Rosé S/W Lambrusco Rosé Light 4%

WINES - SPARKLING

Graham Beck Brut, Hardys Nottage Hill Chardonnay, Lindauer Brut, S/W Cremant de Bourgogne, S/W Sparkling Spumante Brut

WINES - WHITE

Australian: Hardys Barossa Valley Chardonnay 1994, Hardys Nottage Hill Chardonnay, Hardys Stamp Semillon/Chardonnay, Penfolds 'The Valleys' Clare & Eden Valley 1997, S/W Chardonnay, S/W Chardonnay / Sauvignon 1995 Clare Valley, S/W Dry White, S/W Oak Chardonnay, S/W Semillon/Chardonnay; *Bordeaux & Atlantic:* Mouton Cade 1994, S/W Bergerac Blanc, S/W Bordeaux Blanc Demi-Sec, S/W Bordeaux Blanc Sec 1998, S/W Oak Aged Bordeaux Blanc; *Burgundy:* S/W Macon Villages, S/W Montagny 1ER Cru; *Côtes du Rhône:* Fait Accompli, S/W DOM Manoir de Maransan White, S/W VDP de l'Ardeche

Blanc; *Eastern European:* S/W Hungarian Country Wine, S/W Irsai Oliver 1998 Nieszmely, S/W Matra Mountain Sauvignon; *German:* Devils Rock Reisling, S/W Hock, St Ursula Morio Muskat 1995; *Italian:* d'Istinito Trebbiano Insolia, S/W Lambrusco Bianco, S/W Lambrusco Light 4%; *Midi:* Colombard Sauvignon VDP de Gers, Dom Brial Muscat de Rivesaltes, S/W Vin Blanc; *New Zealand:* Montana Chardonnay Marlborough 1995, Montana Sauvignon Marlborough 1995; *North American:* Ironstone Chardonnay, S/W Californian Oak Aged Chardonnay 1995; *South African:* Kleinezalze Sauvignon Blanc, S/W South African Chardonnay; *South American:* S/W Chilean Sauvignon, S/W Chilean White; Spanish S/W Moscatel de Valencia

FOOD

BISCUITS

Basics: Bourbon Creams, Ginger Nut, Rich Tea Fingers; Coconut Crumble Cream, Coconut Rings, Fruit Shortcake, Ginger Crunch, Ginger Thins, Morning Coffee, Rich Tea Finger,

BREADS, ROLLS, PIZZA BASES, ETC

Bake Off: **Organic White Bread**, **Organic Wholemeal Bread**, Flour Coated Softgrain, Flour Coated Softgrain w Fibre, Seeded White Bloomer, White Bloomer, White Farmhouse Bread, White Split Tin, Wholemeal Bread, Wholemeal Tin; *Baps:* Giant White x 4, Soft white, White Burger, Wholemeal; *Batch Loaf:* Stoneground Wholemeal, White; *Bread:* Basics White, Basics Wholemeal (All Sliced Sizes), Brown Medium Sliced, Danish Soft White, Soft Bake White & Wholemeal Twin Pack, Softgrain Sliced (All Sizes), Sour Dough, Tomato & Basil; *Farmhouse:* Sliced White, Sliced Wholemeal, Soft Loaf; *Garlic & Herb Focaccia:* Mini x 4, Standard Size; Good Intentions Garlic Baguette, *Long Life:* Premium Wholemeal, Sliced White, White Pitta, White Rolls x 12, Wholemeal Bread - All slice sizes, Wholemeal Pitta Bread x 6; Mini Sundried Tomato Focaccia, *Part Baked Traditional:* Coburg Loaf, Shell Loaf; Pizza Base Mix, Pugliese, *Rolls:* Bakers Best Premium White x 6, Basics Brown x 12, Basics White x 12, Soft Brown x 6 & 12, Soft White x 6 & 12; Seeded Gallego, Soft Bake White Split Tin Twinpack, Spiced Fruit Buns x 4, *White Bread:* All slice sizes; *Wholemeal Bread:* All slice sizes

BREAKFAST FOODS

Basics Corn Flakes, Breakfast Bran, *Muesli:* Luxury Fruit, Luxury Fruit & Nut, Wholewheat

CAKES & CAKE MIXES

Apricot & Peach Lattice, Part Baked Doughnut

CHOCOLATE

Chocolate Mint Crisps, Dark Continental French Chocolate

CONFECTIONERY & SWEET SNACKS

American Hard Gums, Clear Fruits, Clear Mints, Fruit Sherbets

COOKING AIDS – SAVOURY

Luxury Stuffing Mix: Apricot, Port & Cranberry, Sultana & Amaretto, Vine Fruit; *Stuffing:* Apple & Herb, Chestnut Stuffing, Garlic & Herb, Sage & Onion

COOKING AIDS - SWEET

Custard Powder, Cut Mixed Peel, Glace Cherries, Golden Marzipan, *Mincemeat:* Luxury w Brandy & a Hint of Orange, Traditional; Vermicelli, White Marzipan

CRACKERS, CRISPBREADS, ETC

Breadsticks: Classic, Garlic, Sesame; Brown Rye Crispbread, *Cream Crackers:* Basics, Sesame Cream, Standard; Healthy Selection Wheat Biscuits, High Bake Water Biscuits, Mini Poppadoms, *Savoury Biscuit Thins:* Poppy & Sesame, Sesame & Onion

DESSERTS

Ready to Serve Custard, Redcurrant Jelly

DIPS & DRESSINGS

Dips: Barbeque, Fresh Extra Hot Salsa, Salsa; *Fresh Dressings:* Balsamic, French, Oil-Free, Tomato & Basil; Houmous

'ICE-CREAMS' SORBETS, ETC

10 Double Lickers, 10 Orange Flavour Ice Lollies, 10 Rocket Lollies, Basics 10 Assorted Fruit Lollies, *Sorbets:* Lemon, Mango

PASTRY

Short Crust Pastry Mix

PICKLES, SAUCES, VINEGARS, ETC

Basics: Malt Vinegar, Sweet Pickle, Sweet Pickled Onions; *Healthy Selection Pickled:* Onions In Light Vinegar, Red Cabbage In Vinegar, Silverskin Onions, Sweet Crinkle Cut Beetroot, Sweet Onions, Sweet Sliced Beetroot; Malt Vinegar, *Mustard:* English, Piccalilli; *Pasta Sauce:* Traditional, w Chunky Vegetables, w Mushrooms, w Onion & Garlic, w Peppers; *Sauces:* **Organic Tomato & Herb**, Basics Brown, Black

Bean, Bramley Apple, Brown, Chilli Culinary, Cranberry, Mint, Rogan Josh Curry Culinary, Sweet & Sour Culinary, Tomato & Herb; Sweet Piccalilli, Sweet Pickle, Tomato Ketchup (Glass & Plastic Bottles)

SAVOURIES – CANNED/BOTTLED

Baked Beans: Healthy Selection In Tomato Sauce, In Tomato Sauce; *Basics:* Baked Beans In Tomato Sauce, Spaghetti in Tomato Sauce; Ratatouille, *Spaghetti:* In Tomato Sauce, Rings In Tomato Sauce, Wholewheat In Tomato Sauce

SAVOURIES – CHILLED/FRESH

Lemon & Coriander Cous Cous, *Mini Indian Selection:* Celebrations Onion Bhaji, Celebrations Vegetable Pakora, Onion Bhajis Deli Counter, Vegetable Pakoras, Vegetable Samosas; *Onion Bhajis:* 6 Pack, Deli Counter; *Oriental Selection Celebrations:* Mini Vegetable Spring Rolls, Sweet & Sour Vegetable Parcels; Vegetable Pasta Salad, Vegetable Samosas, *Vegetable Spring Rolls:* 4 Pack, Single; White Pudding Links,

SAVOURIES - DRIED

Sundried Tomato Cous Cous

SAVOURIES - FROZEN

3 Way Cook Chips: Crinkle Cut, Steak Cut, Straight Cut; *American Style 3 Way Cook:* Chips, Fries; *Basics Chips:* Deep Fry, Frying, Oven; Battered Onion Rings, *Chips:* Healthy Selection Straight

Cut Oven, Steak Cut, Straight Cut;
Onion Rings In Crispy Breadcrumbs,
Rice & Vegetable Mix, Roast Potatoes

SEASONAL FOODS

Standard Hot Cross Bun, Xmas Line -
Shallow Fill Mince Pies x 6

SNACKS - SAVOURY

Basics: Dry Roasted Peanuts, Ready
Salted Crisps; Onion Rings, Potato
Rings, Potato Triangles, Salt & Vinegar
Twirls, *Tortilla Chips:* Chilli Flavour,
Lightly Salted, Salsa Flavour

SOUPS

Fresh Tomato & Basil, Homestyle
Chunky Vegetable & Lentil

SPREADS - SAVOURY

Peanut Butter: Basics Smooth, Crunchy,
Smooth

DRINKS

BEERS

Biere de Belgique, French Premier Lager,
German Pilsner

SOFT

American Ginger Ale: Low Calorie,
Normal; Apple & Blackcurrant Drink,
Basics: Cola, Lemonade; *Basics Juice
Drink Variety Packs:* Blackcurrant,
Orange, Orange, Pineapple & Lemon;
Bitter Lemon: Low Calorie, Normal;
Cherryade, *Cola:* American Style,
Caffeine Free Diet Cola, Diet American
Style, Original, Original Diet, Original
Diet Caffeine Free, Standard; *Cranberry
Juice Drink:* Standard, w Blueberry &
Sweeteners, w Sweeteners; *High Juice:*
Blackcurrant Drink, Orange Squash;
Indian Tonic Water: Low Calorie,
Standard; *Juice Drink:* Apple &
Grapefruit, Apple w Sweeteners, Fruit &
Barley, Peach & Apricot, Pineapple w
Coconut Flavour, Pink Grapefruit Fruit &
Barley, Tropical Fruit, Tropical Fruit w
Sweeteners; *Juice Drink Multipack:*
Apple w sweeteners, Blackcurrant w
sweeteners, Orange w sweeteners;
Lemon Drink, Lemon & Lime Drink,
Lemonade: Diet, Diet Sugar Free, Diet
Traditional, Standard, Still, Traditional;
Lime Juice Cordial, Limeade, *Low
Calorie Indian Tonic w:* Lemon, Lime;
No Added Sugar: Apple & Blackcurrant
Drink, Apple Crush, Apple Drink,
Blackcurrant Crush, Cherryade, Lemon
Drink, Limeade, Orange Crush, Orange
Drink, Orangeade, Pineapple &
Grapefruit Crush, Strawberry Drink;
Orange Drink: Standard, w Lemon &
Pineapple, w Mango, w Peach, w
Sweeteners; Orange Juice Drink,
Orangeade, *Slightly Sparkling Spring
Water Fused w:* a hint of Raspberry
Flavour, Apple & Blackberry, Cranberry,
Grapefruit, Lemon & Lime, Peach,
Tropical Fruit; Soda Water, *Sparkling
Juice:* Apple, Red Grape, White Grape;
Tonic Water w A Dash Of Lemon,
Traditional Style: Cream Soda, Ginger
Beer

FOOD

BISCUITS

Fruit Shortcake, Ginger Nuts, Rich Tea, 25% Less Fat Rich Tea, Biscuits, Rich Tea Fingers; *Value:* Bourbon Creams, Digestive, Rich Tea

BREADS, ROLLS, PIZZA BASES, ETC

10 Mini White Pitta Breads, 4 Potato Farls, 6 Potato Cakes, 8 Pikelets, 8 Potato Farls, *Baps:* 12 White, 16 Sliced White, 4 Giant White, 4 Giant Wholemeal, 4 Granary, 4 Large Malted Brown, 4 Large White, 4 Large Wholemeal, 6 Large White; *Brown Bread:* Bakers Premium Gold Malted, Organic Thick Sliced Malted, Standard Medium Sliced; *Buns:* 12 Sliced Sesame Seeded Burger, 12 Stayfresh White, 4 Currant, 6 Large White Burger; Ciabatta, Crusty White Bloomer, Crusty Wholemeal Bread Mix, Finest Barra Gallega Baguette, Finest Seeded Batch, Finest Sfilantino Trio, *Homebake Bread & Rolls:* 2 Half Baguettes, 6 Mini Petit Pains; *Mega Value Packs:* 24 White Rolls, 32 White Finger Rolls; Oatmeal White Thick, **Organic Crumpets, Organic Malt Loaf,** Pizza Base Mix, *Rolls:* 12 Wholemeal Snack, 4 Bakers Premium Granary Brown, 4 Large White Hot Dog, 4 White Deli, 4 Wholemeal Deli, 6 Brown, 6 Brown Finger, 6 Brown Morning, 6 Scottish White Morning, 6 Soft White, 6 White Finger, 6 White Morning, 6 Wholemeal, Coffee Shop Loose White Morning; *Rye Bread:* Continental Style Light Brown, Finest Country, Finest German Crusty; Scotch Batch, Sliced Fruit Loaf, Softgrain Medium Thick White Bread, *Standard White Bread:* Medium, Plain, Stayfresh Medium, Stayfresh Thick, Thick, Thin, Toaster Extra Thick, Traditional, Value Thick; Sundried Tomato & Basil Ciabatta, *Value Packs:* 12 White Rolls, 12 Wholemeal, 4 Teacakes, 6 White Pitta, Medium Wholemeal Bread; *White Danish Bread:* Medium, Thick; *Wholemeal Bread:* Bakers Premium Gold, Multigrain, Stayfresh Medium, Stayfresh Thick

BREAKFAST FOODS

Frosted Flakes, Golden Wheat Pillows, Healthy Eating Wheat Biscuits, Hi Fibre Bran, Instant Hot Oat Cereal, Malt Wheats, *Muesli:* Healthy Eating Fruit, Healthy Eating Tropical, Wholewheat; Tropical Feast, *Value:* Bran Flakes, Cornflakes, Frosted Flakes, Fruit & Fibre; Wheat Biscuits

'BURGERS', 'SAUSAGES', 'MEAT' SLICES ETC

Organic Vegetable Burgers

CAKES & CAKE MIXES

2 Healthy Eating Summer Fruit Pudding, 5 Jam Doughnuts, 6 Value Apple Pies, Finest Summer Pudding, Luxury Crumble Mix, Value Twin Apple Pies

CONFECTIONERY & SWEET SNACKS

15 Lolly Mix, American Hard Gums, Coffee Shop Caramel Popcorn, Fruit Sherbets, Sparkling Mints, Value Lollies

COOKING AIDS - SAVOURY

Sage & Onion Stuffing Mix

COOKING AIDS - SWEET

Glace Cherries: French, Natural Coloured, Standard; Luxury Continental Dark Chocolate, Ready Ice White, *Sweeteners:* Granulated, Tablet

CRACKERS, CRISPBREADS, ETC

Breadsticks: Garlic, Mini, Original, Sesame; *Crackers:* **Organic Wholemeal**, Multigrain, Onion & Sesame, Poppy & Sesame; High Baked Water Biscuits, Plain Mini Puppadums, Rough Oatcakes

DESSERTS

Strudel: Apple, Apple & Strawberry, Woodland Fruit

DIPS & DRESSINGS

Finest Dipping Oils: Balsamic, Chilli & Garlic; *Humous:* Lemon & Chilli, Reduced Fat, Standard, w Red Pepper; *Salad Dressing:* 95% Oil Free, Finest French, Finest French Vinaigrette, Finest Salsa, Garlic Vinaigrette, Healthy Eating Less Than 4% Fat, Mustard & Tarragon, Original Fresh Style Vinaigrette, Sun-Dried Flavour, Vinaigrette; *Salsa Dip:* Cool, Hot

ICE-CREAMS, SORBETS, ETC

Lollies: **Organic Apple & Blackcurrant**, Assorted 10 Real Fruit, Fines Orange & Cranberry, Finest Frechly Squeezed Orange Juice, No Added Sugar Assorted Fruit, Orange Juice, Slimey Limey, Value Assorted Fruit; *Sorbet:* Lemon, Mango, Raspberry & Peach Harlequin

MARGARINES, FATS, OILS, ETC

Baking Margarine, Soya Spread

PICKLES, SAUCES, VINEGARS, ETC

Beetroot In Vinegar: Crinkle Cut Sweet, Pickled Sliced, Value, Whole Baby, Whole Baby Sweet; *Chinese Cooking Sauce:* **Organic Sweet & Sour**, Better Value Sweet & Sour, Blackbean Stirfry, Stirfry Szechuan, Sweet & Sour Stirfry; *Chutney:* **Organic Sweet**, Curried Fruit, Finest Apple & Flame Roasted Tomato & Garlic, Hot Mango, Mango, Peach; Cornichons, *Finest Tapenade:* Green Olive & Lemon, Sweet Red Pepper; *Fresh Sauce:* Arrabiata, Napoletana, Pepperonata; *Gherkins:* Crinkle Cut, Sweet & Sour; *Marinated Olives:* Green, Mixed; Mint Jelly, *Mustard:* **Organic Coarsegrain**, Dijon, English, Finest Horseradish, Wholegrain; *Pasta Sauce:* Chunky Vegetable, Healthy Eating, Mushroom, Onion & Garlic, Original, Original Better Value, Value; *Piccalilli:* Sandwich, Standard, Sweet; *Pickle:* Original Sweet, Sandwich, Value Sweet; *Pickled Onions:* Dark Spiced, Hot & Spicy, Hot & Spicy

Shallots, Sharp Silverskin, Sweet Silverskin, Traditional, Value; Pickled Red Cabbage, *Relish:* Sweetcorn, Tomato & Chilli; *Sauces:* BBQ Squeezy, Bramley Apple, Cranberry, Finest Cranberry, Finest Mustard & Dill, Fresh Garden Mint Sauce, Fruity Brown (Bottle, Squeezy), Jalfrezi Indian Cooking, Mint, Ready To Serve Mint Squeezy, Rogan Josh, Smooth Bramley Apple, Value Brown (Bottle, Squeezy), Value Mint Sauce; *Tomato Ketchup:* Reduced Calorie, Value; *Vinegar:* Finest Balsamic, Malt

SAVOURIES – CANNED/BOTTLED

Baked Beans: **Organic**, 50% Less Sugar & Salt, In Tomato Sauce, Value; Lentil Dahl, Saag Aloo, *Spaghetti:* In Tomato Sauce, Letters, Rings In Tomato Sauce, Value; Vegetable Curry

SAVOURIES – CHILLED/FRESH

Bombay Potatoes, Colcannon, Gobi Aloo Saag, *Mini:* Assorted Indian Snacks, Onion Bhaji; Mushroom & Spinach Bhaji, New York Style Healthy Eating Potato Wedges, Onion Bhajis, Potato Wedges, Saffron Rice, Tex Mex Style Vegetable Chilli, Vegetable Chilli & Rice, Vegetable Dhal, Vegetable Spring Rolls

SAVOURIES - DRIED

Savoury Rice Mild Curry, Special Byriani Savoury Rice, Spicy Curry Snack Pot, Value Instant Mashed Potato

SAVOURIES - FROZEN

American Style Thin Fries, Family Fries, Frying Chips, **Organic Roasting Potatoes,** *Oven Chips:* American Cut, American Style Thin, Crinkle Cut, Steakhouse, Straight Cut, Value; Oven Crunchies, Potato Jigsaw Pieces, Steakhouse Fry Chips

SEASONAL FOODS

Cross Buns: 4 Brown Hot, 4 Healthy Eating, 9 Mini

SNACKS - SAVOURY

Garlic Bread Snacks, Lightly Salted Pretzels, Lightly Salted Tortilla Chips, **Organic Ready Salted Crisps,** *Potato:* Chips, Rings, Triangles; Ready Salted 25% Less Fat Crisps, Ready Salted Crunchy Sticks, Select Ready Salted Crisps, Thick & Crunchy Texas BBQ

SOUPS

Organic Lentil

SPREADS - SAVOURY

Yeast Extract

SPREADS - SWEET

Conserve: Black Cherry & Amaretto, Finest Apricot & Brandy, Finest Strawberry & Champagne; Finest w Whisky Marmalade

DRINKS

'HOT'

Instant Lemon Tea Granules,

LOW & NON-ALCOHOLIC

Traditional Style Shandy

SOFT

Cola: **Organic**, Best Ever, Best Ever Diet, Sparkling, Standard, Value; Dandelion & Burdock, Finest Morello Cherry Drink, *Hi Juice:* Apple Squash, Blackcurrant Squash, No Added Sugar Pink Grapefruit, No Added Sugar Blackcurrant, No Added Sugar Orange, Orange Squash, Pineapple Squash, Pink Grapefruit Squash; *Hint Flavoured Spring Water:* Apple & Raspberry, Blackberry & Grape, Elderflower & Lemon, Grapefruit, Lemon & Lime, Passionfruit, Peach; Iron Brew, *Kick Stimulation Drink:* Cola, Diet, Standard; *Lemonade:* **Organic**, Diet, No Added Sugar, Sparkling, Sparkling Diet, Standard, Still, Sugar-Free, Traditional Style Pink, Value, Value Low Sugar; Lime Juice Cordial, *Mixers:* **Organic Dry Ginger Ale**, **Organic Tonic Water**, American Ginger Ale, Bitter Lemon, Dry Ginger Ale, Low Calorie Tonic w Lemon, Low Calorie Tonic w Twist Of Lime, Low Calorie Tonic Water, Tonic w Twist Of Lemon, Tonic Water; No Added Sugar Appleade, *No Added Sugar Barley Water:* Blackcurrant & Raspberry, Peach Apricot, Pink Grapefruit, Strawberry, Tropical; No Added Sugar Orangeade, *No Added Sugar Single Juice Multipacks:* Apple & Blackcurrant, Strawberry, Tropical Juice Drink, Whole Orange Drink; *No Added Sugar Squash:* Apple, Apple & Blackcurrant, Blackcurrant, Grapefruit, Lemon, Mixed Fruit, Orange, Orange Lemon & Pineapple, Summer Fruit, Tropical; *Orange Crush w:* Apple, Lemon & Lime, Peach, Raspberry; ***Organic Crush:* Apple**, **Grapefruit**, **Orange**; *Squash:* Apple & Blackcurrant, Lemon & Lime, Low Calorie Orange, Mixed Fruit, Orange, Lemon & Pineapple, Whole Lemon, Whole Orange; Sugar Free Strawberryade, Traditional Style Diet Ginger Beer, Traditional Style Ginger Beer, Variety Pack Orange Apple & Pineapple Juice

FOOD

BISCUITS

Apple & Sultana, Bourbons, C/Nut Crumble Cream, Fruit Shortcake, Morning Coffee, *Rich Tea:* Biscuits, Fingers, Low Fat; Shortcake Almond & Lemon

BREADS, ROLLS, PIZZA BASES, ETC

6 Petits Pains, Altamura, *Bagels:* **4 Organic**, 5 Caramelised Onion & Poppyseed, 5 Cinnamon & Raisin Bagel, Plain Bake Off; *Baguettes:* 3 Half, Artisan, Artisan Seeded; *Bake-Off Breads:* **Organic Baguette**, **Organic Brown Bread**, **Organic Heyford Wholemeal**, **Organic White Bread**, Baguette, Brown Flute, Flute, Granary Baton, Granary Long Tin, Granary Sandwich, Granary Tin, Grand Rustique, Pain Au Levain, Pain Rustique, Petit Pain, Poppy Knot, White Bloomer, White Farmhouse, White Long Split Tin, Wholemeal Farmhouse, Wholemeal Long Tin; *Baps:* 4 Giant White, 6 White Floured, 6 Wholemeal, Ex Large Brown, Giant White Sesame, Giant Wholemeal, Large Granary; Bloomer, *Bread:* **Malted Tin Organic Flour**, Ascot Brown Thin, Danish Malt Three Seed, Hovis, Malted Batch, Onion & Sultana, Sliced Richly Fruited, Soft Grain Thick, Walnut; *Buns:* 12 Sliced White Burger, 4 Fruit, 4 Richly Fruited, 6 Sesame Seed Burger, 9 Mini Spiced Fruit, Mini Cinnamon & Raisin, W/Meal Spiced Fruit; Caramelised Garlic Twist, Casareccio, *Ciabatta:* Italian, Mediterranean; *Crumpets:* **Organic Toast**, Standard; Daktyla, Danish Toaster, *Focaccia:* Mediterranean, Trio, w Rosemary; Fougasse w Herbs, *Granary:* Long Tin, Malted Brown Sandwich, Sesame, Thick, Tin; *Grand Mange:* Blanc, Paysan; *Muffins:* **Organic W/Meal**, White; *Organic Bread:* Fruit, **German Recipe Rye**, **Malted White Long Tin**, **Petit Pain**, **Premium Thick**, **Traditional White Bread**, **Traditional Wholemeal**, **White**, **White Medium**, **Wholemeal**; Pain Cirque, *Pane:* Anello, Bruno, Rustico; Paysan Rustique, *Pitta Bread:* **Organic Brown**, Traditional White, Traditional Wholemeal, White Picnic; Poppy Seeded Batard, *Premium:* Extra Thick, Medium, Thick Wholmeal w Seeds, Wholemeal, Wholemeal Medium, Wholemeal Thick; Pretzel, *Ready To Bake:* Baguettes, Petit Pain; *Rolls:* **4 Organic Brown**, 4 Ciabatta, 4 Old Fashion White, 6 White Snack, 9 Soft Brown Snack, 9 Soft White Snack, Granary Malted Brown, Premium W/Meal, White Country, White Soft; *Rye:* & Sultana Ficelle, Light w Caraway Seed, Poppy Seeded Batard; Spanish Seeded Gallego, *White Bread:* **Organic Farmhouse**, **Organic Tin Bread**, Bloomer, Bloomer Seeded, Crusty Tin, Farmhouse, French Stick, Medium, Sandwich, Soft Sandwich Tin, Sour Doughbread, Split Tin, Thick, Tin, Traditional, w Oatmeal; *Wholemeal:*

Organic Farmhouse, **Organic Heyford**, Batch, Farmhouse, Long Tin, Medium, Multi Seed Batch, Oat & Seed, Soft Sandwich Tin, Stoneground Tin Organic Flour, Traditional

BREAKFAST FOODS

High Fibre Bran, *Muesli:* **Organic Luxury**, Luxury Summer Fruit Muesli; Multi Flake Cereal, Puffed Wheat, Wholemeat Cereal Biscuits

CAKES & CAKE MIXES

Assabee, Baklava, Boukage, Fruit Shrewsbury, Kulwuskur, Mulled Wine Pudding, Original Plum, Strawberry & Rhubarb Pie, Treacle Tart, Womble Biscuit

CHOCOLATE

After Dinner Mints, Choc Brazil Nuts, Mint Thins, Peppermint Creams, *Plain Chocolate w:* Cognac, Orange, Peppermint, Woodland Fruit

CONFECTIONERY & SWEET SNACKS

Clear Mints, Crystal Stem Ginger, Mint Imperials

COOKING AIDS - SAVOURY

Croutons Herb & Sea Salt, French Croutons, *Stuffing Mix:* Parsley & Thyme, Sage & Onion

COOKING AIDS - SWEET

Cut Mixed Peel, Glace Cherries *Marzipan:* Golden, White; *Mincemeat:* Special, Traditional; Vegetable Suet

CRACKERS, CRISPBREADS, ETC

Breadsticks: Garlic, Sesame, Traditional; Cream Crackers, *Crispbread:* Garlic, Rosemary; High Bake, *Oatcakes:* **Organic**, Scottish; *Perfect Balance Ricecake:* Lo Salt, No Salt; *Thins:* Onion & Sesame, Poppy & Sesame Thin

DESSERTS

Perfect Balance: Summer Puddings, Tropical Summer Pudding; *Puddings:* Handmade Summer, Summer, Winter

DIPS & DRESSINGS

Dressings: Citrus, Fat Free Vinegarette, French, Lemon, Oil Free French, Pepper& Balsamic, Sundried Tomato, Tomato, Garlic & Basil; *Houmous:* **Organic**, Reduced Fat, Standard; Salsa Dip

ICE-CREAMS, SORBETS, ETC

Ice Lollies: **Organic Apple**, **Organic Summerfruit**, Assorted 10s, Orange Juice; *Sorbets:* Lemon, Mango, Orange & Passionfruit, Pineapple & Mango, Strawberry & Raspberry

PICKLES, SAUCES, VINEGARS, ETC

Beetroot: Baby, Sliced, Sweet Baby, Sweet Sliced; *Chutney:* Apple & Walnut, Apricot & Ginger, Curried Fruit, Date & Apricot, Hot Mango, Mango, Special Peach, Spicy Flame Roast, Spicy Mango; *Cooking Sauces:* Jalfrezi, Madras, Sweet & Sour; Cornichons,

Jelly: Coriander & Sage, Lemon & Dill, Mint, Redcurrant & Port, Savoury Blackberry; *Mustard:* & Dill, Dijon, English, French, Wholegrain; **Perfect Balance Organic Sauces: Balti, Rogan Josh, Sweet & Sour**; *Piccilli:* Mustard, Sandwich, Sweet; *Pickled:* Ginger, Onion, Red Cabbage, Silverskin Onions, Sweet Onion; *Relish:* Olive, Salsa, Tarragon; Sandwich Pickle, *Sauce:* Amaretto & Mascarpone, Apple, Apple & Cranberry, Arrabbiatta, Chilli, Cranberry, Cumberland, Fruity, Lemon, Mediterranean, Mint, Napoletana, Pepperonata, Plum & Ginger, Redcurrant, Roasted Mediterrean Vegetables, Spicy, Tomato & Herb; *Soy Sauce:* Dark, Japan, Light, Teryki; Sweetpickle, *Tapenade:* Olive & Lemon, Sundried Tomato; *Tomato Ketchup:* Reduced Sugar, Sqeazy, Standard; *Vinegar:* **Organic Balsamic w Oregano**, Cider, Malt, Mixed Herb, Tarragon, White Wine

SAVOURIES – CANNED/BOTTLED

Beans: **Organic Baked Beans**, Baked Beans, Curry Sauce, Spicy Tomato; Ratatouille, Spaghetti in Tomato Sauce, Spaghetti Rings, Vegetable Chilli

SAVOURIES – CHILLED/FRESH

4 Vegetable Samosas, 4 Vegetable Spring Rolls, 6 Onion Bhajis, 6 Potato & Spinach Pakoras, Bhindi Bateta, Bistro Al Fresco Bulgar, Bistro Onion Mash, Bombay Potatoes, Crispy Seaweed, Ebly & Roasted Vegetables, Grilled Peppers

Mixed Antipasti, Indonesian Noodles w Potato Coriander, Kalamata Mix, Kanpyo Hosomaki, Mango Nigiri, *Marinated:* Artichoke Hearts, Field Mushrooms; Masala Dal, Minted New Potatoes, Mushroom Dopiazza, Nutty Rice, Nutty Rice & Coucous, *Olives:* Black & Green w Herbs, Marinated Tuscan; Orange & Lime Dressing Tabbouleh, **Organic Falafel, Organic Seasonal Salad Mini Tortillas,** *Perfect Balance:* Sweet & Sour Veg w Rice, Tomato & Pepper Pizza; Phul Gobi Vatana, *Pilau Rice:* Lemon, Spinach & Carrot, Standard, w Spinach; Punjabi Style Onion Bhaji, *Rice:* Coconut, Couscous, Saffron, Thai Fragrant; Ringna Bateta, Seaweed, Spicy Lattice Fry, Sticky Rice, Vagharela Bhaat, Vegetable Jalfrezi

SAVOURIES – FROZEN

American Style Oven Fries, *Chips:* **Organic Oven**, Crinkle Cut Oven, Fry, Oven, Reduced Fat Oven, Steak Cut Oven; Oriental Stir Fry, Oven Crunchies

SEASONAL FOODS

Christmas Relish, *Hot Cross Buns:* **Organic**, 4 Rich Fruit, Cinnamon & Raisin, Mini, Wholemeal; *Mince Pies:* Mini, Shortcrust

SNACKS - SAVOURY

Crisps: **Sea Salt Organic,** Low Fat Crinkle, Low Fat Salted, Ready Salted; Hand Cooked Chips, Low Salt Tortillas, Onion Rings, Oven Baked Potato Chips,

Paquitos Original, *Peanuts:* Dry Roasted, Sweet & Sour Flavour; Potato Rings Ready Salted, Potato Sticks

SOUPS

Gazpacho, Golden Gazpacho, Minestrone w Pasta Shells, **Organic Chickpea & Lentil,** *Perfect Balance:* Mediterranean Vegetable, Moroccan Lentil; Roast Pepper & Tomato, Tomato & Basil In A Cup

SOYA & OTHER 'MILKS'

Organic Soya Milk: **Sweetened, Unsweetened**; Rice Drink w Calcium, *Soya Milk:* Sweetened, Unsweetened; Soyilk Milk Alternative

SPREADS - SAVOURY

Peanut Butter: **Organic**, Crunchy, Smooth, Wholenut

SPREADS - SWEET

Jelly Marmalade: Lemon, Orange; Spiced Christmas Marmalade, Strawberry & Drambuie Preserve

TOFU, TEMPEH, MISO, ETC

Organic Tofu

DRINKS

BEERS

Biere De Flandres, *Bitter:* Midland, Strong, Wessex; *Lagers:* American,
Bavarian Pilsner, Czech, Danish, French, German, German Pilsner, Italian, Lager, Spanish, Strong, Very Strong; Pale Ale

CHAMPAGNE

21st Century Brut, Blanc De Blancs, Blanc De Noirs, Brut Half, Brut Magnums, Brut Non Vintage, Rose, Vintage

CIDERS & PERRIES

Cider: **Organic**, Extra Strong, Strong Scrumpy, Vintage; *Traditional Ciders:* Medium Sweet, Strong Dry; Vintage Perry

LOW AND NON-ALCOHOLIC

Low-Alcohol Cider

SOFT

Bitter Lemon, Cola, *Cordial:* Elderflower, Lime Juice; Diet Cola, Fiery Ginger Beer Light, *Flavoured Water:* Blackberry, Cranberry & Blueberry, Elderflower, Grapefruit Spring Water, Melon & Cinnamon Water, Peach Spring Water, Scottish Water w Lemon, Scottish Water w Lime; *Ginger Ale:* American, Dry; Ginger & Lemon, Grapefruit & Barley, *High Juice:* Apple, Blackcurrant, Grape & Peach, Lemon, Low Sugar Blackcurrant, Orange, Pink Grapefruit; Lemon & Lime, *Lemonade:* Standard, Still, w Lemon, White; *Low-Cal:* American Ginger Ale, Bitter Lemon, Lemonade, Tonic Water; *No added sugar:* Apple & Blackcurrant, Lemon, Orange & Apricot, Orange Squash; *Old*

Fashioned: Ginger Beer, Lemonade; Orange & Mango Drink, *Refresher:* Apple & Rhubarb, Gooseberry & Elderflower; Soda Water, Sparkling Cream Soda, *Squash:* Apple & Blackcurrant, Apple & Raspberry, Orange, Tropical; Summerfruit Barley, *Tonic Water:* Diet w lemon, Standard, w Lemon; *Traditional:* Cream Soda, Ginger Beer

SPIRITS & APERITIFS

Armagnac, Brandy 3yr, Calvados, *Cognac:* Fine, Millennium Vsop, Vsop Fine; Dunkelweiss, *Gin:* **Organic**, Grain; *Rum:* West Indies, White; *Sherries:* Dry Amont, Manzanilla, Oloroso, Rich Cream; *Vodka:* **Organic**, Canadian, Standard; *Whiskies:* Bourbon, Irish Malt, Island Malt 10yr, Islay Malt, Scotch, Single Grain 7 Yr, Single Highland Malt 12yr, Speyside Malt 12yr, Whisky 5yr

WINES - RED

Bistro Rouge, Carnelian Merlot, Cotes du Rhone, Rose D'anjou

WINES - WHITE

Bistro Blanc, Chenin / Torrontes, Colombard Chardonnay, Touraine Sauvignon Chardonnay VDP

HEALTHCARE

VITAMINS & MINERALS

Chew Vit C 500mg 30s, Chewable Calcium & Vit D 30, Folic Acid Tablets 90's, Vit B Complex 60, Vit C 60 Mg 90s

TOILETRIES & COSMETICS

BATH & SHOWER

Shower Gel: Lilacmist, Orchard

CONDITIONERS & HAIRCARE

Conditioner: Deep Nourish , Light / Daily

SHAMPOOS

Cleanse / Refresh, Enhance / Shine, Restore & Balance

TOOTHPASTES & ORAL HYGEINE

Fresh Toothpaste Pump

BABY,
INFANT & CHILDCARE

TOILETRIES ETC

Baby Wipes: Fragranced, Fragrance-Free

HOME & OFFICE

BLEACH

Thick Bleach: Aqua, Citrus, Forest, Original

ANIMAL-FREE CRITERIA

To qualify for inclusion in the Animal free shopper, products must, as far as is possible and practical, be entirely free from animal involvement.

NO ANIMAL INGREDIENTS

The manufacture and/or development of the product, and where applicable its ingredients, must not involve, or have involved, the use of any animal product, by-product or derivative

SUCH AS:

• **animal-derived additives** — (see below) • **animal fibres** — angora, astrakhan, cashmere, mohair, wool • **animal milks** • **animal milk derivatives** — casein, caseinates, lactates, lactic acid, lactose • **bee products** — bee pollen, bee venom, beeswax, honey, propolis, royal jelly • **dairy products and by-products** — butter, cheese, whey, yoghurt • **eggs and their derivatives** (eg albumen, lecithin, lutein • **items obtained directly from the slaughter of animals** — fish (including anchovies), game and their derivatives (eg meat/fish extracts and stocks), poultry, meat • **marine animal products** — ambergris, capiz, caviar(e), chitin, coral, fish scales, fishmeal, isinglass, marine oils and extracts (eg fish oils, shark oil (squalene or squalane), seal oil, whale oil), natural sponge, pearl, roe, seal meat, shellfish, sperm oil, spermaceti wax, whale meat • **miscellaneous** — amniotic fluids, animal and fish glues, carmine/carminic acid, catgut, chamois, cochineal, crushed snails or insects, fixatives (eg musk, civet, castoreum) hormones (eg oestrogen, progesterone, testosterone) ivory, lanolin(e), oil of mink, parchment, placenta, silk, shellac, snake venom, some vitamins (eg D3), urea, vellum, and any carriers, processing aids or release agents containing/comprising substances of animal origin • **slaughter by-products** — animal fats (eg dripping, lard, suet, tallow), amino acids, aspic, bone, bone charcoal, bone meal, bristles, collagen, down, dried blood, fatty acid derivatives, feathers, fur, gelatin(e), glycerin(e)/glycerol, hair, hides (leather, suede etc), hoof & horn meal, oleic acid, oleoic oil, oleostearin, pepsin, proteins (eg elastin, keratin, reticulin), rennet, skins, stearates, stearic acid, stearin(e)

Vegetable, mineral or plant/mineral-derived synthetic forms of these substances are acceptable, as are microbiologically-fermented substances of plant origin.

270

NO ANIMAL TESTING

The development and / or manufacture of the product, and where applicable its ingredients, must not involve, or have involved, testing of any sort on animals conducted at the initiative of the manufacturer or on its behalf, or by parties over whom the manufacturer has effective control.

ADDITIVES

A food additive alters the properties of a basic foodstuff or mixture of foodstuffs for the purpose of achieving one, or a combination of, the following: aiding the production process, preserving, modifying consumer perception. The majority of additives possess no nutritive value.

All the countries of the European Union share a common list of additives. They are preceded with an 'E' to show they have been approved for use within the Union and must be displayed on the labels of all foods containing them. Some additives do not have E-numbers and therefore do not have to be declared. These include solvents, used to dilute other additives such as colourings and to extract flavours. Flavourings constitute the largest group of non-E additives.

The addition of substances to modify food is by no means a new phenomenon. Salt, for example, has been used as a preservative since c3000BC. However, the sheer number of additives available for use today, the routine and insidious use of animal-derived substances, the known health problems associated with some additives (including eczema, hyperactivity, nausea, allergies, asthma and migraine) — hazards of others that may yet come to light, and the totally unnecessary and morally objectionable requirement to test new additives on animals, all provide the animal free shopper with an incentive to avoid additive-containing products where alternatives are available.

Note: All products appearing in the Animal Free Shopper containing additives listed in the **POSSIBLY ANIMAL-DERIVED** category have been judged to be animal free on the basis of manufacturer/distributor declarations.

ANIMAL-DERIVED ADDITIVES

• **E120** carmine/cochineal • **E542** edible bone phosphate • **E901** beeswax • **E904** shellac • **calcium mesoinositol hexaphosphate** • **lactose** • **sperm oil** • **spermaceti**

POSSIBLY ANIMAL-DERIVED

• **E101** riboflavin, lactoflavin, vitamin B12 • **E101a** riboflavin 5'-phosphate • **E153** (believed animal-free version only may be used in food) carbon black, vegetable carbon • **E161(b)** lutein • **E161(g)** canthaxantin • **E236** formic acid • **E237** sodium formate • **E238** calcium formate • **E270** lactic acid • **E322** lecithin • **E325** sodium lactate • **E326** potassium lactate • **E327** calcium lactate • **E422** glycerol (glycerine) • **E430** (believed to be no longer permitted in food) polyoxyethylene (8) stearate, polyoxyl (8) stearate • **E431** polyoxyethylene (40) stearate, polyoxyl (40) stearate • **E432** polyoxyethylene sorbitan monolaurate, polysorbate 20, tween 20 • **E433** polyoxyethylene sorbitan mono-oleate, polysorbate 80, tween 80 • **E434** polyoxyethylene sorbitan monopalmitate, polysorbate 40, tween 40 • **E435** polyoxyethylene sorbitan monostearate, polysorbate 60, tween 60 • **E436** polyoxyethylene sorbitan tristearate, polysorbate 65, tween 65 • **E470(a)** sodium, potassium and calcium salts of fatty acids • **E470(b)** magnesium salts of fatty acids • **E471** glycerides of fatty acids, glyceryl monostearate, glyceryl distearate • **E472(a)** acetic acid esters of glycerides of fatty acids, acetoglycerides, glycerol esters • **E472(b)** lactic acid esters of glycerides of fatty acids, lactylated glycerides, lactoglycerides • **E472(c)** citric acid esters of glycerides of fatty acids • **E472(d)** — tartaric acid esters of glycerides of fatty acids • **E472(e)** mono and diacetyltartaric acid esters of glycerides of fatty acids **E472(f)** mixed acetic and tartaric acid esters of mono- and di-glycerides of fatty acids • **E473** sucrose esters of fatty acids • **E474** sucroglycerides • **E475** polyglycerol esters of fatty acids • **E476** polyglycerol esters of polycondensed fatty acids of castor oil, polyglycerol polyricinoleate; polyglycerol esters of dimerised fatty acids of soya bean oil • **E477** propylene glycol esters of fatty acids; propane-1,2-diol esters of fatty acids • **E478** lactylated fatty acid esters of gylcerol and propane-1,2-diol • **E479(b)** thermally oxidised soya bean oil interacted with mono- and di-glycerides of fatty acids • **E481** sodium stearoyl-2-lactylate • **E482** calcium stearoyl-2-lactylate • **E483** stearyl tartrate • **E491** sorbitan monostearate • **E492** sorbitan tristearate, span 65 • **E493** sorbitan monolaurate, span 20 • **E494** sorbitan mono-oleate, span 80 • **E495** sorbitan monopalmitate, span 40 • **E570** fatty acids (including myristic, stearic, palmitic and oleic), butyl stearate • **E572** magnesium salts of fatty acids (including magnesium stearate); calcium stearate • **E585** ferrous lactate • **E627** guanosine 5'-disodium phosphate, sodium guanylate, disodium guanylate • **E631** sodium 5'-inosinate • **E635** sodium 5'-ribonucleotide • **E640** glycine and its sodium salt • **E920** L-cysteine hydrochloride • **E1518** glyceryl mono-, di- and tri-acetate (triacetin) • **calcium hepatonate** • **calcium phytate** • **diacetin, glyceryl** • **leucine** • **monoacetin** • **oxystearin** • and **any unspecified flavourings**

GLOSSARY OF ANIMAL SUBSTANCES

A '*****' indicates that non-animal (synthetic, vegetable or plant/mineral-derived) versions/sources by the same name are known to exist.

• **albumen/albumin** egg white Use/s: food binder • **alpha hydroxy acids (AHAs)*** naturally occurring chemicals derived from fruit or milk Use/s: cosmetics • **ambergris** morbid concretion obtained from the intestine of the sperm whale Use/s: perfumes • **amino acids*** 'building blocks' of proteins • **amniotic fluid** fluid surrounding the foetus within the placenta Use/s: cosmetics • **amylase*** enzyme in saliva and pancreatic juice • **anchovy** small fish of the herring family. Often an ingredient of Worcester sauce and pizza toppings Use/s: flavour enhancer • **angora** fibre obtained from rabbits or goats Use/s: clothing • **aspic** savoury jelly derived from meat and fish Use/s: glazing agent • **astrakhan** skin of still born or very young lambs from a breed originating in Astrakhan, Russia Use/s: clothing • **beeswax (E901)** secreted by bees to produce combs Use/s: furniture and floor polishes, candles, cosmetics • **bone/bonemeal** animal bone Use/s: horticultural fertiliser, bone china ornaments, crockery, supplements • **brawn** boiled meat, ears and tongue of pig Use/s: foodstuff • **bristle*** stiff animal hair, usually from pigs Use/s: brushes • **calcium mesoinositol hexaphosphate** Use/s: baked goods, soft drinks, processed vegetables • **capiz** shell Use/s: lampshades • **carmine/carminic acid (E120)** red pigment obtained from cochineal Use/s: food and drink dyes • **casein** main protein of milk Use/s: cheese making • **cashmere** fine wool from the cashmere goat and wild goat of Tibet Use/s: clothing • **castoreum** obtained from the anal sex gland of the beaver Use/s: fixative in perfumes • **catgut** dried and twisted intestines of the sheep or horse Use/s: stringed musical instruments, surgical stitching • **caviar(e)** roe of the sturgeon and other fish Use/s: a relish • **charcoal*** charred bone or wood Use/s: clarifying agent • **chitin** organic base of the hard parts of insects and crustacea eg shrimps, crabs Use/s: conditioners and skin care products, thickener and moisturiser in shampoos • **chamois** soft leather from the skin of the chamois antelope, sheep, goats, deer etc Use/s: cleaning cloth • **cholecalciferol** see **D3** • **civet** substance scraped from glands in the anal pouch of the civet cat Use/s: fixative in perfumes • **cochineal (E120)** dyestuff consisting of the dried bodies of scale insects. Used for making carmine Use/s: red food and drink colouring • **cod liver oil** oil extracted from the liver of cod and related fish Use/s: food supplement • **coral** hard calcareous substance consisting of the continuous skeleton secreted by coelenterate polyps for their support and habitation Use/s: ornaments • **collagen** constituent of connective tissue which yields gelatin(e) on boiling Use/s: cosmetics, sausage skins • **D3 (cholecalciferol)** vitamin derived from lanolin or fish oil Use/s: vitamin and food supplements •

deoxyribonucleic acid (DNA) * controls protein synthesis/stores genetic information. Found in all animal and plant cells Use/s: cosmetics, genetically-modified organisms, shampoos • **down** underplummage of fowls (especially duck and goose) Use/s: filling quilts, pillows, sleeping bags, padded clothing • **dripping** melted animal fat Use/s: frying • **eider down** small, soft feathers from the breast of the eider duck Use/s: filling quilts • **elastin** protein uniting muscle fibres in meat Use/s: moisturiser in cosmetics • **fatty acids** * organic compounds: saturated, polyunsaturated and unsaturated • **feather** epidermal appendage of a bird Uses: fashion accessory, feather dusters • **felt** * cloth made of wool, or of wool and fur or hair Use/s: clothing • **gelatin(e)** jelly obtained by boiling animal tissues (skin, tendons, ligaments etc) or bones Use/s: confectionery, biscuits, capsules, jellies, photographic film, match heads • **glycerin(e)/glycerol (E422)** * clear, colourless liquid which may be derived from animal fats, synthesised from propylene or from fermentation of sugars Use/s: solvent for flavours, texture improver, humectant • **hide** animal skin (raw or tanned) Use/s: clothing and footwear, clothing accessories, upholstery • **insulin** * pancreas of cattle, sheep or pigs Uses: managing diabetes **isinglass** very pure form of gelatin(e) obtained from the air bladders of some freshwater fishes, especially the sturgeon Use/s: clarifying alcoholic drinks, jellies • **keratin** protein found in hair, horns, hoofs and feathers Use/s: shampoos and conditioners, fertiliser • **L'cysteine hydrochloride (E920)** * manufactured from animal hair and chicken feathers, or synthetically from coal tar Use/s: shampoo, improving agent for white flour • **lactic acid (E270)** * acid produced by the fermentation of milk sugar but also by fermentation in pickles, cocoa and tobacco Use/s: acidulant in confectionery, soft drinks, pickles and sauces • **lactose** milk sugar Use/s: tablet filler, sweetener, 'carrier' for flavouring agents — especially in crisps • **lanolin(e)** fat extracted from sheep's wool Use/s: cleaning products, an emollient and emulsifer used in cosmetics — especially lipsticks • **lard** fat surrounding the stomach and kidneys of the pig, sheep and cattle Use/s: culinary • **leather** tanned hide (mostly from cattle but also sheep, pigs, goats etc) Use/s: clothing and footwear, clothing accessories, upholstery • **lecithin (E322)** * fatty substance found in nerve tissues, egg yolk, blood and other tissues. Mainly obtained commercially from soya bean, peanut and corn Use/s: emulsifier in baked goods and confectionery • **lutein(E161(b))** * substance of deep yellow colour found in egg yolk. Obtained commercially from marigold Use/s: food colouring • **mohair** cloth or yarn made from the hair of the angora goat Use/s: clothing • **musk** * substance secreted in a gland or sac by the male musk deer Use/s: perfume • **oleic acid** * fatty acid occurring in animal and vegetable fats Use/s: soaps, cosmetics, ointments • **oleoic oil** liquid obtained from pressed tallow Use/s: margarines • **oleostearin** solid obtained from pressed tallow Use/s: soap and candle making • **oestrogen** * female sex hormone from cow ovaries or pregnant mares' urine Use/s: cosmetics, body building supplements, hormone creams • **parchment** * skin of the sheep or goat, dressed and prepared for writing etc • **pearl** ('Mother of',

274

or 'cultured') concretion of layers of pain-dulling nacre formed around a foreign particle within the shell of various bivalve molluscs, principally the oyster Use/s: jewellery and decorative • **pepsin** enzyme found in gastric juices Use/s: cheese making • **placenta** organ by which the foetus is attached to the umbilical cord Use/s: cosmetics • **progesterone*** sex hormone Use/s: hormone creams • **propolis** bee glue. Used by bees to stop up crevices and fix combs to the hive Use/s: toiletries and cosmetics • **rennet*** extract of calf stomach. Contains the enzyme renin which clots milk Use/s: cheese making, junkets • **reticulin** one of the structural elements (together with elastin and collagen) of skeletal muscle • **ribonucleic acid (RNA)** * see **deoxyribonucleic acid (DNA)** • **roe** eggs obtained from the abdomen of slaughtered female fish Use/s: a relish • **royal jelly** food on which bee larvae are fed and which causes them to develop into queen bees Use/s: food supplement • **sable** fur from the sable marten, a small carnivorous mammal Use/s: clothing, artists' brushes • **shellac (E904)** insect secretion Use/s: hair spray, lip sealer, polishes, glazing agent • **silk** cloth made from the fibre produced by the larvae ('silk worm') of certain bombycine moths, the harvesting of which entails the destruction of the insect Use/s: clothing, cosmetics • **sodium 5'-inosinate** occurs naturally in muscle. Prepared from fish waste Use/s: flavour enhancer • **sperm oil** oil found in the head of various species of whales Use/s: candle making • **spermaceti wax** fatty substance found mainly in the head of the sperm whale, other whales and dolphins Use/s: medicines, candle making, cosmetics • **sponge*** aquatic animal or colony of animals of a 'low order', characterised by a tough elastic skeleton of interlaced fibres Use/s. bathing aid • **squalene/squalane*** found in the liver of the shark (and rats) Use/s: toiletries and cosmetics • **stearate*** salt of stearic acid Use/s: body building supplements • **stearic acid (E570)*** organic acid prepared from stearin • **stearin(e)*** general name for the three glycerids (monostearin, distearin, tristearin). Formed by the combination of stearic acid and glycerin; chiefly applied to tristearin, which is the main constituent of tallow or suet Use/s: medicines, skin softener in toiletries and cosmetics • **suede*** kid-, pig- or calf-skin, tanned Use/s: clothing and footwear • **suet*** solid fat prepared from the kidneys of cattle and sheep Use/s: cooking • **tallow** hard animal fat, especially that obtained from the parts about the kidneys of ruminating animals Use/s: soap and candle making • **taurine*** amino acid • **testosterone*** male hormone Use/s: body building supplements • **urea*** waste nitrogen formed in the liver and excreted by the kidneys Use/s: toiletries and cosmetics • **vellum*** fine parchment prepared from the skins of calves, lambs or kids Use/s: writing material • **vitamin A*** (retinol) derived from fish liver oil or egg yolk Use/s: cosmetics, food supplement • **velvet*** fabric made usually of silk but also rayon or nylon Use/s: clothing • **volaise** ostrich meat • **whey** residue from milk after the removal of the casein and most of the fat. By-product of cheese making Use/s: margarines, biscuits, crisps, cleaning products • **wool** hair forming the fleecy coat of the domesticated sheep (and similar animals) Use/s: clothing

ANIMAL TESTING CRITERIA

It remains the case that animal protection groups and manufacturers promote a number of variations on the 'not tested on animals' theme. Depending on one's perspective or strategy, all have their strengths and weaknesses.

The criterion used to complete the Animal Free Shopper recognises that most substances have been, and some may continue to be, animal tested and simply requires that a product's manufacturer, or 'related' company, has not initiated testing on either the finished product or, where applicable, the ingredients.

For those readers who prefer companies using either a fixed cut-off date or the Humane Cosmetics Standard (see below), an appropriate symbol (see **KEY**, page iii) appears in the product listings after the company name.

HUMANE COSMETICS STANDARD

In response to pressure from animal protection groups and consumers across Europe, the European Parliament proposed a ban on the marketing of animal tested cosmetics (Directive 93/35). However, early in 1997, to widespread dismay, the European Union (EU) postponed its 1 January 1998 target date until into the new century. An international coalition of animal protection groups from across the EU and North America drew up an international Humane Cosmetics Standard and launched a major campaign calling on all manufacturers and retailers to adopt it.

Co-ordinated (in the UK) by the British Union for the Abolition of Vivisection (BUAV), the standard requires companies not to conduct, commission, nor be party to any animal testing either now or in the future, and to adopt a fixed cut-off date for ingredients testing. The cut-off date is chosen by the company, but must be before the date that it applies to join the standard.

FIXED CUT-OFF DATE

A company that has adopted a fixed cut-off date has a policy of using only ingredients that have not been tested on animals by, or at the initiative of, either it or its suppliers since a specified date. In addition, the company will not initiate animal tests on its finished products.

The Cosmetics Industry Coalition for Animal Welfare (CICAW) encourages cosmetic companies to adopt an animal testing fixed cut-off date — preferably 1976 (the year the EU required all new ingredients to be safety(animal)-tested).

See 'Vivisection' (page 26) for more details on animal testing.

OTHER ETHICAL CONSIDERATIONS

To qualify for inclusion in the Animal free shopper a product need only be free of animal ingredients and animal testing. However, whilst avoiding products having direct animal involvement is a coherent and far-reaching ethical stance in itself, many animal free shoppers choose to make purchases on a wide range of additional ethical considerations pertaining to humans, animals and the environment — such as:

- **vegan ownership** Some shoppers prefer to support those companies which are wholly or partly owned by vegans (see **KEY**, page iii)
- **product range** Many companies manufacture or distribute both animal and non-animal products. Given the choice, many animal-free shoppers prefer to buy from those companies whose entire range is animal-free (see **KEY**, page iii)
- **company activities** A number of companies manufacturing or distributing animal-free (and animal) products are involved directly in animal abuse — such as the meat and dairy industries.
- **company connections** Some seemingly innocuous companies have parent, sister or subsidiary companies which are involved directly in animal abuse. See company details (page 300) for parent companies of listed brands.
- **company affiliations** Possible animal abuse affiliations include: The British Industrial Biological Research Association (BIBRA), Research Defence Society (RDS), British Field Sports Society (BFSS), Game Conservancy.
- **company sponsorships & donations** Common areas include animal-connected medical research and sporting events.
- **organised boycotts** Even large multi-national companies have ceased an objectionable activity when threatened with, or subjected to, a boycott campaign. Though not always successful, it is argued that boycotts are, nevertheless, a useful means by which to heighten public awareness.

- **use of by-products** The production of animal-free goods may involve the generation of by-products which are then employed for purposes the animal free shopper would not normally support. Examples include: white flour — bran — animal feed; wheat etc — straw — animal bedding; linseed, rapeseed, soya — cake/meal — animal feed; sugar beet — pulp — animal feed.
- **pesticide use** – the excessive use of chemical pesticides and fertilisers damages the environment and kills wildlife. Many animal-free shoppers prefer to avoid contributing to the destruction of our countryside and instead chose organic products – we have printed these products in bold and highlighted those companies whose entire product range is organic (see **KEY** page iii).
- **genetically-modified organisms** See **GENETICALLY-MODIFIED ORGANISMS**, (page 34 and **KEY**, page iii).
- **microbiological testing -** in order to ensure the safety of their products, and to forestall damaging law suits which might arise following the discovery of a defect, many manufacturers test batches of their products for the presence of bacterial contaminants. The nutrient media 'fed' to the bacteria (in order to identify them) are commonly derived from the slaughterhouse or the dairy industry. Virtually all foodstuffs, and most toiletries and cosmetics, are subject to testing involving the use of animal derivatives. Unfortunately, animal free shoppers cannot avoid microbiologically-tested foodstuffs, which not only include processed foods but also unprocessed fruits and vegetables — and even drinking water!

Recognising that human and animal rights are inextricably linked and that all life is dependent upon the well-being of the planet, the animal free shopper might also wish to avoid companies involved in or with: cash crops, environmentally damaging practices, irresponsible marketing, land rights, low wages and poor conditions, and oppressive regimes.

FURTHER INFORMATION

The Ethical Consumer Research Association Unit 21, 41 Old Birley St, Manchester M15 5RF **t** 0161 226 2929 **w** www.ethicalconsumer.org **e** mail@ ethicalconsumer.org

Publishes *The Ethical Consumer*: a magazine providing information on companies behind brand names across a range of ethical issues — including 'Animal Testing', 'Factory Farming' and 'Other Animal Rights'.

ANIMAL FREE SHOPS

The entirely animal free retail outlets listed below are run by vegans and stock a wide range of products.

- **Devon** *Exeter Body Piercing* 17 Fore St Centre, Fore St, Exeter EX4 3AN **t** 01392 494545 **e** piercing@eclipse.co.uk

- **Gwynedd** *Vegonia Wholefoods* 49 High St, Port Madoc LL49 9LR **t** 01766 515195 **e** vegonia@vegonia.worldonline.co.uk

- **Manchester** *Unicorn Grocery* 89 Albany Rd, Chorlton, Manchester M21 0BN **t** 0161 861 0010 **e** office@unicorn-grocery.co.uk

- **Nottinghamshire** *Suma Centre* 188 Mansfield Rd, Nottingham NG1 3HW **t** 0845 458 9595 **e** rainbow@innotts.co.uk

- **West Midlands** *One Earth Shop* 54 Allison St, Digbeth, Birmingham B5 5TH **t** 0121 632 6909 **e** rickards@lineone.net

- **Germany** *Vegan-Shop & Versand* Hohenstrasse 50, D-60385 Frankfurt, Germany **t** 0049 (0)69 440989

ONLINE SHOPS

- **Animal Aid** www.animalaid.org.uk/shop
- **Cruelty Free Shop** www.crueltyfreeshop.com
- **Ethical Wares** www.ethicalwares.com
- **Meadowsweet** www.crueltyfreeshop.com
- **Vegan Society** www.vegansociety.com/shop
- **Veganline** www.veganline.com
- **Veganstore** www.veganstore.co.uk
- **Vegetarian Shoes** www.vegetarian-shoes.co.uk
- **Via Vegan Ltd** www.viavegan.com
- **World's End Trading Company** www.worldsend.co.uk

CONTACT NETWORKS

BUSINESS

- **Vegan Business Connection**, Patrick Smith, c/o Veggies, 245 Gladstone Street, Nottingham, NG7 6HX **t** 0845 458 9595 **e** vbc@veggies.org.uk **w** www.veggies.org/vbc.htm
- **Vegan Village**, Libby & Andy Watts, Imaner House, 14 Wynford Grove, Leeds, West Yorkshire, LS16 6JL **t** 0113 293 9385 **e** info@veganvillage.co.uk **w** www.veganvillage.co.uk

COMMUNITIES & PROJECTS

- **Brynderwen Vegan Community Project**, Malcolm Horne, Brynderwen, Crymlyn Road, Llansamlet, Swansea SA7 9XT **t** 01792 792442 **e** vegancom@btinternet.com
- **Living Land Project**, Living Land Co-Op Ltd, 25a Stanley Road Whalley Range, Manchester, Greater Manchester, M16 8HS **t** 0161 232 9094
- **Plants For A Future**, The Field, Higher Penpoll, Lostwithiel, Cornwall, PL22 0NG **t** 0845 458 4719 **e** veganic@gardener.com **w** www.pfaf.org
- **Sunseed Trust** www.sunseed.org.uk

FAMILIES

- **Vegan Children's Book List**, Pauline Tilbury, 91 Idlecombe Road, SW17 9TD **t** 020 8672 1725
- **Vegan Families Network**, Lesley Dove, 4 Wooster Mews, Harrow, Middlesex, HA2 6QS **t** 020 8861 1233 **e** Lesley@vegan4life.org.uk
- **Vegan Family House**, Lucy Burnett, 29 Burnside Crescent, Stuartfield, Peterhead, Aberdeenshire, AB42 5FL **e** veganfamily@veganfamily.co.uk **w** www.veganfamily.co.uk
- **VegParents NW** **e** vegparentsnw@ukveggie.com

INTERNATIONAL

- **Vegan Society International Contact** c/o The Vegan Society, Donald Watson House, 7 Battle Rd, St Leonards-on-Sea, East Sussex, TN37 7AA **t** +44 (0)20 8265 3277 **e** vegans@parlyweb.demon.co.uk
- **International Vegetarian Union** www.ivu.org **e** editor@ivu.org
- **European Vegetarian Union** www.europeanvegetarian.org **e** evu@ivu.org
- **World Animal Net** www.worldanimalnet.org
- **VegDining** www.vegdining.com
- **Veggies' Animal Contacts Directory** www.veggies.org.uk/acd

---

- **Australia** Vegan society of Australia, PO Box 85, Seaford, Victoria 3198 **w** www.veganaustralia.org **e** info@veganaustralia.org
- **Austria** Vegane Gesellschaft Oesterreich **w** www.vegan.at
- **Denmark** Vegana, Raadmand steins alle 45, 7 DK-2000, Fredriksberg, Denmark **t** +45 70200510 **w** www.vegana.dk **e** info@vegana.dk
- **Finland** Vegaaniliitto Ry, PO Box 320, SF-00151, Helsinki, Finland **w** www.vegaaniliitto.fi
- **Holland** Vereniging Voor Veganisme, Postbus 1087, 6801 BB, Arnhem, Netherlands **t** +31 30 230 0434 **w** www.veganisme.org **e** info@veganisme.non-profit.nl
- **Hong Kong** Hong Kong Vegan Society, GPO Box 6450, Hong Kong **w** www.ivu.org/hkvegan/ **e** annie@hongkongvegan.com
- **Indonesia** The Indonesian Vegan Society, Jakarta Barat, Indonesia **t** +628159927067 **w** www.i-v-s.org **e** info@i-v-s.org
- **Italy** www.vegan.italia.com
- **Latin America** Marly Winckler, Servidao do Nilton, 412, Praia de Cacupe, 88050-170 Florianopolis SC Brazil **t** 0055 48 2351609 **w** www.ivu.org/latinam **e** latinam@ivu.org
- **Luxembourg** De Vegabond, Dr Claude Pasquini, c/o BP 44, l-3701 Rumelange, Luxembourg
- **New Zealand** VEGANZ, PO BOX 4309, Shortland St, Auckland, New Zealand **t** NZ 021 890 629 **e** dwyn@kiwilink.co.nz
- **Spain** Asociación Vegana Española (AVE), Apartado Postal 478, 29740 Torre del Mar (M·laga), Spain **t** 34-95-2513981 **w** www.ivu.org/ave **e** ave@ivu.org
- **Sweden** Veganforeningen I Sverige, Ulla Troeng, Klovervagen 6, S-647 00, Mariefred, Sweden **t** +46 159 12 467 **w** www.vegan.org.se

- **USA** American Vegan Society, 56 Dinshah Lane, P.O. Box 369, Malaga NJ 08328 **t** 856-694-2887 **w** www.americanvegan.org

LOCAL

- **Birmingham Vegetarian and Vegan Group** c/o 5 Esher Road, Kingstanding, Birmingham B44 9QJ **t** 0121 353 2442
- **Bristol Vegetarian & Vegan Society** Jill Greenway **t** 01934 843853 Roger Hards **e** rogerhards-venusmead@breathemail.net
- **Chester & Clwyd Vegetarians & Vegans** Brian Burnett, Nant Yr Hafod Cottage, Llandegla, Wrexham LL11 3BG **t** 01978 790442 **e** indesigneko@aol.com
- **Croydon & Sutton Vegans** Pat Mear, 12 Furze Ct, Ashburton Rd, Croydon, CR0 6AP **t** 0208 654 3740 **e** pat_croydonvegans@hotmail.com
- **East Riding Vegans** Carol Nicholson **t** 01482 471119
- **Essex Vegans** Karin Ridgers **t** 01277 655460 **e** veganessex@hotmail.com
- **Friends Vegetarian Society** Charles Ryder, 9 Astons Close, Woods Lane, Amblecote, Nr Stourbridge, W. Mids DY5 2QT **t** 01384 423899
- **Glasgow Vegans** Jo Crozier **t** 0141 954 6519
- **Gloucester & Hereford Vegans& Vegetarians** 13 Croft Rd, Newent, GL18 1SW **t** 01531 822375
- **Gloucestershire Vegans t** 01666 503892 **e** veganvicky@aol.com
- **Highland Veggies and Vegans** c/o Scottish Voluntary Action, 1 Connel Court, Ardconnel Street, Inverness, IV2 3EY **t** 01463 712945 **e** info@highlandveggies.org **w** www.highlandveggies.org
- **Isle of Wight Vegetarians & Vegans** c/o Keeper's Lock, Youngswoods Way, Alverstone, Sandown **t** 01983 407098
- **Leeds Vegetarian & Vegan Society** Ian Davison, 41 Hillcourt Drive, Leeds, LS132AN **t** 0113 2572760 **e** leedsveg@ukgateway.net
- **Leicester Vegetarians & Vegans** Sue 0116 240 4010 **w** http://myweb.tiscali.co.uk/leicsveg
- **London Vegans** 24-hour info line: 0208 931 1904
- **ManVeg for Vegans** (Manchester) manveg@ukveggie.com
- **Norfolk Vegetarian and Vegan Society** Gabrielle Rose **t** 01603 893620 **e** vegerose@hotmail.com **w** vegfolk.co.uk
- **North Riding Vegetarians & Vegans** Patricia Tricker, Cottage 3, Arrathorne, Bedale, DL8 1NA **t** 0845 458 4714 **e** patricia@p-m-t.freeserve.co.uk
- **North-East Vegans** 12 Taunton Ave, Chirton Grange, North Shields, Northumberland, NE29 8PA **t** 0191 258 6704

- **Northern Ireland Vegetarians & Vegans** Mrs Beth Gourley, 66 Ravenhill Gardens, Belfast, BT6 8GQ **t** 028 90 281640
- **Oxford Vegetarians & Vegans** 57 Sharland Cl, Grove, Wantage, OX12 0AF t 01235 769425 **e** oxveg@ivu.org **w** www.ivu.org/oxveg/
- **Rugby Vegans** Andrea Elson, 4 Keynes Dr, Bilton, Rugby, CV22 7ST **t** 01788 810805 **e** therugbyvegan@yahoo.co.uk
- **Sevenoaks Vegans** Jackie Golding **t** 01732 461701
- **Sheffield Vegan Society** c/o Recyc, 54 Upperthorpe Rd, S6 3EB
- **Shrewsbury Vegans** Ann **t** 01743 360620 **e** ann.henderson5@btopenworld.com
- **Solent Vegetarians & Vegans** John Curtis, 31 Cranbury Road, Eastleigh, Hants SO50 5HB t 023 80573133 **e** solentveg@ivu.org **w** www.ivu.org/solentveg
- **Southend Area Vegetarians** Soo Coleman 59 Stambridge Road Rochford Essex **t** 01702 540903 **e** soocoleman4@aol.com
- **Sussex Vegetarians & Vegans** Rob Sier, 30 Winchcombe Rd, Eastbourne, BN22 8DE **t** 01323 723855 or 01293 857281 **e** gofer59@email.com
- **Swindon & Area Single Vegans** Kathryn **t** 01793 532297
- **Tyne & Wear Vegetarian Group** Mrs Helen Speight, 14 Stephenson Court, North Shields NE30 1PQ **t** 0191 258 7853 **e** helensp8@yahoo.co.uk
- **Ulster Vegetarian Society** Mrs Margaret C Gunn-King, Braidujle, 120 Knockan Road, Nr Broughshane, Ballymena BT43 7LE **t** 028 25861202
- **VeggiTaters** (Nottingham) John Kennedy, **t** 0115 9609825 **e** ceinneidgh@lentils.fsnet.co.uk
- **Young Indian Vegetarians & Vegans** Nitin Mehta, 226 London Rd, Croydon, Surrey CR0 2TE **t** 020 8681 8884 **e** animalahimsa@yahoo.co.uk

SOCIAL

- **Vegan Camp** c/o 245 Gladstone St, Nottingham, NG7 6HX **t** 0845 330 3918 **e** info@vegancamp.org **w** www.vegancamp.org
- **Vegan Summer Gathering**, Brynderwen, Crymlyn Road, Llansamlet, Swansea, SA7 9XT **t** 01792 792442
- **Vegan World Ventures**, 4 Cameron Road, Seven Kings, Ilford, Essex, G3 8LA **t** 020 8220 2003
- **Vegetarian & Vegan Gay Group**, 86 Caledonian Road, N1 9DN **t** 020 8690 5397 **e** vvgg@freeuk.com **w** www.vvgg.freeserve.co.uk
- **Vegetarian Matchmakers**, Concord House 7 Waterbridge Court, Appleton, Warrington, Cheshire, WA4 3BJ **t** 01925 601609 **e** info@veggiematchmakers.com **w** www.veggiematchmakers.com

- **Veggie-Link**, 42 Hawthorne Crescent, Findern, Derby, DE6 6AN
  t 01283 703809
- **Vegi Ventures**, Castle Cottage, Castle Square Castle Acre,
  King's Lynn, Norfolk, PE32 2AJ **t** 01760 755888
  e holidays@vegiventures.com **w** www.vegiventures.com

SPORT

- **James Gorman MSF, MAB, Phys**, 25 Nore Farm Avenue, Emsworth,
  Hampshire, PO10 7NA **t** 07876673559
- **Vegetarian & Vegan Bodybuilding**, 17 Inglewood Road, Rainford,
  St Helens, Lancashire, WA11 7QL **e** david.fairclough5@virgin.net
  w www.veganbodybuilding.org
- **Vegetarian Cycling & Athletics Club**, 13 Peers Lane, Shenley Church
  End, Milton Keynes, Buckinghamshire, MK5 6BG **t** 01908 503919
  e vegcac@pgen.net **w** www.vegcac.co.uk

VEGAN SOCIETY LOCAL CONTACTS

An up-to-date list of our Local Contacts is published on our website and in
'*The Vegan*' every quarter or can be obtained by sending a SAE to our 'Local
Contacts Co-ordinator' c/o The Vegan Society.

USEFUL ADDRESSES

Many of the groups listed below have limited funds and therefore would probably
appreciate receiving an SAE with your enquiry.

ANIMAL EXPERIMENTS & ALTERNATIVES

• **British Anti-Vivisection Association**, PO Box 73 Chesterfield, Derbyshire S41
0YZ **e** bava@esmail.net **w** www.eurosolve.com/charity/bava • **British Union for the
Abolition of Vivisection**, 16a Crane Grove, Islington, London N7 8LB **t** 020 7700
4888 **e** info@buav.org **w** www.buav.org • **Doctors & Lawyers for Responsible
Medicine**, PO Box 302, London N8 9HD **t** 020 8340 9813 • **Dr Hadwen Trust for
Humane Research**, Dr Hadwen Hse, 84a Tilehouse St, Hitchin, Hertfordshire SG5
2DY **t** 01462 436819 **e** info@drhadwentrust.org.uk **w** www.drhadwentrust.org.uk
• **FRAME**, 96-98 North Sherwood St, Nottingham NG1 4EE **t** 0115 958 4740
e frame@frame.org.uk **w** www.frame.org.uk • **Humane Research Trust**, Brook

Hse, 29 Bramhall Lane South, Bramhall, Stockport SK7 2DN **t** 0161 439 8041 **e** members@humane.freeserve.co.uk **w** www.btinternet.com/~shawweb/hrt • **Lord Dowding Fund for Humane Research** see National Anti-Vivisection Society • **National Anti-Vivisection Society**, 261 Goldhawk Rd, London W12 9PE **t** 020 8846 9777 **e** info@navs.org.uk **w** www.navs.org.uk • **Nurses' Anti-Vivisection Movement**, PO Box 32, Matlock, Derbyshire DE4 3YJ **t** 01629 824664 • **People Against Vivisection**, PO Box 70, North Shields, Tyne & Wear NE29 0YP **t** 0191 296 3478 **e** djurs@cableinet.co.uk **w** http://wkweb5.cableinet.co.uk/djurs • **Plan 2000**, 234 Summergangs Rd, Hull HU8 8LL **t** 01482 786855 **w** www.eurosolve.com/charity/Plan2000 • **Quest Cancer Research**, Woodbury, Harlow Rd, Roydon, Harlow, Essex CM19 5HF **t** 01279 792233 **w** www.questcancer.org • **Save the Newchurch Guinea Pigs** SNPG, PO Box 74, Evesham, Worcs WR11 3WF **t** 01902 564734 **e** info@guineapigs.org.uk **w** www.guineapigs.org.uk • **Stop Huntingdon Animal Cruelty (SHAC)** **t** 0845 458 0630 **e** info@shac.net **w** www.shac.net • **Uncaged Campaigns**, 2nd Floor, St Matthew's House, 45 Carver St, Sheffield S1 4FT **t** 0114 272 2220 **e** uncaged.anti-viv@dial.pipex.com **w** www.uncaged.co.uk

BLOODSPORTS

• **Campaign for the Abolition of Angling**, BM Fish, London WC1N 3XX **t** 0870 458 4176 **e** pisces@pisces.demon.co.uk **w** www.anti-angling.com • **Conservative Anti-Hunt Council**, 38 Holway Ave, Taunton, Somerset TA1 3AR **t** 01823 286398 • **Hunt Saboteurs Association**, PO Box 5254, Northampton NN1 3ZA **t** 0845 458 0727 **e** info@huntsabs.org.uk **w** www.huntsabs.org.uk • **League Against Cruel Sports**, Sparling House, 83-87 Union St, London SE1 1SG **t** 020 7403 6155 **e** info@league.uk.com **w** www.league.uk.com • **National Anti-Hunt Campaign**, PO Box 66, Stevenage, Hertfordshire SG1 2TR **t** 01442 240246 **e** nahc@nahc.freeserve.co.uk • **Surrey Anti-Hunt Campaign**, BM Box 7099, London WC1N 3XX **t** 0771 903 1066 **e** surreyantihunt@yahoo.com **w** sahc.org.uk

CIRCUSES & ZOOS

• **Captive Animals Protection Society**, PO Box 43, Dudley, West Midlands DY3 3YP **t** 01384 456682 **e** caps-uk@dircon.co.uk **w** www.captiveanimals.org

'DEVELOPING WORLD'

• **Help International Plant Protein Organisation (HIPPO)**, The Old Vicarage, Llangynog, Carmarthen SA33 5BS **t** 01267 241547 **e** hippocharity@aol.com • **Vegfam**, The Sanctuary, nr Lydford, Okehampton, Devon EX20 4AL **t** 01822 820203 **e** vegfam@veganvillage.co.uk **w** www.veganvillage.co.uk/vegfam

DIET/LIFESTYLE

• **Bristol Cancer Help Centre**, Grove Hse, Cornwallis Gr, Clifton, Bristol BS8 4PG **t** 0117 980 9500 **w** www.bristolcancerhelp.org • **FRESH** (Fruitarian & Raw Energy Support & Help) Network PO Box 71, Ely, Cambridgeshire CB7 4GU **t** 0870 800 7070 **e** info@fresh-network.com **w** www.fresh-network.com • **Institute for Plant Based Nutrition**, 333 Bryn Mawr Ave, Bala Cynwyd, Pennsylvania 19004-2606, USA **t** 610 667 6876 **w** www.plantbased.org • **International Vegetarian Union t** 020 8265 3277 **e** info@ivu.org **w** www.ivu.org • **London Vegetarian Info Centre**, 2 Melcombe Gdns, Kenton, Harrow, Middlesex HA3 9RH **t** 020 8204 1231 • **Movement for Compassionate Living**, Burrow Farm, Highampton, Beaworthy, Devon EX21 5JQ **t** 01409 231264 **w** www.MCLveganway.org • **Physician's Committee for Responsible Medicine**, 5100 Wisconsin Ave, NW, Suite 400, Washington, DC 20016, USA **w** www.pcrm.org • **Raw Times w** www.rawtimes.com • **Vegan Information Network & ESCAPE**, PO Box 2801, Brighton BN1 3NH • **Vegan Views**, Harry Mather, Flat A15, 20 Dean Pk Rd, Bournemouth BH1 1DB **t** 01202 555712 **e** info@veganviews.org.uk **w** www.veganviews.org.uk • **Vegan Village** www.veganvillage.co.uk • **Vegetarian Society**, Parkdale, Dunham Rd, Altrincham, Cheshire WA14 4QG **t** 0161 925 2000 **e** info@vegsoc.demon.co.uk **w** www.vegsoc.org • **Vegetarian & Vegan Foundation**, 12 Queen Square, Brighton, BN1 3FD **t** 0845 456 1437 **e** info@vegetarian.org.uk **w** www.vegetarian.org.uk • **World Vegan Day**, c/o The Vegan Society, Donald Watson House, 7 Battle Rd, St Leonards-on-Sea, East Sussex, TN37 7AA **t** 0845 45 88244 **e** media@vegansociety.com **w** www.worldveganday.org • **Young Indian Vegetarians**, 226 London Rd, W Croydon CR0 2TF **t** 020 8681 8884 **e** animalahimsa@yahoo.co.uk **w** www.indian-vegetarians.org

DIRECT ACTION

• **Animal Liberation Front Press Office**, BM 4400, London WC1N 3XX **t** 07752 107515 • **Animal Liberation Front Supporters Group**, BM 1160, London WC1N 3XX 0870 138 5037 **e** info@alfsg.co.uk

FARMING & GROWING

• **Compassion in World Farming**, Charles Hse, 5a Charles St, Petersfield GU32 3EH **t** 01730 264208 **e** compassion@ciwf.co.uk **w** www.ciwf.co.uk • **Farm & Food Society**, 4 Willifield Way, London NW11 7XT **t** 020 8455 0634 • **Farm Animal Welfare Network**, PO Box 40, Holmfirth, Huddersfield HD7 1QY **t** 01484 688650

enry Doubleday Research Association, Ctre for Organic Gardening, Wolston
e, Ryton-on-Dunsmore, Coventry CV8 3LG t 024 7630 3517 • National
anisation Working Against Live Exports, St Josephs, Souldern, Bicester,
ordshire OX6 9LA t 01869 345243 • Plants for a Future 1 Lerryn View, Lerryn,
withiel, Cornwall PL22 0QJ t 01208 872 963 e veganic@gardener.com
www.pfaf.org • Soil Association, Bristol Hse, 86-88 Colston St, Bristol BS1 5BB
17 929 0661 e info@soilassociation.org w www.soilassociation.org • Vegan
anic Network, Anandavan, 58 High Lane, Chorlton, Manchester M21 9DZ t
1 860 4869 e veganorganic@supanet.com w www.veganorganic.com •
anic Garden Supplies/Information, c/o Weavers Way, Heath Farm Rd,
stead, N Walsham, Norfolk NR28 9AH t 01692 404570

R & LEATHER

ampaign Against Leather & Fur (CALF), BM 8889, London WC1N 3XX
lf@alrob.freeserve.co.uk • Campaign to Abolish the Fur Trade (CAFT)
Box 38, Manchester M60 1NX e caft@caft.demon.co.uk w www.caft.org.uk

NERAL

dvocates for Animals, 10 Queensferry St, Edinburgh EH2 4PG
31 225 6006 e advocates.animals@virgin.net
www.advocatesforanimals.org.uk • Animal Aid, The Old Chapel, Bradford St,
oridge TN9 1AW t 01732 364546 e info@animalaid.org.uk
www.animalaid.org.uk • Animal Concern, PO Box 5178, Dumbarton G82 5YJ
389 841639 e animals@jfrobins.force9.co.uk • Animal Cruelty Investigation
up, PO Box 8, Halesworth, Suffolk IP19 0JL t 01986 782280
ike@acigawis.freeserve.co.uk w www.acigawis.freeserve.co.uk • Animal
enders see National Anti-Vivisection Society • Chickens' Lib see Animal Aid •
thkind, Enefcohouse, Town Quay, Poole, Dorset BH15 1HJ t 01202 682366
o@earthkind.org.uk w www.earthkind.org.uk • IFAW, 8th Floor, 87-90 Albert
bankment, London SE1 7UD t 020 7587 6700 e info@ifaw.org w www.ifaw.org
ndon Greenpeace, 5 Caledonian Rd, London N1 9DX t 020 7713 1269
clibel@globalnet.co.uk w www.mcspotlight.org • People for the Ethical
atment of Animals (Europe), PO Box 3169, London SW18 4WJ t 020 8870
6 e info@petaeurope.org.uk w www.PETAEurope.org • Petsearch Register of
mals Lost & Found, 851 Old Lode La, Solihull, West Midlands B92 3JE
21 743 4133 e ukpetsearch@freeuk.com w www.ukpetsearch.freeuk.com •
ect for Animals, PO Box 6500, Nottingham NG4 3GB t 0115 952 5440
fo@respectforanimals.org w www.respectforanimals.org • RSPCA, Wilberforce
, Southwater, Horsham RH13 7WN t 0870 010 1181 e webmail@rspca.org.uk

w www.rspca.org.uk • **Viva!**, 12 Queen Sq, Brighton BN1 3FD **t** 0845 456 8220
e info@viva.org.uk **w** www.viva.org.uk • **World Society for the Protection of Animals**, 89 Albert Embankment, London SE1 7TP **t** 020 7793 0540
e wspa@wspa.org.uk **w** www.wspa.org.uk • **World Wide Fund for Nature**, Panda Hse, Weyside Pk, Catershall Lane, Godalming GU7 1XR **t** 01483 426444
w www.wwf-uk.org

MARINE ANIMALS

• **Breach Marine Protection**, 3 St John's St, Goole, East Yorkshire DN14 5QL
t 01405 769375 **e** breachenv@aol.com **w** www.members.aol.com/breachenv/home.htm
• **British Divers Marine Life Rescue**, 39 Ingram Rd, Gillingham, Kent ME7 1SB
t 01634 281680 • **Cetacea Defence**, PO Box 78, Shaftesbury, Dorset SP7 8ST
e cetaceadefence@hotmail.com **w** http://free.freespeech.org/cetaceadefence/ •
Marine Conservation Society, 9 Gloucester Rd, Ross-on-Wye, Herefordshire
HR9 5BU **t** 01989 566017 **e** info@mcsuk.org **w** www.mcsuk.mcmail.com •
Shellfish Network, Springside, Forest Rd, E Horsley, Leatherhead, Surrey
e shellfish_uk@hotmail.com KT24 5AZ **t** 01483 282995
w http://arc.enviroweb.org/shellfish/ • **Whale & Dolphin Conservation Society**,
Alexander Hse, James St West, Bath BA1 2BT **t** 01225 334511 **e** info@wdcs.org
w www.wdcs.org

MISCELLANEOUS

• **McLibel Support Campaign**, c/o 5 Caledonian Rd, London N1 9DX
t 020 7713 1269 **e** mclibel@globalnet.co.uk **w** www.mcspotlight.org • **Vegan
Bikers e** vb@eloi.nildram.co.uk **w** www.nildram.co.uk/veganmc • **Vegan /
Vegetarian Esperanto Group**, Brian Burnett, Nant Yr Hafod Cottage, Llandegla,
Wrexham, Denbighshire LL11 3BG **t** 01978 790442 **e** brianthesquirrel@compuserve.com
• **Vegetarian Housing Association** (Homes For Elderly Vegetarians) Chancery
House, St Nicholas Way, Sutton, Surrey, SM1 1JB **t** 020 8652 1934 **e**
office@veghousing.org.uk **w** www.veghousing.org.uk

PRISONERS' SUPPORT (ANIMAL RIGHTS/VEGAN)

• **Vegan Prisoners Support Group**, POB 194, Enfield, Middlesex EN1 3HD
t (emergencies only) 020 8292 8325 **e** hvpc@vpsg.freeserve.co.uk

RELIGIOUS

• **Anglican Society for the Welfare of Animals**, PO Box 7193, Hook, Basingstoke RG27 8GT **t** 0118 932 6586 **e** AngSocWelAnimals@cs.com **w** www.aswa.org.uk • **Animal Christian Concern**, PO Box 70, Horsforth, Leeds LS18 5BG **t** 0113 258 3517 • **Catholic Study Circle for Animal Welfare**, 12 Swan Court, Witney, Oxfordshire OX29 6EA **e** djonesark@waitrose.com **w** www.catholic-animals.org • **Christian Ecology**, Link, 20 Carlton Rd, Harrogate, North Yorkshire HG2 8DD **t** 01423 871616 **e** info@christian-ecology.org.uk **e** cel2000@christian-ecology.org.uk **w** www.christian-ecology.org.uk • **Christian Prayer Fellowship for the Protection of Animals**, 5 Wemyss Pl, Peebles EH45 8JT • **Jewish Vegetarian and Ecological Society**, 853-855 Finchley Rd, London NW11 8LX **t** 020 8455 0692 **e** jvs@ivu.org **w** www.ivu.org/jvs/ • **Kindness Unlimited**, The Old Vicarage, Llangynog, Carmarthen SA33 5BS **t** 01267 241547 **e** springoftruelinf@aol.com • **Pagan Animal Rights**, 110 Geoffrey Rd, Brockley, London SE4 1NU

WILD ANIMALS

• **Born Free Foundation**, 3 Grove Hse, Foundry La, Horsham, West Sussex RH13 5PL **t** 01403 240170 **e** wildlife@bornfree.org.uk **w** www.bornfree.org.uk • **British Hedgehog Preservation Society**, Knowbury Hse, Knowbury, Ludlow, Shropshire SY8 3LQ **t** 01584 890287 • **Care for the Wild International**, 1 Ashfold, Horsham Rd, Rusper, Horsham, West Sussex RH12 4QX **t** 01293 871596 **e** info@careforthewild.org.uk **w** www.careforthewild.org.uk • **Fox Project**, The Old Chapel, Bradford St, Tonbridge TN9 1AW **t** 01732 367397 **e** a.r.wilson@btinternet.com **w** www.innotts.co.uk/~robmel/foxproject.html • **International Primate Protection League**, 116 Judd St, London WC1H 9NS **t** 020 7837 7227 • **Jenita Fox Rescue**, Oak Tree Cattery, Main Rd, Colden Common, Winchester SO21 1TL **t** 023 8069 2309 • **London Wildlife Trust**, Harling Hse, 47-51 Gt Suffolk St, London SE1 0BS **t** 020 7261 0447 **e** londonwt@cix.co.uk **w** www.wildlondon.org.uk • **National Federation of Badger Groups**, 2 Cloisters Business Centre, 8 Battersea Pk Rd, London SW8 4BG **t** 020 7498 3220 **e** elaine.king@ndirect.co.uk **w** www.nfbg.org.uk • **Seal Sanctuary**, Gweek, near Helston, Cornwall TR12 6UG **t** 01326 221361 **e** seals@sealsanctuary.co.uk **w** www.sealsanctuary.co.uk • **St Tiggywinkle's**, see Wildlife Hospital Trust • **Wildlife Hospital Trust**, Church Farm, Aston Rd, Haddenham, Aylesbury HP17 8AF **t** 01844 292292 **e** tiggys@globalnet.co.uk

YOUTH GROUPS

• **Animal Aid Youth Group** see Animal Aid (General) • **Animal Defenders** see National Anti-Vivisection Society (Animal Experiments & Alternatives) • **Animal Freedom** see Hunt Saboteurs Association (Bloodsports) • **Earthlings** see Earthkind (General) • **Farm Animal Rangers** see Compassion in World Farming (Farming) • **Go Wild Club** see World Wide Fund for Nature (General) • **Junior Elefriends** see Born Free Foundation (Wild Animals) • **Junior RSPCA** see RSPCA (General) • **VC21** see Vegetarian Society (Diet/Lifestyle) • **Vegilantics** see Vegan Society magazine and website for details • **Viva! Activists** see Viva! (General)

SUGGESTED READING

A '*****' before a title indicates it is available from the Vegan Society. Ring 01424 427393 for current price details or send an SAE marked 'Publications & Merchandise'. For details of the Vegan Society's range of Information Sheets send an SAE marked 'Information Sheets' to: The Vegan Society, Donald Watson House, 7 Battle Road, St Leonards-on-Sea, East Sussex TN37 7AA.

Note: Many of the titles listed below are not written from an entirely animal free viewpoint but are included on the basis of their educational or practical value. A number of the books may no longer be in print, but may be available from your local library.

ADDITIVES

- **A Consumer's Dictionary of Food Additives** Ruth Winter, Three Rivers Press (1999)
- **Additives — Your Complete Survival Guide** Felicity Lawrence, Century (1986)
- **Animal Ingredients A-Z** The EG Smith Collective, AK Press (1997)
- **Food Additives — Taking the Lid off What We Really Eat** Erik Millstone, Penguin (1986)
- **Food Additives, Nutrients and Supplements** Eileen Renders, Clear Light Publishing (1998)
- **The Additives Guide** Christopher Hughes, John Wiley & Sons (1987)
- **The New E for Additives** Maurice Hanssen, Thorsons (1987)
- **Understanding Additives** Consumers' Association and Hodder & Stoughton (1988)

ANIMAL CARE

- ***Vegetarian Cats and Dogs** James Peden, Harbingers of a New Age (US) (1995)

ANIMAL EXPERIMENTS & ALTERNATIVES

- **Animal Experimentation: The Consensus Changes** Gill Langley (Ed.), MacMillan Publishers, London (1991)
- **Animals in Education: The Facts, Issues and Implications** Lisa Ann Hepner, Richmond Publishers, Albuquerque NM. (1994)
- **Faith, Hope & Charity** Gill Langley, BUAV (1990)
- **Health With Humanity** Steve McIvor, BUAV (1990)
- **Naked Empress: The Great Medical Fraud** Hans Ruesch, CIVIS, Klosters, Switzerland (1982)
- ***Sacred Cows and Golden Geese**, Dr C R Greek & J S Greek, Continuum International Publishing Group (2002)
- **Science on Trial: The Human Cost of Animal Experiments** Dr Robert Sharpe, Awareness Books (1994)
- **Secret Suffering** Sarah Kite, BUAV (1990)
- **Slaughter of the Innocent** Hans Ruesch, Civitas Publications, Swaine, NY. (1983)
- ***Specious Science** C Ray Greek & Jean Swingle Greek, Continuum (2002)
- **The Cruel Deception: The Use of Animals in Medical Research** Robert Sharpe, Harper Collins (1988)
- **Victims of Science: The Use of Animals in Research** Richard Ryder, National Anti-Vivisection Society, Centaur Press Publishers, Fontwell. (1983)
- **Vivisection or Science**, Pietro Croce, Zed Books (1999)
- **Vivisection Unveiled** Dr Tony Page, Jon Carpenter (1997)
- **Why Animal Experiments Must Stop** Vernon Coleman, EMJ (1994)

ANIMALS AND LAW

- **Animals & Cruelty & Law** Noíl Sweeney, Alibi (1990)
- **Animals and their Legal Rights** The Animal Welfare Institute, Washington D.C. (1990)
- **Up against the Law** J. J. Roberts, Arc Print, London (1987)

ANIMAL RIGHTS – LIBERATION & ETHICS

- ***Animal Century** Mark Gold, Jon Carpenter (1998)
- ***Animal Liberation** Peter Singer, Pimlico (1995)

- **Animal Liberation: A Graphic Guide** Lori Gruen, Peter Singer and David Hine, Camden Press (1987)
- **Animal Rights — Extending the Circle of Compassion** Mark Gold, Jon Carpenter (1995)
- **Animal Welfare: A Cool Eye Towards Eden** John Webster, Blackwell Science (1997)
- **Animals and their Moral Standing** Stephen Clark, Routledge (1997)
- **Animals and Why They Matter: A Journey Around the Species Barrier** Mary Midgley, Penguin Publishers, London. (1983)
- **Animals' Rights** Henry Salt, Centaur (1980)
- **Animals, Politics & Morality** Robert Garner, Manchester University Press (1993)
- ***Campaign Against Cruelty** Alex Bourke and Ronny Worsey, Scamp Media (2001)
- **Caught in the Act** Melody MacDonald, Jon Carpenter (1994)
- **Created from Animals: The Moral Implications of Darwinism** James Rachels. (1990)
- **Fettered Kingdoms** John Bryant, Fox Press (1990)
- ***Free the Animals!** Ingrid Newkirk, PETA (2001)
- **In Defense of Animals** Peter Singer, Harper Collins (1986)
- **Inhumane Society: The American Way of Exploiting Animals** Michael W. Fox, St. Martins Press, New York. (1990)
- **Living Without Cruelty** Lorraine Kay, Sidgwick & Johnson (1990)
- **Morals, Reason and Animals** Steve Sapontzis. (1987)
- **No Room, Save in the Heart** (Poetry,Prose)
- **Political Theory & Animal Rights** Paul Clarke and Andrew Linzey, Pluto Press (1990)
- **Rape of the Wild: Man's Violence against Animals and the Earth** Andree Collard with Joyce Contrucci. (1989)
- **The Animal Welfare Handbook** Barry Kew, Fourth Estate (1993)
- **The Case for Animal Rights** Tom Regan, Routledge (1988)
- **The Dreaded Comparison: Human and Animal Slavery** Marjorie Spiegel, Heretic Books (1988)
- **The Nature of the Beast: Are Animals Moral?** Stephen Clark, Oxford University Press (1982)
- **The Pocketbook of Animal Facts & Figures UK** Barry Kew, Green Print (1991)
- **The Savour of Salt: A Henry Salt Anthology** G. and W. Hendrick, Centaur Press Publishers, Fontwell. (1989)
- **The Silent Ark** Juliet Gellatley, Thorsons (1996)
- **The Struggle for Animal Rights** Tom Regan, ISAR (US) (1987)
- **The Unheeded Cry: Animal Consciousness, Animal Pain and Science** Bernard Rollin. (1989)

- **Voiceless Victims** Rebecca Hall, Wildwood House (1984)

BLOODSPORTS

- **Outfoxed** Mike Huskisson (1983)

BABIES & CHILDREN

- ***Happy, Caring, Healthy & Sharing – a book for young green vegans** Graham Burnett, Land & Liberty
- ***Pregnancy, Children & the Vegan Diet** Michael Klaper MD, Gentle World (US) (1994)
- ***Vegan Infants Case Histories** Plamil Foods

CIRCUSES AND ZOOS

- **Animals in Circuses and Zoos - Chiron's World?** Marthe Kiley -Worthington, Little Eco Farms Publishing, Basildon, UK (1990)
- **Beyond the Bars** Virginia McKenna, William Travers, Jonathan Wray (eds.), Thorsons Publishers, Wellingborough, UK (1987)
- **The Rose-Tinted Menagerie** William Johnson, Heretic (1990)

CONSUMERISM

- **The Ethical Consumer Guide to Everyday Shopping** ECRA (1993)
- **The Good Shopping Guide** The Ethical Marketing Group (2002)

COOKBOOKS

- **365 Plus One Vegan Recipes** Leah Leneman, Thorsons (1993)
- **A Vegan of India** Linda Majzlik, Jon Carpenter (2002)
- ***A Vegan Taste of Italy** Linda Majzlik, Jon Carpenter (2000)
- ***A Vegan Taste of the Caribbean** Linda Majzlik, Jon Carpenter (2001)
- **An Allergy Cookbook** (vegetarian edition) Patricia Carter, Ian Henry Publications (1993)
- ***Authentic Chinese Cuisine** Bryanna Clark Grogan, Book Publishing Company (2000)
- **Cook Vegan** Richard Youngs, Ashgrove Press (1993)
- ***Cooking with PETA** PETA, Book Publishing Company (1997)
- ***Everyday Vegan** Dreena Burton, Arsenal Pulp Press (2001)
- ***Fabulous Beans** Barb Bloomfield, Book Publishing Company (1994)
- ***Fat-Free & Easy** Jennifer Raymond, Book Publishing Company (1997)

- **Gourmet Vegan** Heather Lamont, Gollancz (1988)
- **Green Gastronomy** Colin Spencer, Bloomsbury (1996)
- ***Healing Foods Cookbook: The Vegan Way to Wellness** Jane Sen, HarperCollins (2000)
- ***Japanese Cooking** Miyoko Nishimoto Schinner, Book Publishing Company (1999)
- ***Nonna's Italian Kitchen** Bryanna Clark Grogan, Book Publishing Company (1998)
- ***Rainbows and Wellies — The Taigh Na Mara Cookbook** Jackie Reading & Tony Weston, Findhorn Press (1995)
- **Simply Vegan** Debra Wasserman & Reed Mangels, Vegetarian Resource Group (US) (1995)
- ***So What Do You Eat?** Liz Cook (1999)
- **The Absolutely Animal Free Cookbook** Wendy Turner, Book Guild (1997)
- **The Caring Cook: Cruelty-Free Cooking for Beginners** Janet Hunt, Vegan Society (1987)
- ***The Cake Scoffer** Ronny, Vegan International Cake Engineers (2000)
- ***The Health Promoting Cookbook** Alan Goldhammer, Book Publishing Company (1997)
- ***The Joy of Vegan Cooking** Amanda Grant, Metro Publishing Ltd (2002)
- **The Single Vegan** Leah Leneman, Thorsons (1989)
- ***The Uncheese Cookbook** Joanne Stepaniak, Book Publishing Company (1997)
- ***The Vegan Cookbook** Alan Wakeman and Gordon Baskerville, Faber & Faber (1996)
- **The Vegan Gourmet** Susann Geiskopf-Hadler & Mindy Toomay, Prima (US) (1995)
- **The Vegan Health Plan** Amanda Sweet, Arlington Books (1987)
- **The Vegan Kitchen Mate** David Horton, Vegan Society (NSW) (1995)
- ***Vegan Baking** Linda Majzlik, Jon Carpenter Publishing (2000)
- ***Vegan Barbecues & Buffets** Linda Majzlik, Jon Carpenter Publishing (1999)
- ***Vegan Cooking** Eva Batt, Thorsons (1985)
- ***Vegan Cooking for Everyone** Leah Leneman, HarperCollins (2001)
- ***Vegan Cooking for One** Leah Leneman, HarperCollins (2000)
- ***Vegan Dinner Parties** Linda Majzlik, Jon Carpenter Publishing (1998)
- ***Vegan Feasts** Rose Elliot, Thorsons (1997)
- ***Vegan Rustic Cooking for all Seasons** Diana White, Vegan Organic Trust (2002)
- ***Vegan Vittles** Joanne Stepaniak, Book Publishing Company (1996)
- ***Warming Up to Living Foods** Elysa Markowitz, Book Publishing Company (1998)

COSMETICS

- **Cover Up — Taking the Lid off the Cosmetics Industry** Penny Chorlton, Thorsons (1988)
- **Herbal Cosmetics** Camilla Hepper, Thorsons (1987)

ECOLOGY — HOME

- **Conservation at Home: A Practical Handbook** Michael Allaby, Unwin (1988)
- **Home Ecology** Karen Christensen, Arlington Books (1989)
- **The Green Home** Karen Christensen, Judy Piatkus (1995)

FARMING (ANIMAL PRODUCTION)

- **Alternative to Factory Farming** Paul Carnell, Earth Resources Research Publishers, London (1983)
- **Animal Factories** Jim Mason and Peter Singer, AAVS, 801 Old York Rd, Suite 204, Jenkintown, PA 19046-1685 (1980, 1990)
- **Assault & Battery** Mark Gold, Pluto Press (1983)
- **Chicken and Egg — Who Pays the Price?** Clare Druce, Green Print (1989)
- **Do Hens Suffer in Battery Cages?** Michael Appleby, The Athene Trust, 5a Charles St, Petersfield, Hants GU32 3EH (1991)
- **Factory Farming: The Experiment That Failed** Animal Welfare Institute, P.O. Box 3650, Washington, DC 20007 (1988)
- **Facts about Furs** G. Nilsson, et. al., Animal Welfare Institute (1980)
- **Lethal Legacy: BSE — The Search for the Truth** Dr Stephen Dealler, Bloomsbury (1996)
- **Pulling the Wool** Christine Townend, Hale and Ironmonger Publishers, Sydney, Australia (1985)
- **Taking Stock: Animal Farming and The Environment** Alan Durning and Holly Brough, Worldwatch Paper 103, WorldWatch Institute, 1776 Mass. Avenue N.W., Washington, DC 20036-1904 (1991)
- **The Meat Business - Devouring A Hungry Planet** Geoff Tansey & Joyce D'Silva (eds) Earthscan (1999)
- **The Price of Meat** Danny Penman, Gollancz (1997)

FEMINISM & ANIMAL RIGHTS

- **Animals & Women: Feminist Theoretical Explorations** CJ Adams & J Donovan, Duke University Press (1995)
- ***Feminism, Animals & Science — The Naming of the Shrew** Lynda Birke, Open University (1994)

FOOD

- **Food For Free** Richard Mabey, Harper Collins (1996)
- ***Profit From Emerging Dietary Trends** John Hartley, Go Publish (2000)

GARDENING

- **Forest Gardening** Robert A de J Hart, Green Books (1991)
- ***Permaculture: A Beginners Guide** Graham Burnett, Land & Liberty (2000)
- ***Sprout Garden** Mark M Braunstein, Book Publishing Company (1999)
- **The Natural Garden Book** Peter Harper, Jeremy Light & Chris Madsen, Gaia Books (1994)
- **The Organic Gardener's Handbook** Margaret Elphinstone & Julia Langley, Thorsons (1995)
- **Veganic Gardening** Kenneth Dalziel O'Brien, Thorsons (1986)

GMOS

- **Animal Genetic Engineering** Peter Wheale & Ruth McNally (Ed), (1995)
- **Genetic Engineering, Food and our Environment** Luke Anderson, Greenbooks (1999)

LAND USE

- **Beyond Beef — The Rise and Fall of the Cattle Culture** Jeremy Rifkin, Thorsons (1992)
- **Food: Need, Greed & Myopia** Geoffrey Yates, Earthright Publications (1986)

LEATHER & FUR

- **Killing for Luxury** Michael Bright, Franklin Watts (1988)

NON-VIOLENCE

- **The Non-Violent Revolution — A Comprehensive Guide to Ahimsa** Nathaniel Altman, Element (1988)

NUTRITION & HEALTH

- ***10 Days to Better Health** Kirsten Hartvig & Dr Nic Rowley, Piatkus Books (1998)
- **Alternatives to Drugs** Arabella Melville & Colin Johnson, Fontana (1987)

- ***Becoming Vegan** Brenda Davis & Vesanto Melina, Book Publishing Company (2000)
- ***Feel Good Food** Susie Miller & Karen Knowler, The Women's Press (2000)
- ***Foods That Cause You to Lose Weight: The Negative Calorie Effect** Neal Barnard MD, Magni Group (US) (1996)
- ***Foods That Fight Pain** Neal Barnard, Bantam Books (1999)
- **Holistic First Aid: A Handbook for the Home** Michael Nightingale, Optima (1988)
- **Love Yourself, So Hate the Weight!** Brother Craig, Woodbridge Press (US) (1997)
- **The Home Herbal** Barbara Griggs, Pan (1986)
- **Vegan Nutrition** Gill Langley, Vegan Society (1995)
- ***Vegan Nutrition: Pure & Simple** Michael Klaper MD, Gentle World (US) (1997)

PRODUCTS — 'TRADITIONAL' ALTERNATIVES

- **1,001 Handy Household Hints** Lizzie Evans, Octopus (1989)

QUOTATIONS

- **Fruits of Paradise: A Vegetarian Year Book** Rebecca Hall, Simon & Schuster (1993)
- **The Extended Circle: A Dictionary of Humane Thought** Jon Wynne-Tyson, Cardinal (1990)

REFERENCE

- **Animals' Contacts Directory** Veggies (2002/03)

RELIGIOUS

- **Animal Sacrifices -- Religious Perspectives on the Use of Animals in Science** Tom Regan (Ed.), Temple University Press, PA. (1986)
- **Animals and Christianity** Andrew Linzey and Tom Regan, SPCK (1989)
- **Christianity & the Rights of Animals** Andrew Linzey, SPCK (1987)
- **Replenish the Earth** Lewis Regenstein, SCM (1991)

TRAVEL

- **Good Vegetarian Food** Italian Vegetarian Association (2002)
- ***The New Spain** Jean Claude Juston (2001)
- ***The Vegan Passport** George Rodger (ed), The Vegan Society
- ***Vegetarian Britain** Alex Bourke & Katrina Holland, Vegetarian Guides (2002)
- ***Vegetarian France** Alex Bourke & Alan Todd, Vegetarian Guides (1998)
- ***Vegetarian Europe** Alex Bourke, Vegetarian Guides, Vegetarian Guides (2000)
- ***Vegetarian London** Alex Bourke & Jennifer Wharton, Vegetarian Guides, (2002)
- **Vegetarian Journal's Guide to Natural Foods Restaurants in the U.S. and Canada** Vegetarian Resource Group
- **Vegan Guide to New York** Rynn Berry, available from www.vegetarianguides.com
- **Vegetarian Nottinghamshire** now available as an information sheet from Veggies Catering Campaign. See www.veggies.org.uk
- **Vegetarian Brighton** Viva! www.viva.org.uk
- **Vegetarian & Vegan Guide to the Lake District** published annually by Viva!
- **Vegetarian Oxfordshire** Paul Appleby, available from www.ivu.org/oxveg

VEGANISM & VEGETARIANISM

- ***Abundant Living in the Coming Age of the Tree** Kathleen Jannaway, MCL (1991)
- *** Being Vegan** Joanne Stepaniak, Lowell House (2000)
- **Compassion — the Ultimate Ethic** Victoria Moran, American Vegan Society (1991)
- **Diet for a New America**, John Robbins, H J Kramer (1998)
- **Food for a Future** Jon Wynne-Tyson, Thorsons (1988)
- ***Go Vegan** The Vegan Society (2001)
- **Living Without Cruelty** Mark Gold, Green Print (1988)
- **McLibel — Burger Culture on Trial** John Vidal, MacMillan (1997)
- ***Plants for a Future** Ken Fern, Permanent Publications (1997)
- ***Shazzie's Detox Delights** Sharon Holstock, Rawcreation Ltd (2001)
- ***The Food Revolution** John Robbins, Conari Press (2001)
- **The New Why You Don't Need Meat** Peter Cox, Bloomsbury (1992)
- **The Realeat Encyclopedia of Vegetarian Living** Peter Cox, Bloomsbury (1994)
- **The Sexual Politics of Meat** Carol Adams, Polity Press (1990)
- ***The Vegan Sourcebook** Joanne Stepaniak & Virginia Messina, NTC Publishing Group (2000)
- **Vegan: The New Ethics of Eating** Erik Marcus, McBooks Press (2000)

- * **Vegan Stories** Julie H Rosenfield, The Vegan Society (2002)
- *** Why Vegan?** Kath Clements, Heretic (1995)

VERSE

- *** 21st Century Toys** BJ Laprade, InfoDirect Ltd (1999)
- *** Explicit Vegan Lyrics: The Little Book of Vegan Poems**
  Benjamin Zephaniah, AK Press (2000)
- *** Talking Turkeys** Benjamin Zephaniah, Penguin (1994)

MAGAZINES

- **Agscene** CIWF, Charles Hse, 5a Charles St, Petersfield, Hants GU32 3EH
- **Animal Action** RSPCA, Causeway, Horsham, W Sussex RH12 1HG
- **Animal Times** PETA, PO Box 3169, London SW15 3ZG
- **Animals Defenders** 261 Goldhawk Rd, London W12 9PE
- **Arkangel** BCM 9240, London WC1N 3XX
- **Campaign Report** NAVS, 261 Goldhawk Rd, London W12 9PE
- **Ethical Consumer** ECRA Publishing, Unit 21, 41 Old Birley St, Manchester
  M15 5RF
- **FRESH** PO Box 71, ELY, CB7 4GU
- **Green Futures** 13-17 Sturton Street, Cambridge, CB1 2SN
- **HOWL** HSA, PO Box 5254, Northampton NN1 3ZA
- **New Consumer** 0800 389 4728
- **Outrage** Animal Aid, The Old Chapel, Bradford St, Tonbridge, Kent TN9 1AW
- **Pisces** BM Fish, London WC1N 3XX
- **The Ecologist** PO Box 326, Sittingbourne, Kent ME9 8FA
- **The Vegan** The Vegan Society, Donald Watson Hse, 7 Battle Rd,
  St Leonards-on-Sea, E Sussex TN37 7AA
- **The Vegetarian** VSUK, Parkdale, Dunham Rd, Altrincham, Cheshire WA14 4QG
- **Vegan Views** 6 Hayes Ave, Bournemouth BH7 7AD
- **Viva Active!** (under 18s) Viva!, 12 Queen Sq, Brighton, East Sussex BN1 3FD
- **Viva Life** 12 Queen Sq, Brighton, East Sussex BN1 3FD
- **Wales Vegan** Montpelier, Llandrindod, Powys, Wales
- **Wildlife Guardian** LACS, Sparling Hse, 83-87 Union St, London SE1 1S

COMPANY INDEX

- **4-20** ahanmagic@hotmail.com 07967 440989
- **Absolute Aromas Ltd** www.absolute-aromas.com 01420 540400
- **Ainsley Harriot** see Morehands Ltd
- **Aldi Stores Ltd** www.aldi-stores.co.uk 01827 711800
- **Allied Domecq Spirits & Wines Ltd** www.allieddomecqplc.com 01403 222600
- **Alpro (UK) Ltd** www.provamel.co.uk 01536 720 605
- **Ambrosian Vegetarian Foods** ambrosian@btopenworld.com 01283 225055
- **Amphora Aromatics Ltd** www.amphora-aromatics.com 0117 9087770
- **Andutra Ltd** www.andutra.co.uk 01992 700 106
- **Anglia Oils Ltd** www.angliaoils.co.uk 01482 701271
- **Animal Aid** www.animalaid.org.uk 01732 364546
- **Animal Free Cosmetics** www.animalfreecosmetics.com 07957958058
- **Anne-Marie Borlind** see Simply Nature
- **AquaSource** www.aquasourcealgae.com 01392 822155
- **Arbonne** see Animal Free Cosmetics
- **Arkopharma (UK) Ltd** www.arkopharma.co.uk 0208763 1414
- **Aromakids** see Hippychick
- **Aromist Sprays** see Savant
- **Ascent** www.hayspace.co.uk 1497 847 788
- **Asda Group Plc** www.asda.co.uk 0500 100055
- **Ashbourne Biscuits Ltd** www.ashbournebiscuits.co.uk 01335 342 373
- **Aspall** www.aspall.co.uk 01728 860 510
- **Auro Organic Paints** www.auroorganic.co.uk 01799 543077
- **Australian Nougat** Company www.ausnougat.com.au australia 617 5855 3132
- **Avalon Vineyards** www.pennardorganicwines.co.uk 01749 860393
- **Baby Naturals** see Power Health Products
- **Babynat** see Organico
- **Bac to Nature** see Savant
- **Bacardi-Martini** www.bacardi.com
- **Bakebest** 0191 442 4400
- **Banfi Naturelle** see Power Health Products
- **Barefoot Botanicals** www.barefoot-botanicals.com 0207288 2977
- **Barry M Cosmetics** www.barrym.com 020 8349 2992
- **Bass** 0845 7112244
- **Baxters of Speyside Ltd** www.baxters.co.uk 01343 820393
- **Bay House Aromatics** www.bay-house.co.uk 01273 601109
- **Beanie's Health Foods** www.beanieshealthfoods.co.uk 01489 574593

- **BeauCaire** see Seven Wives of St Ives
- **Beauty Through Herbs** www.bth.co.uk 01847 822208
- **Bennett Natural Products** www.healthremedies.co.uk 01257 404659
- **Bentley Pearl** bentleypearl@edgeware.co.uk 0208 381 1334
- **Bertolli** see Unilever Bestfoods
- **Betterware** www.betterware.co.uk 0845 121 1010
- **Bickiepegs Ltd** www.bickiepegs.co.uk 01224 790626
- **Biddy Merkins** Celtic House, Gaerwen, Anglesey, Wales LL60 6HR 01248 422011
- **Biocare** see Savant
- **Biocosmetics** see Power Health Products
- **Bio-D Co. Ltd.** bio-d@ecodet.keroo.co.uk 01482 229950
- **Bio-Health Ltd** www.bio-health.ltd.uk 01634 290115
- **Bionade** see Beanie's Health Foods
- **biOrganic Hair Therapy Ltd** www.biorganic.co.uk 01384 877951
- **Birds Eye Walls Ltd** www.birdseye.com 01932 263115
- **Bisto** see Centura Foods
- **Bite Me Vegan Treats**, 46 Park Road, Ilford, Essex 020 8554 8273
- **Black Sheep Brewery Plc** www.blacksheep.co.uk 01765 689227
- **Blackmores** 0208 842 3956
- **Body Reform (UK) Ltd** www.bodyreform.co.uk 01354 610550
- **Bodywise (UK) Ltd** www.natracare.com 01275 371764
- **Booja Booja Company Ltd** www.boojabooja.com 01508 499049
- **Brakspear & Sons Plc** www.brakspear.co.uk 01491 570 200
- **Branston** see Nestlé
- **Brewhurst Healthfood Supplies** www.brewhurst.com 01932 354211
- **Broughton Ales** www.broughtonales.co.uk 01899 830 345
- **Broughton Pastures Organic Fruit Wine** www.BroughtonPastures.co.uk 01442 823 993
- **Brunel Healthcare** www.bruhealth.co.uk 0117 946 5511
- **Bulmer Ltd** www.bulmers.co.uk 01432 352000
- **Bute Island Foods** www.scheese.co.uk 01700 505117
- **Buteful Sauce Company** www.butefulsauce.co.uk 0141 889 2468
- **Calder Valley Soap** www.uksoaps.net 01422 362202
- **Caledonian Curry Co** info@caledoniancurry.co.uk 01863 766025
- **Calypso Soft Drinks** www.calypso.co.uk 01978 668400
- **Cambridge Bioceuticals** www.bio-kult.com 01353 723234
- **Camilla Hepper Ltd** www.camillahepper.com 01491 826196
- **Campbell's Grocery Products Ltd** www.campbellsoup.com 01553 692266
- **Capitelli Oils** The Meadowbank Clinic, 2 Meadowbank Terrace, Edinburgh EH8 7AR 0131 6617275
- **Cat Country (CC UK)** 01949 845 111

- **Cauldron Foods Ltd** www.cauldronfoods.co.uk 01275 818448
- **Celestial Designs Aromatherapy** www.aroma-shop.co.uk 01745 550 411
- **Cellande Midlands** www.cellande.co.uk 0121 472 2903
- **Celtic Chocolates Ltd** 00353-405 57077
- **Centura Foods** www.sharwoods.com 01606 834747
- **Chesswood** see Westler Foods
- **Chicken Tonight** see Unilever Bestfoods
- **Chikpe** www.chikpe.co.uk 01743 244466
- **Chiman's** chimans@sosi.net 01271 883864
- **Christy** see Network Management
- **Clearspring** www.clearspring.co.uk 01332 200636
- **Colman's** see Unilever Bestfoods
- **Commex Foods Ltd** www.jollyswagman.co.uk 020 88613871
- **Community Foods Ltd** www.communityfoods.co.uk 0208208 2966
- **Compassion in World Farming** www.ciwf.co.uk 01730 264208
- **Condomi Health UK Ltd** www.condomi.com 01628 781 432
- **Cookeen** see Unilever Bestfoods
- **Co-operative Group Ltd** www.co-op.co.uk 0800 0686 727
- **Cooplands Ltd** 01302 818000
- **Cotswold Health Products** www.cotsherb.co.uk 01453 843694
- **Crawford's** see United Biscuits
- **Crazy Jack's** see Community Foods
- **Crisp 'n' Dry** see Unilever Bestfoods
- **Crosse & Blackwell** see Nestlè
- **D & D Chocolates** www.d-dchocolate.com 02476 370909
- **Daler Rowney Ltd** 12 Percy St, Tottenham Ct Rd, London W1A 2BP 020 7636 8241
- **Daloon Foods (UK) Ltd** sales@daloonuk.com 01636 701000
- **Daniel Field** Freepost Nottingham www.danielfield.com
- **Dannex** see Power Health Products
- **Dany Bernard** see Power Health Products
- **Davenport Vineyards** www.davenportvineyards.co.uk 01892 852 380
- **Davina Sports Nutrition** see Power Health Products
- **Delhi Kuts** delhikuts@ntlworld.com 01162 207360
- **Dene's Natural Pet Care Ltd** www.denes.com 01273 325364
- **Dental Herb Co.** see Savant
- **Deodorant Stone (UK) Ltd** www.deodorant-stone.co.uk 01559 384856
- **Desert Essence** 0800 146 215
- **Dextro Energy** see Unilever Bestfoods
- **Dipak Foods Ltd** 25 Silverstone Drive, Leicester LE4 7RR 0116 251 1300
- **Dolma** www.veganvillage.co.uk/dolma 0115 963 4237
- **Doves Farm Foods** www.dovesfarm.co.uk 01488684884

- **Dr Hadwen Trust** www.drhadwentrust.org.uk 01462 436819
- **Dragonfly Foods** www.beany.co.uk 01364 642700
- **Dri-Pak Ltd** sales@dripak.co.uk 0115 932 5165
- **Droyt Products Ltd** www.droyts.com 01257 417251
- **Dunkerton's Cider Company** www.dunkertons.co.uk 01544 388653
- **Earth Friendly Baby** see Natural Woman
- **Earth Friendly Products** www.earthfriendlyproducts.co.uk 01892 616871
- **Eco-babes** www.eco-babes.co.uk 01353 664941
- **Ecolino** www.ecolino.be +320331288
- **Ecomil** see Organico
- **Ecos Paints** www.ecospaints.com 01524 852 371
- **Ecotec** see Old House Store
- **Ecover** www.ecover.com 01635 528240
- **Eco-Zone** www.sea-vegetables.co.uk 020 8962 6399
- **Elco** see Dri-pak
- **Elizabeth Shaw Ltd** www.elizabethshaw.co.uk 0117 301 3300
- **Elkes Biscuits** www.elkes.com 01889 563131
- **Ella Drinks** www.bouvrage.com 01786 834342
- **Enjoy Organic Co Ltd** www.enjoyorganic.com 01628 478 484
- **Equal Exchange Trading** www.equalexchange.co.uk 0131 220 3484
- **Escential Botanicals Ltd.** www.escential.com 01884 257612
- **Essential Oil Company** www.eoco.org.uk 01256 332737
- **Essentially Yours** sales@essentially-yours.co.uk 01372 465 414
- **Ethical Wares** www.ethicalwares.com 01570 471155
- **Faith Products Ltd** www.faithproducts.com 0161 764 2555
- **Fayrefield Foods Ltd** www.fayrefield.co.uk 01270 589311
- **Fentimans Ltd** www.fentimans.com 01434 682300
- **First Foods** www.first-foods.com 01494 431355
- **First Quality Foods** www.firstqualityfoods.co.uk 01454 880044
- **Flora Margarines** see Unilever Bestfoods
- **Flora** see Savant
- **Florentino** see Morehands Ltd
- **Food Safe Ltd** www.food-safe.com 01788 510 415
- **Fox's Biscuits** www.foxs-biscuits.co.uk 01924 444333
- **Freerangers** www.freerangers.co.uk 01661 831781
- **Frutina** www.fruitina.com 0870 600 2007
- **Fry Light** see Morehands Ltd
- **Fry's** see Beanie's Health Foods
- **FSC** see Health & Diet Co.
- **George Bateman & Son** mjcullimore@bateman.co.uk 01754 880317
- **Get Real Organic Foods** www.get-real.co.uk 01939 210925

- **Glanbia** www.cheese.co.uk 01691 678 403
- **GNC** www.gnc.co.uk 0870 750 4527
- **Go Organic Ltd** www.goorganic.co.uk 0131 220 8248
- **Golden Wonder** 01858 410410 www.goldenwonder.com
- **Goodlife Foods** www.goodlife.co.uk 01925 837810
- **GR Lane** www.laneshealth.com 01452 524012
- **Granose** see Haldane Foods
- **Granovita UK Ltd** www.granovita.co.uk 01933 273717
- **Green & Blacks**, 2 Valentine Place, London www.greenandblacks.com
- **Green & Organic** www.greenandorganic.co.uk 01420 520838
- **Green Ark Animal Nutrition** www.greenark.co.uk 01282 606810
- **Green Building Store** www.greenbuildingstore.co.uk 01484 854 898
- **Green Paints** see Green Shop 01507 327362
- **Green People Co.** www.greenpeople.co.uk 01444 401444
- **Green Shoes** www.greenshoes.co.uk 01803 864997
- **Green Shop** www.greenshop.co.uk 01452 770 629
- **Greencity Wholefoods** www.greencity.co.uk 0141 554 7633
- **Groomers Ltd** www.groomersshampoo.com 01635 581958
- **Growganic** www.growganic.com 01380 871050
- **H J Heinz** www.heinz.com 0208 573 7757
- **Haldane Foods Group** www.haldanefoods.co.uk 01908 211311
- **Hambleden Herbs** www.hambledenherbs.co.uk 01823 401205
- **Happidog Petfood** 0800 0182955
- **Harbourne Vineyard** www.harbournevineyard.co.uk 01797 270420
- **Health & Diet Co.** www.gnc.co.uk 0870 759 4012
- **Health Plus** www.healthplus.co.uk 01323 737374
- **Healthpol** www.delacet.co.uk 020 8360 0386
- **Healthquest Limited** www.healthquest.co.uk 020 8206 2066
- **Hellmann's** see Unilever Bestfoods
- **Hemp Shop Ltd** www.thehemp-shop.com 07041 313233
- **Hemp Union** www.hemp-union.karoo.net 01482 225328
- **Herb UK Ltd** 01202 477188
- **Herbs Hands Healing** www.herbshandshealing.co.uk 0870 755 4848
- **Herbs of Grace** www.herbsofgrace.co.uk 01638 750140
- **Hermitage Oils** www.hermitageoils.com 01274 565957
- **Heron Quality Foods Ltd** heronfoods@eircom.net 00 353 2339006
- **Higher Nature** www.higher-nature.co.uk 01435 883484
- **Hippychick** www.hippychickltd.co.uk 01278 671461
- **Hollytrees** see J & D Black
- **Homecare Products** www.homecareproducts.co.uk 020 8871 5027
- **Homestrip** see Green Shop

- **Honesty Cosmetics Ltd** www.honestycosmetics.co.uk 01629 814888
- **Humane Research Trust** www.btinternet.com/~shawweb/hrt 0161 439 8041
- **Iceland Frozen Foods PLC** www.iceland.co.uk 01244 842842
- **Imagine** www.imaginefoods.com
- **Impact RTR** 0800 783 7548
- **Innocent** www.innocentdrinks.co.uk 020 8600 3939
- **Interbrew** www.interbrew.com 01582 391166
- **It's Soya Good** see Organico
- **J & D Black Ltd** sales@jdblack.co.uk 01252 344010
- **J. L. Bragg Ltd** www.charcoal.uk.com 01473 748345
- **J.P. Textiles** (evergreen) www.ever-green.co.uk 01226 232630
- **Jacobs** Ruscote Avenue, Banbury, Oxfordshire 0151 525 3661
- **Jan De Vries** see Power Health Products
- **Jonathan Crisp** www.jonathancrisp.co.uk 01865 882514
- **Jophiel** www.jophieloils.com 0161 626 1549
- **Jordan (Cereals) Ltd** 01767 319454
- **Jurlique** 020 8841 6644
- **Just Wholefoods** www.justwholefoods.co.uk 01285 651910
- **Kallo Foods** www.kallofoods.com 01428 685100
- **Kelloggs** www.kelloggs.co.uk 0161 869 2000
- **Kent Cosmetics** www.kentcos.com 01622 859898
- **Kettle Foods** www.kettlefoods.co.uk 0800 616996
- **Kingfisher Natural Toothpaste** www.rainbowwholefoods.co.uk 01603 630484
- **Kiss My Face** www.milfordcollection.com 01686 629919
- **Knorr** see Unilever Bestfoods
- **Kobashi** www.kobashi.co.uk 01392 217628
- **KP Foods** see United Biscuits
- **Kudos Vitamins and Herbals Ltd** www.kudosvitamins.com 020 8392 6524
- **La Tienda** see Green Shop
- **Lafe** see Seven Wives of St Ives
- **Lavinia** see Power Health Products
- **Leafcycle**, Coombe Farm, Cove, Tiverton, Devon EX 16 7RU 01398 331808
- **Leeora Vegetarian Food** info@sunshinehealing.co.uk 01206 514966
- **LG Harris** www.lgharris.co.uk 01527 575441
- **Liberon Waxes Ltd** www.liberonwaxes.co.uk 01797 367555
- **Life** see Morehands Ltd
- **Lifeplan Products Ltd** www.lifeplan.co.uk 01455 556281
- **Lifestyle Healthcare Ltd** www.glutenfree.co.uk 01491 570000
- **Lindt & Sprungli** www.lindt.com 01895 424 062
- **Linfit Brewery** 01484 842370
- **Lipton** see Unilever Bestfoods

- **Little Miracles / Aphrodite's Rose** www.littlemiracles.co.uk 020 7435 5555
- **Little Salkeld Mill** www.organicmill.co.uk 01768 881523
- **Loyd Grossman** www.loydgrossmansauces.co.uk 0800 3898548
- **Lunapads** see Natural Woman
- **Lush** www.lush.co.uk 01202 668545
- **Lyme Regis Fine Foods Ltd** www.lymeregisfoods.com 01428 722900
- **Lyons** see Mr Kipling
- **MacSween of Edinburgh** www.macsween.co.uk 0131 440 2555
- **Made to Last Workers Co-operative** www.scribe.demon.co.uk/mtl 0113 230 4983
- **Malibu Health Products Ltd** www.malibusun.com 020 8758 0055
- **Marigold Health Foods** 020 7388 4515
- **Marks & Spencer** www.marksandspencer.com 020 7935 4422
- **Marmite** see Unilever Bestfoods
- **Martha Hill** www.marthahill.com 0800 980 6662
- **Mason's Products** www.dogoil.co.uk 01706 379817
- **Matthew Clark plc** www.mclark.co.uk 01275 836100
- **Matthews Foods** www.matthews-foods.co.uk 0800 0284499
- **Maxicrop International Ltd** www.maxicrop.co.uk 01405 762777
- **Maxim Marketing Company** 4 Allison Road, London W3 6JE 020 8998 2357
- **McCain Foods** GB Ltd www.mccain.com 01723 584141
- **McDougalls** see Centura Foods
- **McVitie's** See United Biscuits
- **Meadowsweet** www.meadowsweet.co.uk 01449 676940
- **Micheline Arcier Aromatherapy** michelinearcier.com 020 7235 3545
- **Millers Damsel** see Ashbourne Biscuits
- **Missing Link** see Savant
- **Modern Organic Products** see Molton Brown Cosmetics
- **Molton Brown Cosmetics** www.moltonbrown.co.uk 0207625 6550
- **Montagne Jeunesse** www.montagnejeunesse.co.uk 01792 310306
- **Monteith Home Bakeries**, Stanford Close, Hampton monteith@btinternet.com
- **Morehands Ltd** www.mhfoods.net 01322 337711
- **Mother Hemp Ltd.** www.motherhemp.com 01323 811909
- **Moulin de Valdonne** see Organico
- **Mr Kipling** Customer Care Dept, Leigh Road, Eastleigh, Hants SO50 9YY
  www.mrkipling.co.uk
- **Nairns** www.simmers-nairns.com 0131 620 7000
- **Napiers Dispensary** www.napiers.net 0906 802 0117
- **Naté** see Organico
- **National Trust Enterprises** www.nationaltrust.org.uk 0870 609 5381
- **Natracare** see Bodywise / Natural Woman
- **Natural Collection** www.naturalcollection.com 01225 404010

- **Natural Feast Corporation** www.naturalfeast.com USA 508 785 3322
- **Natural Shoe Store** www.birkenstock.co.uk Covent Garden Branch: 020 7836 5254 Please phone for availability
- **Natural Woman** www.natural-woman.com 0117 968 7744
- **Naturalife** see Savant
- **Nature Knows Best** see Power Health Products
- **Nature's Aid Ltd** www.naturesaid.co.uk 01772 686231
- **Nature's Dream** www.naturesdream.co.uk 01788 579 957
- **Nature's Mother** see Power Health Products
- **Nature's Plate** naturesplate@yahoo.com 01392 413578
- **Nature's Plus** www.naturesplus.co.uk
- **Nature's Remedies** naturesremedies.com 01494 727 888
- **Naturewatch** www.naturewatch.org 01242 252871
- **NDS Healthcare** www.ndshealthcare.com 08700 11 11 88
- **Neal's Yard Remedies** www.nealsyardremedies.com 020 7627 1949
- **Nestle` UK Ltd** www.nestle.co.uk 0800 00 00 30
- **Network Management** 01252 533 333
- **Network of Wholefood Wholesale Co-Operatives** now@essential-trading.co.uk 0117 958 3550
- **New Seasons** www.newseasons.co.uk 01235 821110
- **New York Bagel Co. Ltd** www.nybagel.co.uk 01733 233405
- **Nutritional Healthcare** www.nhi.co.uk 0800 917 1669
- **Old House Store** www.oldhousestore.co.uk 0118 969 7711
- **Opal** see Dri-pak
- **Optima Health** www.optimah.com 029 20388422
- **Ord River Tea Tree Oil** see Absolute Aromas
- **Organic Botanics** 01273 773182
- **Organic Gardening Catalogue** www.OrganicCatalog.com 01932 253666
- **Organic Pudding** sales@wildpuddings.com 015395 36330
- **Organic** see Haldane Foods
- **Organic Supplies** info@organicsupplies.ltd.uk 020 8677 9769
- **Organic Wine Company** www.organicwinecompany.com 01494 446557
- **Organico** www.organico.co.uk 0118 9510 518
- **Organix Brands Plc** www.babyorganix.co.uk 0800 39 35 11
- **Orgran** see Community Foods
- **Original Source** see Health & Beauty Solutions
- **Oscar Bars** www.oscarbars.com 01544 231228
- **OSMO** www.osmouk.com 01296 481 220
- **OXO** 0800 374 342
- **Pantri Nolwenn** www.pantrinolwenn.co.uk 0845 330 6193
- **Pataks Foods Ltd** www.pataks.co.uk 01942 272300

- **Paul's Tofu** 66-68 Snow Hill, Melton Mowbray, Leics 01664 560572
- **People Tree** www.ptree.co.uk 0207808 7060
- **Perfumers Guild Ltd** perfumersguild@aol.com 01923 260502
- **Pertwood Organic Cereal Company Ltd** www.pertwood.co.uk 01747 820 719
- **Pharma Nord (UK) Ltd** www.pharmanord.com
- **Phytofoods** www.micropix.demon.co.uk/tempeh 01547 510242
- **Pitfield Brewery** www.pitfieldbeershop.co.uk 02077393701
- **Pitrok Ltd** www.pitrok.co.uk 0208 563 1120
- **Plamil** www.plamilfoods.co.uk 01303 850588
- **Plantation Trading Ltd** 39 Flower Lane, Mill Hill, London 020 8959 6588
- **Polyco Ltd** www.superglove.co.uk 020 8443 9000
- **Potions and Possibilities** www.potions.co.uk 01394 386 161
- **Potter's Herbal Medicine** www.potters-herbal-medicines.com 01942 405103
- **Power Health Products** 01759 302595
- **Primo D'Oro** see Kallo Foods
- **Principle Healthcare** Principle House, Airedale Business Centre, Millennium Road, Skipton, North Yorkshire BD23 2TZ 01756 792600
- **Pritchitt Foods** www.pritchitt.com 020 8290 7020
- **Probiotics International Ltd.** enquiries@probiotics-international.ltd.uk 01935 822921
- **Prosta Kit** see Savant
- **Pure Wine Company** www.purewine.co.uk 0808 100 3123
- **Purple Flame Aromatherapy** www.purpleflame.co.uk 01676 542 542
- **Quaker Oats Ltd** 020 8574 2388
- **Quest Vitamins** www.questvitamins.co.uk 0121 359 0056
- **Quinessence Aromatherapy** www.quinessence.com 01530 814171
- **R J Foods Limited** www.rjfoodslimited.co.uk 01202 481471
- **Radfords of Devon** 01803 316020
- **Ragu** see Unilever Bestfoods
- **Rakusen's** www.rakusens.co.uk 0113 278 4821
- **Real Samosa Co.** realsamosa@aol.com 01223 212254
- **Real Soup Co.** www.realsoup.com 01434 602503
- **Realeat** see Haldane Foods
- **Red Bull** 020 7434 0100 www.redbull.co.uk
- **Redwood Wholefood Company** www.redwoodfoods.co.uk 01536 400557
- **Reevecrest Healthcare** see Power Health Products
- **Reliv UK** www.reliv.co.uk 01494 539733
- **Retone Products** www.retone.co.uk 0161 832 7788
- **Rhema UK Ltd** 020 8488 8111
- **Rich Products** www.richs.com/intl/uk.html 01789 450030
- **Ridpath Pek Ltd** www.ridpathpek.com 020 7474 0555

- **Ritter Sports** Alfred Ritter, GmbH & Co KG, D-71108 Waldenbuch, Germany www.ritter-sport.de
- **Robert McBride Ltd** www.plp.co.uk 0800 0181217
- **Rocks Organic Cordials** www.rocksorganic.com 0118 934 2344
- **Rococo Chocolates** www.rococochocolates.com 020 7352 5857
- **Rogue Development** www.roguedevelopment.co.uk 020 7274 7048
- **Romany** see Power Health Products
- **RR Tofu** 01653 690235
- **Ryvita** www.ryvita.co.uk 01202 743090
- **Sabel** sabel@sabel_cosmetics.co.uk 01422 366400
- **Safeway Stores Plc** www.safeway.co.uk 01622 712987
- **Sage Nutritionals** www.sagenutritionals.com 01672 872907
- **Salus** 01925 825679
- **Samuel Smith** High Street, Tadcaster, N Yorkshire LS24 9SB 01937 832225
- **Sanchi** www.goodfooddelivery.co.uk 020 8450 9419
- **Sanitarium Health Food Co (UK)** www.sanitarium.com.au
- **Santa Fe Natural Tobacco Co.** www.sfntc.co.uk 0800 731 1500
- **Sarc Health Foods** www.soyahealth.co.uk 01432 820695
- **Sauflon Pharmaceuticals** 0208 322 4200
- **Savant** www.savant-health.com 0845 0606070
- **Saxa & Cerebos** see Centura Foods
- **Scent By Nature** www.scentbynature.net 01493 369 678
- **Scottish Courage Ltd** www.scottish/newcastle.co.uk 0845 302 3000
- **Scottish Herbal Supplies** 108 Kinnell Avenue, Glasgow G52 3RZ 0141 882 7001
- **Seabrook Potato Crisps Ltd** www.seabrookcrisps.com 01274 546405
- **Seagreens Co Ltd** www.seagreens.com 01444 400403
- **Sedlescombe Organic Vineyard** www.englishorganicwine.co.uk 0800 980 2884
- **Seeds of Change** www.seedsofchange.co.uk 01664 415490
- **Seven Seas** www.seven-seas.ltd.uk 01482 375234
- **Seven Wives of St Ives** Soap Co sales@7wives.co.uk 01736 741274
- **Shanti Health & Beauty Products** www.shantiproducts.co.uk 01304 820129
- **Sharwood & Company Ltd** 01784 473000 www.sharwoods.com
- **Shearer Candles** www.shearer-candles.com 0141 445 1066
- **Shepherdboy** www.shepherdboy.co.uk 0116 260 2992
- **Simply Nature** 01580 201687
- **Simply Organic** www.simplyorganic.co.uk 0131 4480440
- **Simply Soaps** www.simplysoaps.com 01603 720869
- **Skane Dairy UK Ltd** www.proviva.com 0845 60 11 754
- **Smilde** www.smildefood.com 01892 669616
- **So Good** see Haldane Foods

- **Solano Trading** 11 Summer Hill, Frome, Somerset BA 11 1 LT 01373 473809
- **Solgar Vitamins Ltd** www.solgar.com/ 01442 890355
- **Solo Nutrition Ltd** www.solonutrition.co.uk 01273 628747
- **Somerfield** www.somerfield.co.uk 0117 935 9359
- **Soto Tofu** see Organico
- **Soya Health Foods** www.soya-group.com 0161 924 2214
- **Spatone** www.spatone.com 0800 7311 740
- **Spice Village Ltd** info@spicetrail.com 01673 844114
- **Stamp Collection** www.stamp-collection.co.uk 020 7637 5505
- **Stargazer** www.stargazer-products.com 020 8655 7005
- **Stiletto Foods** 020 8840 2244
- **Sukar** www.sukar.co.uk 01937 572 711
- **Suma Wholefoods** www.suma.co.uk 0845 458 2291
- **Sun Pat** see Nestlé
- **Swizzels Matlow Ltd** www.swizzels-matlow.com 0800 9700480
- **Taifun** www.taifun-tofu.de/engl +49 761 - 152 10 0
- **Tamar Organics** www.tamarorganics.co.uk 01822 834887
- **Tanjero** rosie@tanjero.co.uk 0114 256 2977
- **Tara Toiletries** see Dri-pak
- **Tastee Foods** www.tasteefoods.co.uk 01509 557030
- **Taylor Jackson Health Products** www.taylor-jackson.com 01923 856 246
- **Tesco** www.tesco.com 0800 505555
- **Thorncroft** www.thorncroft.ltd.uk 01642 791792
- **Thorntons Plc** www.thorntons.co.uk 0845 121 1911
- **Thursday Plantation** see Optima Health
- **TIGI** www.tigi.co.uk 020 8338 1300
- **Tiki** see GR Lane
- **TLC** Collection 020 7323 2222
- **Tofutti UK Ltd** www.tofutti.co.uk 020 8861 4443
- **Tom's of Maine** PO Box 1873, Salisbury SP4 6WZ www.tomsofmaine.com
- **Tree-harvest** www.tree-harvest.com 01531 635 284
- **Trefriw Wells Spa** see Spatone
- **Trufree** www.trufree.co.uk 01225 711801
- **Udo's Choice** see Savant
- **UHU (UK) Ltd** www.uhu-uk.co.uk 020 8847 2227
- **Unilever Bestfoods** www.unilever.com 0207 822 5252
- **United Biscuits Ltd** www.unitedbiscuits.co.uk 0500 011 710
- **Urtekram** www.urtekram.dk 01403 786460
- **Vecon** see GR Lane
- **Vega Nutritionals** www.vegavitamins.com 01932 267337
- **Vegamp** www.vegamp.co.uk

- **Veganline** www.veganline.com 0800 458 4442
- **Veganstore.co.uk** www.veganstore.co.uk 01273 302979
- **Vegepet** www.vegepet.com 406 295-4944
- **Vegetarian Shoes** www.vegetarianshoes.co.uk 01273 691913
- **Vegetarians Choice** 01202 889900
- **Veggies Catering Campaign** www.veggies.org.uk 0845 458 9595
- **Village Bakery** www.village-bakery.com 01768 881515
- **Vinceremos** www.vinceremos.co.uk 0113 244 0002
- **Vindotco UK Ltd** www.citra.co.uk 01652 652444
- **Vintage Roots** www.vintageroots.co.uk 0800 980 4992
- **Viridian** www.viridian-nutrition.com 01327 878050
- **Vita Youth** see Power Health Products
- **Vitalinea** see Jacobs
- **VIVA!** www.viva.org.uk 01273 777688
- **Waitrose** www.waitrose.co.uk 0800 188884
- **Walkers Snack Foods Ltd** walkers.corpex.com 0116 234 2345
- **Warburtons Soreen** www.warburtons.co.uk 0800 243684
- **Wassen International Ltd** www.wassen.com 01372 379828
- **Wayfarer** see Westler Foods
- **Weetabix Ltd** www.weetabix.co.uk 01536 722181
- **Weleda** 0115 944 8222 www.weleda.co.uk
- **Westler Foods Ltd** www.westlerfoods.com 01653 693971
- **Weston & Sons Ltd** www.westons-cider.co.uk 01531 660233
- **Whitewave** see Haldane Foods
- **Whitworths Ltd** www.whitworths.co.uk 01933 653000
- **Whole Earth Foods Ltd** www.freshfood.co.uk 020 8749 8778
- **Wholebake Ltd** www.wholebake.co.uk 01490 412297
- **Wicken Fen** www.wickenfen.co.uk 01361 883150
- **William Santus & Co Ltd** www.uncle-joes.com 01942 243464
- **Winsor & Newton** www.winsornewton.com 020 8424 3415
- **Wolverhampton & Dudley Breweries plc** www.fullpint.co.uk 01902 711811
- **Worlds End Trading** www.worldsend.co.uk 01872 501988
- **Wrigley Co Ltd** www.wrigley.com 01752 701107
- **Xynergy Health Products** www.xynergy.co.uk 01730 813642
- **Yarrah** www.yarrah.com 00 31 341 432623
- **Yin Yang Beauty Care** www.yinyang.co.uk 01993 868912
- **Yoah** www.yaoh.co.uk 0117 923 9053
- **York Foods** OPSA House, 5a High Ousegate, York Y01 2RZ 01904 647721
- **Your Body** sales@yourbody.co.uk 020 8808 2662/3
- **Zedz Foods** www.zedzfoods.co.uk 0161 835 1442

INDEX

NOTES

Membership / Renewal

THE
Vegan
SOCIETY

◯ I wish to become a member and support the work of the Vegan Society.

◯ I wish to renew my membership. Membership No. (if known)

....

Name:...Address:...

....Postcode:...............................

Tel:...email:...

Date of Birth: (for security purposes) ..../........./........

Occupation:...

A copy of the Society's rules (Memo & Articles of Association) can be viewed on our website or at our office. Alternatively you may buy a copy for £5.

◯ Please tick this box if you are a dietary Vegan.
This entitles you to voting rights in the Society's elections if aged 18+.

◯ Please treat my membership subscription as Gift Aid. I have paid UK income or capital gains tax equal to the amount the Society reclaims.

◯ My income is less than £8000 per year and I qualify for the low income discount of 33%.*

◯ I wish to enrol other members of my household for an additional £7 each.**

Please give full names of additional members and specify if dietary vegan and / or under 18. (If more than six additional members please attach separate sheet.)

contiued overleaf

Membership

Individual **£21**	
* Less **£7** low-income deduction (if applicable)	
** Add **£7** per additional household member	
Life **£350**	
Memo & Articles of Association **£5**	
Overseas: Europe **+£5** / Rest of World **+£7**	
Donation	
Total:	

How to pay

Payment must be made by credit card, sterling International money order or sterling cheque drawn on a British bank.

- **Cheque / PO** payable to *The Vegan Society*   ● **Credit / Debit card** (below)
- **Direct Debit** ◯   Please send me a form   ● **Website:** www.vegansociety.com

☐☐☐☐☐☐☐☐☐☐☐☐☐☐☐☐☐☐☐☐☐☐

Please debit my Visa / Mastercard / Visa Delta / Connect / Switch / Solo card number

Name on card:...Signature:..................................

Today's date.........../.........../.........Start date:.........../...........Expiry date.........../...........

Switch Issue No.:..................

Please return to: **Membership Dept.**
The Vegan Society | **Donald Watson House** | **7 Battle Road**
St Leonards on Sea | **East Sussex** | **TN37 7AA** | **UK.**
Tel: **0845 45 88244** | Fax: **01424 717064**
Visit: **www.vegansociety.com**   email: **membership@vegansociety.com**

This form may be photocopied